A COMPREHENSIVE

STUDY

OF A PORTION OF THE

RED HILLS REGION OF GEORGIA

Prepared
by

The Thomas College
Regional Resource Center

The Thomas College Press
1501 Millpond Road
Thomasville, Georgia 31792
ISBN 0-9643826-0-1

Printed By
Barnes Printing Company, Inc.
Thomasville, Georgia

Cover art courtesy of
Dr. Steve Gatewood

AUTHORS

Dr. Steve Gatewood

Dr. Kenneth W. Johnson

Richebourg G. McWilliams
and
Candace Trimble, Associate

Neil G. Sipe

Nancy Tinker

PROJECT DIRECTOR

Richard W. Search

EDITOR

James E. Hodges

PROJECT PHOTOGRAPHER

Katherine Lisenby

TABLE OF CONTENTS

ACKNOWLEDGEMENTS

A project of this nature involves synthesizing and assessing existing information; consequently, it draws upon the knowledge of many people and institutions. The authors of this study wish to acknowledge the following organizations and individuals for their assistance and contributions:

1. Tall Timbers Research Station, with special thanks to Wilson Baker, Julie Moore, Jim McKinley, Cathy Genest-Godfrey and Deborah Blair.

2. The Tallahassee office of The Nature Conservancy.

3. Dr. Paul Huddleston, Chief Stratigrapher, Georgia Geological Survey; Dr. Walt Schmidt, State Geologist of Florida; Dr. Tom Scott, Chief Stratigrapher, Florida Geological Survey; Frank Rupert, Florida Geological Survey.

4. Ray Gainey, manager of Mistletoe Plantation; Carrol (and Mary) Weaver, manager of Arcadia Plantation; Mr. Warren Bicknell, owner, Sinkola Plantation; Mr. and Mrs. Jeptha Wade, Arcadia Plantation; many other plantation owners who volunteered access to their property for field work; Sue Flieder.

5. Molly Aldritch, Soil Conservation Technician, U.S.D.A-S.C.S, Cairo, Georgia; Johnny Eubanks, District Conservationist, U.S.D.A-S.C.S, Thomasville, Georgia; Jerry Pilkinton, Area Soil Scientist, U.S.D.A-S.C.S, Albany, Georgia.

6. Alice Gordon and Deborah McKeel, Florida Geological Survey Librarians.

7. Wilma Cashman and Linda Elliott of Thomas College.

8. Thomasville Landmarks, Inc.

9. Those persons who live within the Red Hills region who have provided financial support, access to their lands, historical information, and a myriad of other contributions which they have provided in order to allow us to assemble the research contained within this document.

10. Dr. Homer R. Pankey, president of Thomas College.

INTRODUCTION

The Red Hills project that follows is the result of the work of five professionals in the fields of biology, economics, archaeology, history, and geology. The report is divided into five chapters, each standing as a complete document.

Many people have studied the Red Hills region of South Georgia and North Florida from many aspects, but we were unable to find any documents that compiled the information known about this region into one source. We further discovered that the portion of the region that lies north of the Florida-Georgia border was vastly under-represented in the literature. Thomas College therefore proposed to undertake a project that would address both these problems. We envisioned a multi-phase project that would begin with collecting existing knowledge about the region into a single report. The next several phases were to be directed by the gaps in the information discovered in the first phase and would include establishing centers of study for each of the areas of interest to continue research on an on-going basis. We also decided to establish the Thomas College Regional Resource Center to provide ready access to a reference collection of data relevant to the Red Hills region.

This report is not an exhaustive effort to compile every scrap of data known about the Red Hills region. Rather, we focused our efforts on the region north of the Florida-Georgia border and the border region itself. We sifted through the available data on our study region and have compiled a representative picture of the region without attempting to find and present every detail currently known. Indeed, future endeavors will continue to expand the compilation of known data while investigating and reporting data unreported elsewhere. When these investigations are finished, the study region will be the most well-documented region in the country, and the data gathered will make planning for future growth and environmental quality possible in a way not available to other regions of the country. Governments and citizens will have an unprecedented opportunity to use wisely and to conserve for future generation the resource found in this unique region.

Each chapter presents an overview of the current state of knowledge, a discussion of the area of the study focus, and recommendations for future areas of investigation. The report relates new data on economic trends and geologic features, and it discusses implications. Taken together, these five study areas show that the Red Hills region in general, and our study area in particular, is a unique area that needs the utmost care and protection to preserve its special qualities for succeeding generations. The state of Georgia is currently involved in a process that will designate the Red Hills region as a "Regionally Important Resource." This fact lends additional emphasis to the contention that this region must be protected and studied.

We have begun the vast undertaking of studying the Red Hills region in an integrated way, and we hope that this study and subsequent studies will form the strong foundation for the protection of the entire Red Hills region.

EXECUTIVE SUMMARIES

CHAPTER 1: ECOLOGICAL RESOURCES

The Red Hills region encompasses an area of rolling topography, rich clayey sands and karst formations. These physiographic conditions provide a variety of settings for natural community development. Sands and clays occupy hilltops and uplands, which are bisected by ravines and drainageways with silty and organic soils. Underlying the entire area is the highly soluble Suwannee limestone, resulting in numerous sinkhole depressions and distinctive "internal" drainage. Key ecological processes interacting with these physiographic conditions have created a distinctive mix of plant and animal communities and have greatly influenced the resulting settlement patterns.

Fire and weather are two natural processes that have a significant impact on natural community composition and structure. Growing season fire is essential to the perpetuation of most plant communities and to the long-term survival of many species of plants and animals. Normal seasonal variability of weather patterns affects fire behavior, while extremes of drought, flooding or storms can quickly change the character of regional biota. In addition to these two natural processes, two human-induced processes have shaped the region significantly: virgin or untouched plant communities have been replaced by man-induced disturbance/succession communities of entirely different composition; and fragmentation of formerly contiguous natural communities by development threatens the ecological integrity of the historic Red Hills ecosystem.

Natural communities are distinct assemblages of plants and animals that exist along ecological gradients. Xeric and mesic uplands are found on hills and ridgetops. Mesic flatlands occupy extensive flats. At the base of hills, seepage slopes and wet flatlands support transitional wetland communities. Floodplain wetlands line the various types of riverine communities, while basin wetlands fill depressions or surround lacustrine lakes and ponds. Unique rockland habitats are associated with sinkholes and steep depressions. Several plant communities characteristic of the region include: long-leaf pine/wiregrass sandhills, mixed hardwood forest, pine/palmetto flatwoods, wet prairies, pitcher plant seepage bogs, bottomland forests, cypress swamp, mixed floodplain forest, freshwater marsh, sinkhole lake, seepage stream and alluvial stream.

Among the hundreds of plants and animals that occur in the region, 43 animals and 22 plants are identified as endangered or potentially endangered by the Georgia Natural Heritage program are indigenous to the Red Hills region. Only 11 listed species have been documented during biological surveys of local plantations. One federally listed endangered bird, the red-cockaded woodpecker, reaches its highest population levels on private lands found in the extensive mature pine forests of the study area.

Although a field survey of the area was not conducted, certain types of natural areas are identified and their occurrence classified as a significant natural area. These include undisturbed "virgin" soils, old growth long leaf pine stands, mature hardwood forests and other pine stands, wetlands, sinkholes, and habitat for endangered, threatened or rare species. In addition, the Red Hills region as a whole represents a significant natural area in and of itself.

There has been a long history of human use of the area. As economic, political and other conditions changed over time, the nature and intensity of use varied to reflect the new conditions. Agricultural use by native peoples, cotton farming, consolidation of abandoned cotton plantations into winter retreats and hunting reserves, and current suburbanization all have played their part in making the region what it is today. The process continues and the future of the Red Hills region will be shaped by how the current generation deals with the elements of change. Significant issues facing owners today include: pressure to develop or break up plantations due to property tax changes or estate tax requirements; linear projects like pipelines and transmission lines targeting this green area with large landowners as an easy route; changes in timber management and harvest practices away from single tree selection of mature timber; and game bird management practices, specifically increasing growing-season prescribed burning and elimination of the creation of new food plots on virgin soil.

The natural and historical resource values of the area are being recognized locally, regionally, and nationally. Individual plantation owners are granting conservation easements over significant natural areas to non-profit conservation corporations such as Tall Timbers Research Station and The Nature Conservancy. Collectively, many plantation owners have formed the Red Hills Conservation Association under the auspices of Tall Timbers to advocate for the owners and provide a forum for information exchange. Funding has been secured by 1000 Friends of Florida to design the Apalachee Greenways Project to link the ecological, recreational, and cultural resources of the Red Hills region with those of the Gulf coast of Florida.

To fill information gaps and create a better data base for decision making about regional resources, a vegetation and land cover map of the area must be developed. This map should be supplemented by detailed biological surveys of listed species habitats, virgin soil areas and old growth forest communities. The existing research programs need to be expanded and additional methods of providing technical assistance developed. The future of the region will rely on our ability to integrate man's activities into the natural world while minimizing disruption and maintaining economic return or other desirable productivity.

CHAPTER 2: ECONOMICS AND DEMO-GRAPHICS

This economic/demographic analysis of the Red Hills establishes an economic and demographic database for a portion of the Red Hills region; quantifies the role that plantations play in the local economy; and examines the impacts of regional economic and demographic trends on the plantations.

The northern portions of Leon County have been and will continue to be the fastest growing areas in the region. The primary limiting factor to even more growth in this region is the availability of land. The degree to which plantation land is converted to residential development will dictate the rate and amount of growth in the region. Between 1976 and 1991, more than 35,000 acres of plantations were converted into subdivisions — with most of this conversion taking place in northern Leon County. The northward movement of growth from Tallahassee combined with the fact the land development is cheaper and quicker in Georgia means that the study area will be subject to significant development pressures over the next several decades.

Leon County is the employment center for the region with more than three times the employment of the other counties, combined. Manufacturing is the most important employment sector in the Grady and Thomas counties. Thomas County has 70 percent more manufacturing jobs than Leon County. Farming, which was once important in all counties, is now only significant in Jefferson County. Retail trade, services and governmental employment are important to the economies of all four counties.

Plantations contribute to the local economy through expenditures for operations and maintenance activities as well as timber harvesting. The plantations in the study area spend almost $3.2 million annually for operations and maintenance in terms of salaries, supplies, etc. Timber production contributes another $0.7 million per year. Thus, the plantations in the study area directly contribute more than $3.9 million to the local economy. These expenditures result in an indirect impact of an additional 102 jobs, increased earnings of $1.9 million, and increased economic output of $8.4 million.

Plantations in the study area paid property taxes of more then $280,000. On average, plantations paid more taxes per acre than similar large parcels being used for forestry and/or farming. On a fiscal impact basis, plantations provide more taxes than they require in terms of governmental services.

From an environmental perspective, the plantations provide a number of benefits. First, the study area provides for an average daily water recharge of 53 million gallons. Second, the plantations provide more than 57,000 acres of nearly contiguous wildlife habitat which in many cases is professional managed. Third, the plantations have low amounts of impervious surfaces and thus low levels of storm water runoff.

CHAPTER 3: ARCHAEOLOGY

This archaeological study is part of a larger investigation of the Red Hills region in Grady and Thomas counties, Georgia. The goals are to determine what is already known about the region, to generate potential questions for future research, and to help educate the public of the value of cultural resources as finite, non-renewable resources. Research activities included interviews with informants, literature review, and limited field work. The chapter provides an overview of each culture period, summarizes current knowledge, identifies future research questions, and serves as a framework for evaluating the significance of particular sites. The project was not a comprehensive survey of archaeological sites in the region, but a preliminary statement of existing knowledge and future potentials.

The chapter concludes with a recommendation for archaeological surveys and historic structure surveys to locate and evaluate sites. Significant sites need to be preserved and may be eligible for nomination to the National Register of Historic Places.

The chapter is organized into fourteen culture periods or themes: Paleo-Indian; Archaic; Woodland, including Deptford, Swift Creek and Weeden Island; Mississippi period Fort Walton; European contact/Hernando do Soto; the Spanish Mission period; Early 19th Century Native American, European American and African American interactions; Antebellum Plantations; 19th century towns; the Civil war; and tenant farms, hotels and hunting plantations.

Interviews with residents and examination of collections verify that Paleo-Indian artifacts (12,000-9500 years before present [B.P.]) are present in the region but in low numbers. Archaic artifacts (9500-3000 B.P. or 1000 B.C.) are abundant and widespread, though often described as isolated finds representing hunters' "campsites"; surveys are needed to determine if larger sites are also present. The Woodland period, subdivided into Deptford (500 B.C. to A.D. 100), Swift Creek (A.D. 100-300) and Weeden Island (A.D. 300-900), is a time of the first settled villages, domesticated plants and mounds. Deptford Check Stamped pottery sherds are present in collections from Grady and Thomas counties, but site locations are uncertain. Few Swift Creek sherds were seen, though likely more exist, as few people collect pottery. A large mound along the Ochlocknee River may contain Deptford and Swift Creek components. The Weeden Island "heartland" blanketed Southwest Georgia, including the Balfour Mound in Grady County; two possibly related sites are nearby. Fort Walton (A.D. 900-1600), a variant of the Mississippian culture, is known from sites just across the state line in Florida; several Fort Walton sherds in Grady and Thomas counties verify the extension into Georgia. Hernando de Soto's army probably marched through current Grady or Thomas County in A.D. 1540, but no sites or artifacts are known. Equally little is known about Spanish mission period sites, though at least one sherd was seen in a collection from the region.

Potential future research questions deal with chronology, regional settlement patterns, local community patterns, cultural adaptations to changing environmental conditions, subsistence strategies, mobility, demography, and social organization. For example, how are the sites distributed across the landscape during different time periods? How are they situated in relation to environmental features? What are the site sizes and number of sites in each period? What were the consequences of plant domestication? Of European contact?

Southwest Georgia offers opportunities for the study of interactions among three ethnic groups — Native Americans, African Americans, and European Americans. Archaeological sites and historical data are also available for the study of what frontier settlements looked like - blacksmith shops, livery stables, stagecoach stops, taverns, stores (by 1827 in Thomasville), churches, homes, and later a Civil War prison camp. Also, many existing antebellum plantations offer outstanding opportunities for the study of slave, overseer and planters' housing, diet and lifestyles, for comparison with coastal Georgia tidewater plantations already studied by archaeologists. Finally, the sites of tenant farms, resort hotels and hunting plantations represent the system by which the Red Hills region prospered economically after the Civil War while other regions of Georgia stagnated. All these cultural patterns contained factors which may still be relevant to today's continued economic prosperity, community identity, and community survival.

CHAPTER 4: HISTORY

The historic overview of a portion of the Red Hills region is intended to provide a historic context for the consideration and understanding of the other sections of this document.

The information which follows was limited to material presently on file with Thomasville Landmarks, Inc. No additional research, either primary or secondary, was conducted due to the time constraints placed upon the organization. The historic component provides an overview of Thomas and Grady County history and focuses primarily upon those properties and communities currently listed on the National Register of Historic Places.

Readers should understand this is not a definitive history since much research outside the Red Hill's Region's "Resort Era" and its associated properties should be undertaken. Research seeking knowledge of the region's original English speaking settlers, information about tenant farming tradition, and material concerning Southwest Georgia's black experience are but a few of the areas in which research could be gathered.

The chapter presents themes in Southwest Georgia history. It also discusses settlement patterns, transportation routes, rural properties, and the establishment of Cairo and Thomasville, Georgia. This portion of the document relates some of the area's local history and conveys the need for protecting and preserving the region's fragile and unique architectural and environmental resources.

CHAPTER 5: GEOLOGY

For most of the last 100 million years (and more) the south Grady - south Thomas county area was dominated by a marine environment, periodically separating mainland Georgia from the Florida Peninsula. By the end of the Miocene Epoch (more than five million years ago), the last of the local inter-connection between Gulf and Atlantic waters had been filled with sediments, and the area became more typically marginal marine. For about the last two million years, the area has been above sea-level and subject to continental-type erosion processes.

Thick sediments deposited in the last Gulf-Atlantic interconnection, the Apalachicola Embayment-Gulf Trough, consist of both marine and land-derived materials and exert a strong geological influence over the western part of the area. Equivalent sediments in eastern portions are often more typically marine in origin. The most recent sedimentary layer (about three million years old) is land-derived and blankets the entire area, except where erosion has removed it.

Groundwater in the project area is mainly produced from the Floridan Aquifer, which is an important source of water in Alabama, Florida, Georgia and South Carolina. The Floridan locally consists mainly of permeable limestones and dolostones and ranges from about 850 feet thick near Metcalf to about 400-500 feet in western parts of the area. The aquifer normally produces acceptable quantities of fairly good quality water, although both the quantity and quality are often reduced in the Apalachicola Embayment-Gulf Trough area (west part of study area). Water in the Floridan is recharged locally, often at high rates, by rainfall (up to about twenty inches per year). In some areas, sediments overlying the Floridan are of relatively low permeability and serve to reduce local recharge, especially in western parts of the area. The aquifer is often artesian, locally, and has been described as "semi-confined or un-confined" by overlying sediments.

The combination of all water withdrawals in the area (including the City of Thomasville, at over four million gallons per day) does not appear to tax the aquifer.

Given the local importance of surface-groundwater interactions, sink holes and other evidences of "internal" drainage as well as thickness of sediments overlying the Floridan were considered good indicators for analysis. Nearly 200 sinkholes were identified in and immediately adjacent to the area by the use of topographic maps. A great majority of these were in the eastern and southern parts of the area. Field observations indicated that a very substantial number of sinks do not appear on the topographic maps.

Surface drainage (streams) is dendritic and continuous in western portions of the area, while it was found to be often disorganized and discontinuous in eastern and southern area, with low stream density and a number of stream disappearances. Relative impermeability of soils was found to decrease from the west to the east, generally, which, along with the prevalence of sink holes, probably influences the drainage patterns.

Thickness of sediments overlying the Floridan Aquifer was found to vary from about 75 feet (or less) in low-lying southern and eastern localities to over 200 feet in areas that have not been as deeply eroded. In general, overlying sedimentary thicknesses were greater in western parts of the area.

The area has a rather substantial need for more information. Lack of adequate subsurface control and other determinations causes difficulties in structural, lithologic and hydrologic analyses, although general conclusions are warranted by existing data. Based on existing information, the quality of waters within the Floridan Aquifer is influenced by the quality of local surface waters (and vulnerable to any changes in them). The degree of influence surely varies from one locality to another; however, it is generally greatest and most direct in southern and eastern portions of the area, where capture of surface drainage by sink holes can be observed in the field.

CHAPTER 1: ECOLOGICAL RESOURCES

Steve Gatewood,
Ph. D.

This chapter describes and summarizes the species and natural communities present in the Red Hills area.

It also analyzes important ecosystem processes and indicates where existing data is inadequate.

INTRODUCTION

Project Description

This ecological resource assessment is designed to provide an initial description and summary of the species and natural communities present in the Red Hills area (identified in Figure 1.1). The study also offers an analysis of key ecological processes that drive ecosystem function. These aims are achieved through 1) the collection and assessment of existing information, 2) synthesis of data into a resource description, and 3) an indication of existing data inadequacies.

This investigation was designed as an assessment of the status of existing information. Extremely limited field time precluded any attempt to create new vegetation maps or develop detailed descriptions of localized conditions. Although such resource information will be essential to future planning, such an effort is well beyond the scope and budget for this portion of the project.

Structure

This chapter on ecological resources is divided into three sections. The regional setting is described, including a brief description of settlement patterns. Next, a resource description is provided that describes the natural communities found in the area. Species lists identify the expected and observed animal species from the Red Hills region and study area. Endangered, threatened and rare taxa are discussed, as well as significant natural features. Finally, a discussion of resource trends, protection tools and information gaps completes the body of the chapter.

The references section identifies the key literature used. Included are individuals and institutions especially valuable in understanding the ecology of this area.

The appendices include long lists, publications, and brochures inappropriate for the text of the chapter. A large amount of other information collected during this study has been given to Thomas College for inclusion in the Thomas College Regional Resource Center.

At this time, individual plantations will not be identified due to the confidential nature of the data collected and at the request of the plantation owners.

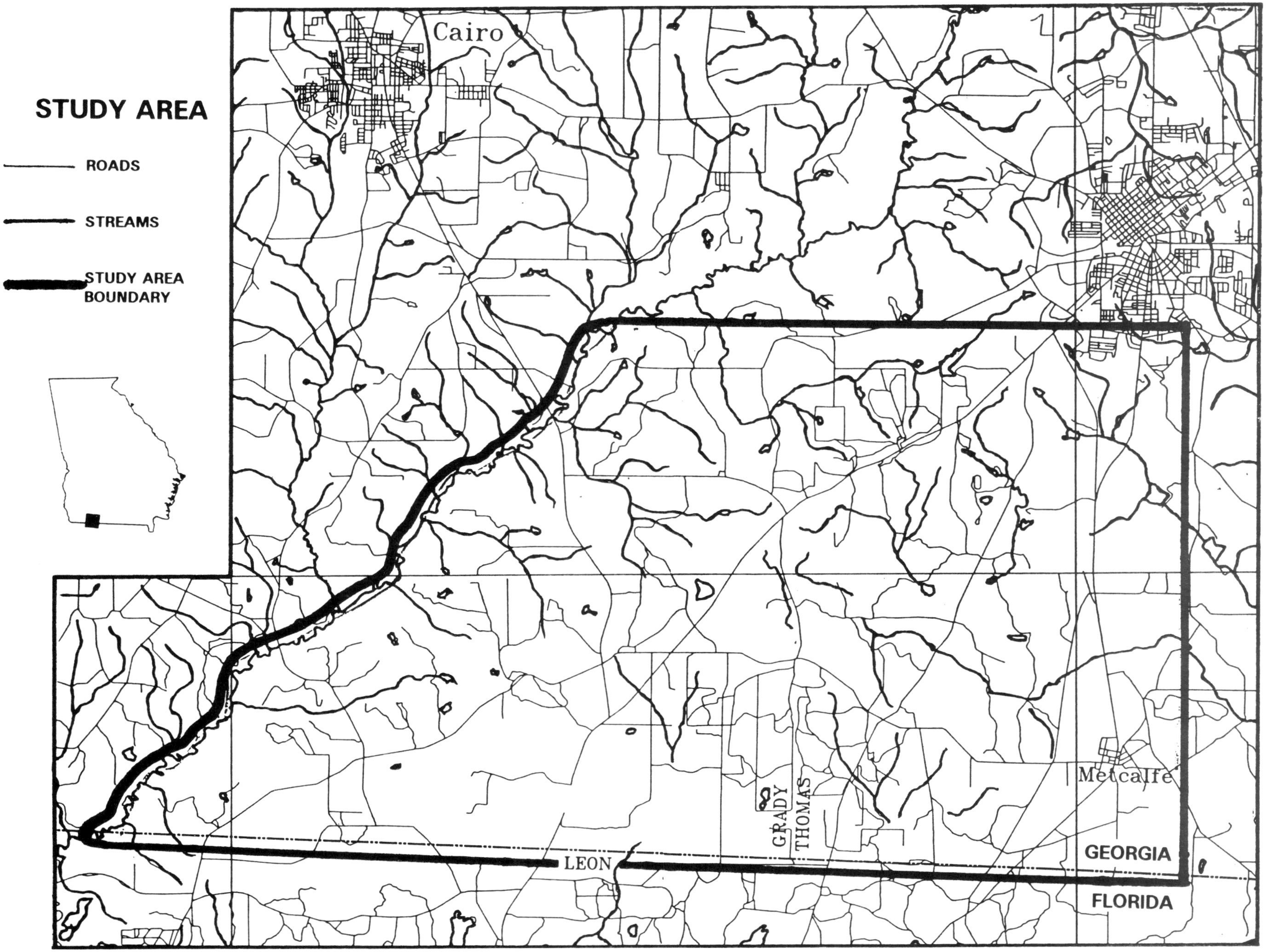

STUDY AREA

——— ROADS

——— STREAMS

━━━ STUDY AREA BOUNDARY

Cairo

LEON

GRADY
THOMAS

Metcalfe

GEORGIA
FLORIDA

FIGURE 1.1   Location and Base Map of the Study Area.

REGIONAL SETTING

Physiography

The Red Hills region of South Georgia and North Florida encompasses an area of rolling topography, rich clayey sands and karst formations. Burleigh (1958), Clewell (1978) and Paisley (1989) each provide a discussion of the region's physiography. Key characteristics will be described in more detail in the companion portion of the project addressing geology and groundwater resources. Certain characteristics of the physiography help define the ecological systems found here and are described below.

The rolling topography, which results from the influences of erosion, soil characteristics and karst geology, provides a variety of settings for natural community development. Hilltops and uplands are bisected by ravines and drainageways. Creek bottoms and large basins are scattered throughout the landscape contributing to a diversity of landforms. The underlying Suwannee limestone is overlain by dense clays of the Hawthorn Formation, which is then overlain by the surficial clayey sands of the Miccosukee Formation.

Three major soil groups from the Thomas County soil survey (USDA/UGA, 1979) are used to characterize the study area. They are as follows:

> Orangeburg-Dothan-Faceville — Well drained soils on nearly level to sloping uplands with a reddish or brownish sandy or loamy sand surface layer and a loamy or clayey subsoil. (38% of Thomas Co.)

> Tifton-Alapaha-Fuquay — Well drained soils on gently sloping uplands and along drainageways with a brownish sandy or loamy surface layer and a loamy mottled subsoil. Also nearly level, somewhat poorly drained soils in depressions or on flats with a grayish sandy surface layer and grayish or brownish loamy mottled subsoil. (54% of Thomas Co.)

> Osier-Pelham-Ocilla — Poorly drained soils on floodplains, stream terraces, and low uplands with a grayish or brownish sandy surface layer and a grayish or brownish mottled sandy subsoil. (8% of Thomas Co.)

The upland clayey and loamy sands are rich in nutrients and cation exchange capacity and produce large amounts of plant biomass. A complex combination of plant communities developed on these rich soils, generally shaped by the influences of fire regime and soil moisture. The high, sandy soils exhibit xeric/mesic conditions, the intermediate loamy and clayey soils a mesic environment, and the flat sands and depressions have mesic/hydric conditions. Deep organic soil (Dasher muck) supports hydric and aquatic communities.

Due to the highly soluble nature of the Suwannee limestone beneath the region, numerous karst features are present. Generally, the thick clays of the Miccosukee and Hawthorn formations shield the limestone from surface runoff. However, these clays were laid on an unstable base that has collapsed in places and allows runoff to enter fissures, sinkholes, and other openings at many locations. Creeks disappear underground or drain into solution basins with no surface outlet. Although limestone is rarely exposed at the surface, its influence on the topography and drainage is pronounced. As discussed earlier, this subject will be addressed in greater detail in the groundwater/geology chapter.

Climate

Southwest Georgia supports a temperate climate just north of the sub-tropics. Summers are warm and humid with winters being short and mild. Due to its proximity to the Gulf of Mexico and Atlantic Ocean, relative humidity is high. Convective thunderstorm activity characterizes the warmer months and continental frontal activity the cooler season. Major weather events occurring on an infrequent but consistent basis include tornados, hurricanes, and drought.

Average annual temperature at Thomasville is 67.6° F, with extremes of 104° and 7°. The highest monthly average is for July at 80.9°, and the lowest is January at 51.3°. An average of 84 days per year are above 90° degrees, and 34 days fall below 32°. The first freeze usually occurs around November 25, and the last freeze around March 3.

Precipitation at Thomasville averages 51.76 inches per year. The highest monthly average is associated with summer thunderstorms in July, and totals 6.15 inches. Monthly maximum was 15.84 inches, and the daily max was 8.99 inches. Fall is the dry season with October's average totaling only 2.15 inches. Some droughts have seen more than one month pass without rainfall and annual totals of less than 20 inches.

Ecological Processes

Numerous processes affect the ecological systems of an area, including nutrient cycling, decomposition, food webs, and others. Two key ecological processes will be discussed in reference to the study area because of their unique and profound impact: fire and weather. In addition, the response of the biota to several man-induced conditions fall into the arena of processes: plant community succession and habitat fragmentation/ecosystem integrity.

Fire. Natural ignition fires were one of the most influential processes on the ecological systems of the study area. The frequency, intensity, seasonality, and spread of fire all contribute to its ability to shape natural community composition and structure. Early naturalists described the uplands of South Georgia as dominated by open, park-like pine forests with a grassy ground cover. This condition is maintained by frequent, low intensity ground fires ignited by lightning, primarily in the early summer thunderstorm season. The fire may burn over entire areas for thousands of acres, or result in patchy burns over only a few square miles. Usually hardwood forests and swamps were spared, but they too were occasionally burned. Many factors affected its behavior. Most plants and animals are adapted to fire and many species are dependent on fire for their long term survival. Three examples of this dependance within fire maintained communities are longleaf pine (*Pinus palustris*), wiregrass (*Aristida stricta*), and the red-cockaded woodpecker (*Picoides borealis*).

Native Americans recognized fire as a tool to alter their environment and probably used it to maintain game populations, open up the forest for travel, and clear land for agriculture. European man viewed wildfire as dangerous and sought to control, suppress, and eliminate all fire. Through development of the landscape with towns, fields, and roads, he inadvertently blocked fire's historic spread. Then when fire was finally recognized as a tool to enhance grazing, for wildlife habitat improvement and for enhanced timber management, the seasonality was shifted to winter to aid in control and fire management. The recent development of the principles of ecologically prescribed fire by natural resource land managers has resulted in efforts to mimic the natural fire regime to the greatest degree possible.

<u>Weather</u>. Variability of weather patterns has a great deal of influence on ecological systems. As discussed in the climate section, variations, and extremes of rainfall and temperature are experienced, and affect plants and animals. The relationship of rainfall to groundwater is also important, especially as it relates to wetland communities. Tropical storms, however, are the weather factors most likely to have recurring, significant impact on regional biota. Because the region is a forest-dominated landscape, the strong winds associated with powerful hurricanes that sweep over the area can level large regional landscapes and dramatically change the environmental conditions in a matter of days. Intense rainfall also affects the area due to prolonged flooding. It is difficult for individual species or entire ecosystems to adapt to such forces when most of the forest structure is destroyed and the process of plant community succession must proceed from the conditions that resulted from the storm's impact.

<u>Plant Community Succession</u>. When some form of disturbance removes the forest community, the vegetation proceeds through a process of recolonization and renewal leading over time to the original community. Succession from recurring natural events usually leads to essentially the same community over predictable time periods. However, when man is the cause of the disturbance, many conditions may change and the end product of succession may not be the same.

Most of the study area has been disturbed by man to the degree that the existing communities do not represent the species composition and structure that existed naturally. Where the ground has not been disturbed and "virgin" land (undisturbed soils) exist, the intact natural communities represent significant ecological resources. Communities that develop on old field lands may appear similar to native communities, but species composition, especially in the ground cover vegetation, is radically different.

<u>Habitat Fragmentation/Ecosystem Integrity</u>. The Red Hills ecosystem once covered hundreds of thousands of acres and consisted of a mosaic of distinct natural communities that were interrelated through fairly stable climatic and geologic conditions. Although conditions were quite different just 10,000 years ago, for the past few thousand years the same basic communities have occupied or recolonized this region. Native Americans altered the landscape to a certain degree, but not until colonization by European man did large scale development of the landscape proceed to where undisturbed habitat fragments now exist in a sea of disturbed communities.

Towns, farms, roads, utility corridors and other types of land use effectively isolate patches of native land from each other and from historically contiguous community types. Wetlands may now be next to farm fields and pastures instead of native pine or hardwood forest. Pine forests are surrounded by development that interferes with the natural spread of wildfire, resulting in a pinelands invasion by hardwoods formerly excluded by fire. Large free-ranging mammals, like panthers, can no longer roam around the 50,000 plus acres they need as a home range. Entire watersheds are altered as hydrology changes and sources of pollution are introduced. Exotic species are brought in, or formerly benign native species are "released" to overpower the natural balance of native communities.

All of these factors and others combine to isolate fragments of natural communities from each other and from natural processes. The long term viability of native populations may be compromised as patches become smaller and more isolated. Larger areas of habitat are better able to support the species and processes that formerly occupied large areas. Rare, endemic or critical species may lose the narrow set of conditions that allowed them to survive. Some communities, such as isolated wetlands, were small patchy habitats originally. But unless they remain surrounded by the large natural landscape within which they developed, their long term stability is unknown.

Settlement Patterns

Evidence of hunter and gatherer native peoples dates back almost to 10,000 years BP (before present). They lived near the coast but traveled inland for game and other materials. Evidence of crops such as maize and beans appears about 1,000 BP. Agriculture developed such that when the first Spanish explorers arrived in the early to mid 1500's, the area between Thomasville, Georgia, and Tallahassee, Florida was almost entirely cropland. European missions replaced the Indian fields, and by the 1700's, much of the land lay fallow.

The cotton era began in the early 1800's with the creation of large plantations supported by slave labor. Stoddard (1969) estimated that 75-90% of the area between Thomasville and Tallahassee was cleared before the Civil War. By the late 1800's, the cotton market had declined and many plantation fields were abandoned. Some were farmed by sharecroppers or small plot farmers. Successional forest cover quickly occupied fields that were not farmed.

In the late 1800's and early 1900's, most of the remaining cotton plantations were purchased by Northern industrialists as winter residences and hunting preserves. The preferred game species was bobwhite quail, and plantation managers developed a system of land management that favored open forests of mature trees and an open grassy ground cover. Winter fire was introduced to maintain the open park-like conditions. Small fields and wildlife food plots replaced the extensive croplands of previous agricultural operations. Timber management practices were adopted that favored single tree selection of large diameter, high value products. This type of management continues today over most of the study area. Existing plantation boundaries for the study area and Red Hills region are mapped in Figure 1.2.

RESOURCE DESCRIPTION

Natural Communities

The Red Hills region supports a diverse mix of natural communities. However, no map or detailed description of local conditions could be found. Two principal sources were used to create a description of 27 natural communities known to be present from previous field work and from the limited field work conducted during this study: "The Natural Environments of Georgia" (Wharton, 1978) and "Guide to the Natural Communities of Florida" (FNAI, 1990). The descriptions in this chapter follow the format of the Florida publication.

Xeric Uplands: Dry ridge tops and hills with deep, well-drained sandy soils and low-moisture adapted species.

> **Sandhill.** This xeric forest is characterized by an open canopy of widely spaced longleaf pine trees with a sparse understory of deciduous oaks and a fairly dense ground cover of grasses and herbs. Typical stands are dominated by longleaf pine, turkey oak, and wiregrass. Other plants include bluejack oak, sand post oak, sparkleberry, persimmon, winged sumac, Indian

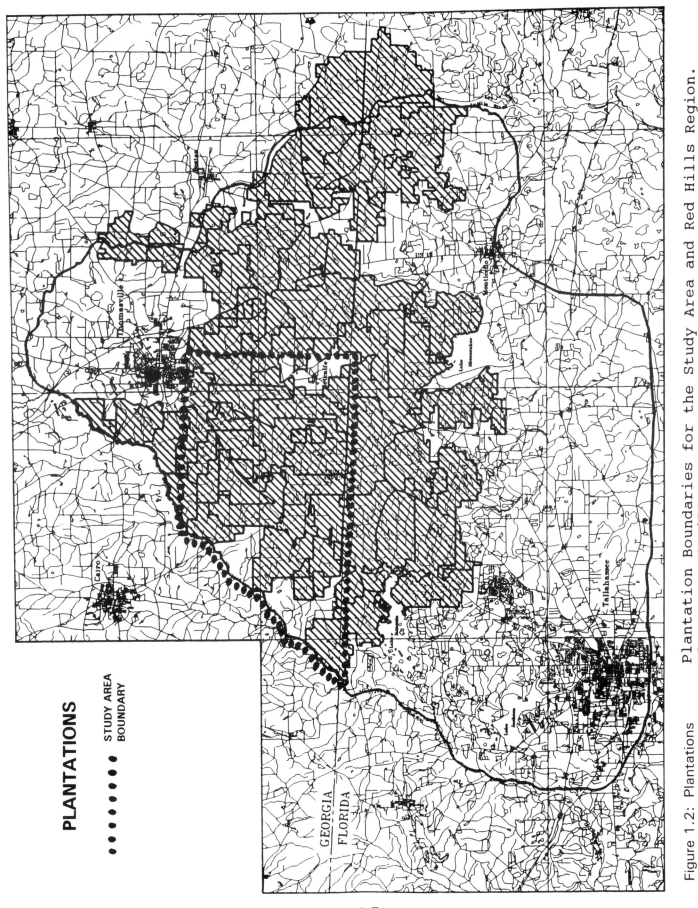

PLANTATIONS

●●●●●●● STUDY AREA
BOUNDARY

Figure 1.2: Plantations

Plantation Boundaries for the Study Area and Red Hills Region.
(Source: Red Hills Conservation Association)

1-7

grass, wild buckwheat, partridge pea, milk pea, wild indigo, gopher apple, golden aster, and bracken fern. Typical animals include spadefoot toad, gopher tortoise, fence lizard, indigo snake, pine snake, coachwhip snake, eastern diamondback rattlesnake, bobwhite quail, red-headed woodpecker, red-cockaded woodpecker, rufous-sided towhee, fox squirrel, and pocket gopher.

Pure sandhill is limited in the study area due to the presence of loam and clay in the soil. It occurs on deep, marine-deposited, yellowish sands that are excessively well drained and relatively sterile. Sandhills are usually important aquifer recharge areas because the porous sand allows water to move quickly through with little runoff and minimal evaporation. Temperature and humidity fluctuations are generally greater than in closed canopy forests.

Fire is a dominant factor in this community. Sandhill is a fire climax habitat, highly dependent on frequent ground fires to prevent hardwood encroachment and perpetuate pines and grasses. Natural fire frequency is estimated at every two to five years.

Mesic Uplands: Dry to moist hills of sand with varying amounts of clay, silt or organic material; diverse mixture of broad leaved and needle leaved temperate woody trees and shrubs.

Upland Pine Forest. This mesic forest community is similar to the drier sandhill with an open forest canopy on rolling upland hills. Pristine areas are dominated by longleaf pine and wiregrass, while disturbed areas are generally dominated by shortleaf and loblolly pine, and old field grasses. Other typical plants include southern red oak, runner oak, bluejack oak, post oak, sassafras, black cherry, mockernut hickory, sweetgum, blackgum, flowering dogwood, gallberry, huckleberry, dangleberry, goldenrod, snakeroot, goats rue, partridge pea, Indian grass, plume grass, grape vines, greenbriar, yellow jessamine, and bracken fern. Typical animals include fence lizard, gopher tortoise, box turtle, eastern diamondback rattlesnake, bobwhite quail, red-bellied woodpecker, red-cockaded woodpecker, gray fox, bobcat, white-tailed deer, cotton mouse, and cotton rat.

Upland pine forest occurs on hills of sand with variable, sometimes substantial, amounts of Miocene clays. The rich soil helps retain moisture and allows for much greater production of biomass than sandhills. This is the most common upland community of the study area, both now and in the past.

Fire is a dominant factor in this community because it reduces hardwood encroachment and facilitates longleaf pine and wiregrass reproduction. Without relatively frequent fire, two to five years, upland pine rapidly succeeds to upland mixed forest and eventually upland hardwood forest. Loblolly and shortleaf pine are more sensitive to fire than longleaf, especially in the seedling and sapling stages.

Upland Hardwood Forest and Upland Mixed Forest. These two upland communities are characterized by well developed, closed canopy forests of hardwoods, with scattered pines in the mixed forest. They have quite similar physical environments and similar species, and are the most diverse of the study area. Trees and shrubs include American beech, southern magnolia, pignut hickory, sweetgum, laurel oak, live oak, swamp chestnut oak, white oak, water oak, basswood, persimmon, red cedar, red mulberry, redbay, laurel cherry, black cherry, black gum, winged elm, spruce pine, loblolly pine, shortleaf pine, wild olive, horse sugar, redbud, flowering dogwood, American holly, American hornbeam, eastern hophornbeam, Hercules's club, devil's walking stick, sparkleberry, beautyberry, strawberry bush, fringe tree, witch hazel, passion vine, trumpet creeper, summer grape, and Virginia creeper. Ground cover is usually sparse, but may include partridge berry, hammock grass, cane, eastern gamma grass, sedges, trilliums, bedstraw, Indian pipes, and beech drops. Typical animals include slimy salamander, gray treefrog, bronze frog, box turtle, green anole, broadhead skink, ground skink, eastern glass lizard, red-bellied snake, coral snake, gray rat snake, rough green snake, woodcock, barred owl, piliated woodpecker, shrews, eastern mole, gray squirrel, flying squirrel, wood rat, cotton mouse, gray fox, and white-tailed deer.

Upland hardwood and mixed forests occur on rolling to steep topography with rich soils. Dense clay or limestone rock is often near the surface. There is usually a thick, well developed organic layer of leaf litter; this helps retain moisture and nutrients. Tree falls and other downed logs are an important component of this community. The dense canopy and multiple vegetation strata keep light penetration and air movement low, making the humidity high and relatively stable.

These are the climax communities for this area. Spruce pine is shade tolerant and can reproduce in the light gaps of tree falls. Fire is uncommon and is usually catastrophic. These communities are most common on locations sheltered from fire by wetlands, slopes or other physical features.

Rockland: Limestone exposed through karst activity.

Sinkhole. The only rockland community known from the study area is the sinkhole, a cylindrical or conical depression generally with steep slopes and limestone exposed. The depression may be quite small like a funnel or large like a basin. Limestone exposed around the edges of a large basin is called a grotto. Those which drain readily and only contain water during or shortly after heavy rains are considered sinkholes, while those which contain permanent water are considered sinkhole lakes. A combination can exist when the lower part is flooded and the upper part exposed. New sinkholes usually fill in over long periods and become marshes and swamps. The distinctions between sinkholes and related communities in the area are subtle as one very gradually succeeds to another.

Typical upland hardwood and mixed forest communities occupy the upper portions of a sink where soil above the collapsing limestone remains. Lower on the slope where the influence of limestone creates a calcareous soil or exposed rock, mosses liverworts, ferns, and a few herbs are characteristic. The sinkhole frequently provides habitat for salamanders, reptiles, and numerous invertebrates.

Sinkholes generally have a very moist microclimate. The depression and forest canopy helps protect the interior from desiccating winds and sunlight. Additionally, seepage from surrounding uplands may moisten the walls and contribute to high humidity. These conditions help buffer temperature and moisture extremes and allow sub-tropical species to be found farther north than would normally be expected.

Mesic Flatlands: Flat, moderately well-drained sandy substrate with a mixture of organic material, often with a hard pan layer.

Mesic Flatwoods. Due to the rolling topography and rich soils of the region, mesic flatwoods are limited in the study area. The community is characterized by an open to moderately dense canopy of pine trees over a dense ground cover of shrubs, herbs, and grasses. Several variations of flatwoods are possible, depending on the mix of dominant species, including longleaf, slash and loblolly pine, gallberry, fetterbush, staggerbush, saw palmetto, wax myrtle, blueberries, St. Johns wort, false foxglove, white topped aster, wiregrass, and yellow-eyed grass. Typical animals include oak toad, narrow-mouth toad, little grass frog, black racer, red rat snake, southeastern kestrel, brown-headed nuthatch, pine warbler, cotton rat, cotton mouse, raccoon, black bear, gray fox, bobcat, and white-tailed deer.

Mesic flatwoods occur on relatively flat, moderately to poorly drained terrain. The soils consist of one to three feet of acidic sand overlying a hard pan or clayey subsoil. The hardpan or subsoil affects water percolation and root penetration. During the rainy season, water frequently perches above the dense layer and briefly inundates the flatwoods; while during the drier season, groundwater below the layer is beyond the confined roots of many plants. Thus the community is under the stress of water saturation during the wet season and the stress of dehydration during the dry season.

As with most pine dominated communities, fire is an important factor in flatwoods. Natural frequency on the order of one to eight years was typical. Without frequent fire, the community will succeed to a hardwood dominated forest or fuel loads build up quickly, and a severe fire will kill most of the forest vegetation.

Wet Flatlands: Flat, poorly drained sand substrate.

Wet Flatwoods. Wet flatwoods are similar to mesic flatwoods in structure, but with a species assemblage typical of longer periods of saturation and inundation. Characteristic species include longleaf, slash or pond pine, sweetbay, loblolly bay, titi, gallberry, spikerush, beakrush, sedges, deer tongue, greenbriar, wiregrass, bluestems, and pitcher plants. Animals include oak toad, cricket frog, chorus frog, yellow rat snake, pygmy rattlesnake, red-shouldered hawk, opossum, cottontail rabbit, cotton rat, cotton mouse, striped skunk, bobcat, black bear, and white-tailed deer.

Substrate conditions are similar to mesic flatwoods as is the presence of frequent fire. Open, herbaceous communities have a fire frequency of one to five years, while thick shrubby types are more like three to eight years.

Wet Prairie. This community is typically a flat, treeless plain with a sparse to dense ground cover of grasses and herbs, including wiregrass, toothache grass, maidencane, beakrush, sedges, hatpins, marsh pink, star grass, meadowbeauty, yellow-eyed grass, sundews, and pitcher plants. Shrubs like titi, wax myrtle, staggerbush and gallberry may be present. Typical animals include cricket frog, chorus frog, little grass frog, black racer, yellow rat snake, pygmy rattlesnake, northern harrier, killdeer, long-billed marsh wren, red-winged blackbird, marsh rabbit, cotton rat, and cotton mouse.

Wet prairie occurs on low, flat, poorly-drained terrain, often adjacent to other deeper wetland communities. Soils usually consist of sands, often exhibiting a substantial clay or organic component. Hydrology and fire are important physical factors: the community remains saturated or shallowly inundated from two to three months each year and burns every two to four years. Shrubs will invade wet prairies quickly if duration of flooding is reduced or fire eliminated. Generally, wet prairies have a much shorter hydroperiod than other wetland communities and are subject to prolonged annual desiccation.

<u>Seepage Wetlands</u>: Sloped or flat sands or peat with high moisture levels maintained by downslope seepage.

Seepage Slope. These wetlands are characterized as shrub thickets or boggy meadows on or at the base of a slope where moisture from upslope saturates the ground constantly but rarely inundates it. They occur where water percolating down through permeable sands reaches an impermeable layer of clay or rock and moves laterally to seep out the side of a hill. Typical plants include pond pine, longleaf pine, slash pine, titi, black titi, fetterbush, myrtle-leaved holly, gallberry, odorless wax myrtle, dog hobble, sweet pepperbush, Virginia willow, wiregrass, beak rush, hatpins, yellow-eyed grass, chain fern, orchids, pitcher plants, and sundews. Typical animals include squirrel tree frog, ribbon snake, rough green snake, cottonmouth, marsh rabbit, and black bear.

Seepage slopes occur on acidic, loamy sands that have low nutrient availability and are constantly saturated except during drought. Small pools and rivulets may be common. Herb bogs have a one- to five-year fire frequency that restricts shrub invasion, while shrub bogs burn no more often than every 20-50 years.

Baygall. The baygall community is generally described as a densely forested, peat-filled seepage depression at the base of a hill. The canopy is typically a densely packed, evergreen hardwoods with sweet bay, swamp bay, and loblolly bay, with occasional dahoon holly, titi, and slash pine. Other plant species include fetterbush, large gallberry, wax myrtle, odorless wax myrtle, dog hobble, hurrah bush, red chokeberry, Virginia willow greenbriar, poison ivy, cinnamon fern, chain fern, netted chain fern, lizard's tail, and sphagnum moss. Typical animals include mole salamander, southern dusky salamander, southeastern shrew, short-tailed shrew, marsh rabbit, opossum, raccoon, southern mink, bobcat, and black bear.

Baygalls are on deep peat that remains saturated and occasionally inundated. The substrate is very acidic and usually subject to a high water table as well as downslope seepage. Since it is so wet, fire rarely burns this community — fire may occur every 50-100 years.

<u>Floodplain Wetlands</u>: Flat, alluvial mineral or organic substrate associated with riverine communities and subject to frequent flooding but not permanent inundation.

Bottomland Forest. This is the highest elevation floodplain community and is characterized by a low-lying, closed-canopy forest of tall, straight trees, primarily hardwoods. Typical plants include water oak, live oak, diamond-leaf oak, sweetgum, southern magnolia, American beech, Florida elm, red maple, spruce pine, loblolly pine, swamp dogwood, American holly, stiffcornel dogwood, American hornbeam, beautyberry, bluestem palmetto, and panicum grasses. Typical animals include marbled salamander, mole salamander, three-lined salamander, slimy salamander, five-lined skink, ringneck snake, gray rat snake, eastern king snake, red-tailed hawk, turkey, yellow-billed cuckoo, screech owl, great horned owl, ruby-throated hummingbird, acadian flycatcher, piliated woodpecker, hermit thrush, yellow-throated warbler, opossum, gray squirrel, flying squirrel, raccoon, mink, gray fox, bobcat, and white-tailed deer.

Bottomland forest occurs on low-lying flatlands that are slightly elevated above adjacent floodplain communities. The water table is high, but the bottomland community is not inundated annually, but only during extreme floods or prolonged rainfall. Soils are generally a mixture of sand, silt, clay, and organic materials. Tree density and species diversity is high.

Like other predominantly hardwood forests, it rarely burns. It is a very stable, advanced successional community found only along major streams and rivers.

Floodplain Forest. This floodplain community occurs on slightly drier soils at higher elevations, such as levees, ridges, terraces, and edges, and are usually flooded annually for a portion of the growing season. Common along alluvial rivers, they also are found along other streams. Primarily hardwood forests; typical trees include, overcup oak, water hickory, diamond-leaf oak, swamp chestnut oak, and sweetgum. The understory may be open and parklike or dense and nearly impenetrable. Other species include bluestem palmetto, green ash, Florida elm, hackberry, water oak, American hornbeam, tulip poplar, coastal plain willow, cottonwood, river birch, sweetbay magnolia, hawthorn, swamp azalea, lanceleaf greenbriar, poison ivy, peppervine, rattanvine, plume grass, redtop panicum, sedges, and wood grass.

Typical animals include a diverse array of residents and transients, such as marbled salamander, mole salamander, southern dusky salamander, two-lined salamander, three-lined salamander, dwarf salamander, slimy salamander, two-toed amphiuma, sirens, southern toad, cricket frog, bird-voiced treefrog, gray treefrog, river frog, southern leopard frog, five-lined skink, broadhead skink, mud snake, rainbow snake, glossy crayfish snake, Mississippi kite, swallow-tailed kite, red-shouldered hawk, woodcock, barred owl, piliated woodpecker, veery, Carolina wren, white-eyed vireo, red-eyed vireo, parula warbler, prothonotary warbler, hooded warbler, cardinal, opossum, southeastern shrew, short-tailed shrew, wood rat, rice rat, cotton mouse, golden mouse, black bear, and raccoon.

Soils of the floodplain forest are variable mixtures of sand, organics and alluvials, which are often distinctly layered. Hydroperiod is the dominant physical feature of the forest, which is typically inundated every year for up to 50% of the growing season. Because of regular flooding, organic material that accumulates on the forest floor can be redistributed within the floodplain or transported downstream to provide a critical source of minerals and nutrients for estuaries. Floodplain forests rarely burn, but forests at the edge of floodplains occasionally may be affected by fire from adjacent uplands.

Floodplain Swamp. This wetland community occurs on flooded soils along stream channels, and in low spots and oxbows within creek, stream and river floodplains. Dominant trees are usually buttressed hydrophytic species such as cypress, tupelo, black gum, water ash, red maple, and river birch. Other plants include dahoon holly, myrtle-leaved holly, swamp titi, hurrah-bush, swamp privet, hazel alder, laurel greenbriar, swamp aster, lizards tail, golden club, royal fern, Virginia chain fern, marsh fern, soft rush, and sedges. The animal community is similar to the floodplain forest with the addition of bullfrog, alligator, river cooter, stinkpot, red-bellied water snake, brown water snake, black swamp snake, cottonmouth, yellow-crowned night heron, wood duck, beaver, and river otter.

As with the floodplain forest community, soils are distinctly layered combinations of sands, alluvials, and organics. Because of the prolonged hydroperiod of the swamp, usually most of the year, substantial peat accumulations can develop. Pockets of anaerobic water can develop, adding further stress to the wetland community. Detrital accumulation and transport are important for downstream systems. Floodplain swamps are also important for cleansing and assimilating materials from upstream flows. Floodplain swamps are usually too wet to support fire, but fire that gets into the system during drought can result in muck fires that consume organic soils.

Floodplain Marsh. These herbaceous wetlands occur primarily as pockets along floodplains and in channels. Typical species include maidencane, pickerelweed, arrowhead, smartweed, buttonbush, spikerush, coreopsis, and blue flag. Animals present may include cricket frog, pig frog, leopard frog, alligator, mud snake, banded water snake, striped swamp snake, numerous wading birds, and waterfowl, red-winged blackbird, beaver, and river otter.

Marsh communities are successional in floodplain situations. They may not be flooded as long as swamps, and without fire will shift to swamp or forest communities.

Basin Wetlands: Shallow, closed basin with outflow usually only in times of high water; peat, sand or loamy substrate, usually inundated; wetland woody or herbaceous vegetation.

Basin Swamp. This swamp wetland community occupies large, irregularly shaped basins that are not associated with rivers and streams. They may have inflow and outflow creeks filling and draining them. Typical plants include cypress, blackgum, tupelo, red maple, bays, slash pine, dahoon holly, swamp redbay, coastal plain willow, buttonbush, laurel greenbriar, titi, Virginia chain fern, lizards tail, and sphagnum moss. Typical animals include southern dusky salamander, cricket frog, little grass frog, chicken turtle, striped mud turtle, ringneck snake, scarlet king snake, crayfish snake, cottonmouth, wood duck, great horned owl, barred owl, piliated woodpecker, gray squirrel, mink, river otter black bear, and bobcat.

Soils in basin swamps are generally acidic, nutrient poor organics, often overlying a clay lens or other impervious layer. A perched water table may slowly release water as surrounding water tables drop during drought. The typical hydroperiod is from 200-300 days. Fire may be regular in cypress swamps, but uncommon in hardwood swamps.

Basin Marsh. This herbaceous or shrubby wetland is situated in a relatively large and irregularly shaped basin. Typical plants include maidencane, cutgrass, southern watergrass, bluestems, penny wort, dollar weed, redroot, soft rush, spikerush, sedges, pickerel weed, arrowhead, knotweed, water lily, water shield, St. Johns wort, buttonbush, saltbush, elderberry, and wax myrtle. Typical animals include two-toed amphiuma, lesser siren, cricket frog, green treefrog, bull frog, pig frog, leopard frog, alligator, mud snake, green water snake, banded water snake, wading birds, waterfowl, northern harrier, marsh rabbit, bobcat, and round-tailed muskrat.

Basin marshes usually develop in large solution depressions that may have been open water lakes in the past. The lake bottom has slowly filled in with sediments from surrounding uplands and from organic soil accumulation. Soils are usually acidic sands and peats. The hydroperiod is generally around 200 days per year, and open water with aquatic vegetation are common in deeper areas. Fire is important in maintaining many marsh communities, especially the edges. The normal fire interval is from one to fifteen years, with grassy marshes having more frequent fire. Without fire, the community will succeed through shrubs to a forested wetland. Fire may also burn the peat soils during drought and move the community back to more open water.

Dome Swamp. Dome swamps are similar to basin swamps except that they occupy smaller, circular depressions and may have small creeks flowing into them but rarely have outflow. The dome shape comes from smaller trees at the edge. Cypress, tupelo, and bays are common trees, with other typical plants such as dahoon holly, red maple, Virginia willow, fetterbush, titi, buttonbush, chain fern, netted chain fern, royal fern, cinnamon fern, maidencane, lizards tail, St. Johns wort, water hyssop, redroot, and sphagnum moss. Typical animals are flatwoods salamander, dwarf salamander, oak toad, southern cricket frog, pinewoods tree frog, little grass frog, narrow-mouth toad, mud turtle, eastern mud snake, cottonmouth, wood duck, barred owl, prothonatory warbler, and hooded warbler.

Dome swamps are common in flatwoods and in karst areas where sand has slumped over a sinkhole forming a conical depression. Soils are generally acidic sands and peat, with an occasional clay lens creating a perched water table. Water comes mostly from rainfall and sheet flow from immediate upland areas, and is very dependent on high groundwater levels in the immediate vicinity. Normal hydroperiod is 200-300 days per year.

Fire is common in cypress-dominated dome swamps, and less frequent in other types. The shorter hydroperiod along the edge of dome swamps allows more fire to influence this fringe, contributing to the dome shape. Severe fire will push the swamp back to a marsh or open water community.

Depression Marsh. This wetland community is characterized as a shallow, usually small rounded depression in a sand substrate with herbaceous vegetation, often in concentric bands. Depression marshes are similar in vegetation to basin marshes, and include maidencane, cutgrass, spikerush, redroot, yellow-eyed grass, sedges, pickerel weed, bladderworts, arrowhead, St. Johns wort, buttonbush, and wax myrtle.

Larger and more permanent depression marshes will have many of the animal species listed as typical of basin marshes. However, because of their isolation and small size, many support a very different assemblage than that found in larger, permanent wetlands. Depression marshes are extremely important in providing breeding or foraging habitat for such species as the flatwoods salamander, mole salamander, tiger salamander, dwarf salamander, striped newt, oak toad, narrowmouth toad, spadefoot toad, gopher frog, cricket frog, barking treefrog, squirrel treefrog, little grass frog, southern chorus frog, white ibis, and wood stork.

Depression marshes are typical of karst regions where sand has slumped over a sinkhole. The substrate is usually acid sand with increasing depths of organic soil towards the center. Hydrologic conditions are highly variable, with most depressions drying out each year. Hydroperiods range widely from as few as 50 days' inundation to more than 200 days per year.

Fire is important in maintaining many depression marshes. It restricts the invasion of shrubs and trees and retards the accumulation of peat. Fire frequency is greatest around the periphery and least toward the center.

Lakes: Permanent, open water with floating or submersed aquatics.

Natural open water is not common in the study area. Succession tends to fill in ponds and lakes, ultimately resulting in marshes and swamps. Where they occur, lakes are surrounded by forested or herbaceous emergent wetland species. Typical aquatic species include American lotus, spatterdock, fragrant water lily, cow lily, coontail, watermilfoil, fanwort, pondweed, bladderwort, duck weed, and water fern. Exotic species, such as water hyacinth, hydrilla, and elodea, may have invaded many aquatic habitats. Typical animals include Florida gar, bowfin, largemouth bass, shad, chain pickerel, shiners, yellow bullhead, mosquitofish, least killifish, flier, swamp darter, redear sunfish, bluegill, warmouth, black crappie, alligator, snapping turtle, Florida cooter, yellow-belly turtle, softshell turtle, waterfowl, egrets and herons, kingfisher, beaver, and river otter.

Clastic Upland Lake. These lakes occur in rolling uplands of rich, clayey soils. They are usually irregular shaped basins with surface inflow and generally limited outflow. Water is dissipated through evaporation and transpiration, but it may also drain out rapidly through sinkholes that connect with the aquifer, especially during prolonged drought. Water can be clear to colored, slightly acidic to circumneutral, and soft with low mineral content. Clastic upland lakes may be oligo-mesotrophic, with relatively low nutrient levels, to eutrophic, with very high nutrient levels, depending on their geologic age and nutrient inputs from surrounding uplands.

River Floodplain Lake. Lakes that occupy river floodplains are normally lentic communities, but exhibit lotic conditions when rivers are at flood stage and flowing through the lakes' basin. Most were formed from old oxbows cut off from the active river channel. They have varying substrates of sand, alluvial deposits or organic material. Water is usually turbid or colored, alkaline or slightly acidic, hard or moderately hard, with high mineral content. They are usually mesotrophic to eutrophic due to frequent river inflow.

Swamp or Marsh Lake. The most common type of lake in the study area is deep, open water in swamps or marshes of large basins. Usually small relative to the surrounding community, they typically occupy the center or deepest part of the basin. The substrate may be sand, clay or peat. Alligators often maintain the open water area. Water levels typically fluctuate widely with shallow groundwater conditions, such that they dry out on an infrequent basis. Usually highly colored from tannic acids, the water is acidic and soft with moderate mineral content. Trophic status tends toward the mesotrophic-eutrophic condition with high primary productivity.

Sinkhole Lake. Where karst formations have not been completely filled with sand, clay or peat, a sinkhole lake may occupy the deep, funnel shaped depression. Although the water is permanent, levels may fluctuate widely with the deep aquifer. These lakes are characterized by clear, alkaline, hard water with high mineral content. Because of their connection to the deep aquifer, these lakes may support a unique fauna associated with the aquatic caves below ground.

Riverine: Flowing, open water in channels or sloughs.

Alluvial Stream. Alluvial streams are perennial or intermittent watercourses originating in rich uplands and carrying variable amounts of sediment. Primarily fed by surface runoff, water is usually turbid due to a high content of suspended particulates, including clays, silts sands, and detritus. Water levels fluctuate widely, often not in response to local conditions. Normal flows are confined to a well defined stream channel, and high flows inundate extensive floodplain systems. High stages typically occur in late winter or early spring, and occasionally in summer. High flows are critical to transport nutrients and detritus downstream to estuaries.

Vegetation is usually limited in the stream due to high flow rates and the turbidity reduces light availability. Water lilies, spatterdock, and other floating-leaved plants may occupy quiet stretches, and pickerelweed, cattails, willows, river birch, and cottonwood occupy the banks. Typical animals include eel, gizzard shad, speckled chub, madtom, pirate perch, striped bass, darter, river frog, alligator snapping turtle, river cooter, beaver, and river otter.

Blackwater Stream. These streams originate in sandy lowlands or areas with extensive swamps and organic soils and get their name from the dark, tea-colored water derived from swamp drainage. They typically have a well-defined channel with high banks, but the stream regularly may disappear into extensive swamps. Substrates are sand or organics. Water levels fluctuate in response to local rainfall and groundwater conditions. The water is usually acidic, with dissolved tannins, particulates, and iron. Very little suspended sediment is carried.

Vegetation is limited in the channel, but may include golden club, smartweed, tapegrass, maidencane, swamp lily, and grasses or sedges. Typical swamp trees line most of the banks. Animals include longnose gar, threadfin shad, redfin pickerel, chain pickerel, shiners, banded topminnow, mosquitofish, flier, red-breasted sunfish, stumpknocker, river frog, snapping turtle, river cooter, stinkpot, brown watersnake, cottonmouth, beaver, and river otter.

Seepage Stream. These small streams originate from shallow groundwaters that have percolated through deep upland soils. The seepage flow is typically clear to lightly colored with a fairly constant temperature of around 70°. The stream is generally short, shallow and narrow, and forms the headwaters of other stream types. When it picks up sediment or color from swamp drainage, it becomes an alluvial or blackwater stream, respectively. Substrate is usually sand, but clay, gravel, and limestone may be present.

Because they are headwater streams and commonly sheltered by dense forest, very little vegetation grows in the channel. Golden club, spikerush, mosses, and liverworts may occupy the stream bank. Typical animals include sailfin shiner, creek chub, speckled madtom, brown darter, blackbanded darter, amphiuma, southern dusky salamander, two-lined salamander, bronze frog, loggerhead musk turtle, rainbow snake, and redbelly water snake.

No vegetation maps are known for the area. The Florida Game and Freshwater Fish Commission's Office of Environmental Services (OES) has prepared a habitat analysis of Florida and has overlap into the study area. Based on LANDSAT imagery, the system defines 22 habitat types, including disturbed communities. Figure 1.3 provides coverage of the study area from that program. An important facet of the OES effort is the ability to assess rapidly future conditions because it is based on satellite imagery.

Flora and Fauna

A detailed plant list for the study area does not exist. There have been numerous botanical investigations in Southwest Georgia and North Florida from which generalized composition of the flora can be implied. The closest list is from Tall Timbers Research Station located just 1 ½ miles south of the south boundary of the study area. That list is included as Appendix I.

The principal components of the fauna are better known. As with plants, the animal list (mammals, birds, and herps) from Tall Timbers is included as Appendix II. In addition, a list of taxa documented from plantations in and adjacent to the study area is included in Appendix III. Added to this list are butterflies documented from one of the plantations.

Endangered, Threatened and Rare Species

Numerous species of plants and animals are indigenous to the study area; many of them are considered rare, endangered, threatened or otherwise of concern for their long term survival. Some are prominent animals with federal listing and extensive research documenting population status and life history - the red-cockaded woodpecker is an example. Others are obscure plants that may be encountered only occasionally by experts and with very little known about their status - the Tallahassee hedge nettle (Stachys hyssopifolia var. lythroides) is an example of this situation.

Federal and state governments maintain officially approved lists of species considered in trouble for various reasons. In addition, state natural heritage programs initiated by The Nature Conservancy maintain lists of taxa in need of protection due to very few known occurrences relative to other taxa. Together these three programs provide a good cumulative list of species tending toward extinction unless they receive attention.

Table 1.1 provides a list from the heritage program of Georgia, the state government list, and the Federal list, of species considered endangered, threatened, rare, or of special concern, or that are candidates for listing, and known to occur in the Red Hills region. It includes 7 fishes, 14 amphibians and reptiles, 16 birds, 6 mammals, and 41 plants.

Based on work conducted primarily by Wilson Baker during biological surveys of plantations within or immediately adjacent to the study area, Table 1.2 identifies those taxa actually encountered during field surveys over the past several years. These plantation surveys do not focus much attention on the aquatic stream and lake environments, except wading birds and waterfowl. Therefore, while not recorded, many of the listed fish are most likely present in the Ochlocknee River drainage.

Of special interest in the study area is the red-cockaded woodpecker (RCW). The Red Hills supports the largest population of RCW's remaining on private land in the Southeast. This woodpecker nests in cavities excavated in live pine trees with red heart disease. Preferring old growth, open pine forests, the current distribution of RCW's directly correlates with the distribution of mature longleaf pine forest, especially forest on virgin soil. Because the RCW is Federally listed as endangered and is a controversial species, the exact location of documented active cavity trees and clans is not readily released by private landowners. Figure 1.4 is a map of the known distribution of the bird in the Red Hills region. Its presence outside the shaded area is extremely limited.

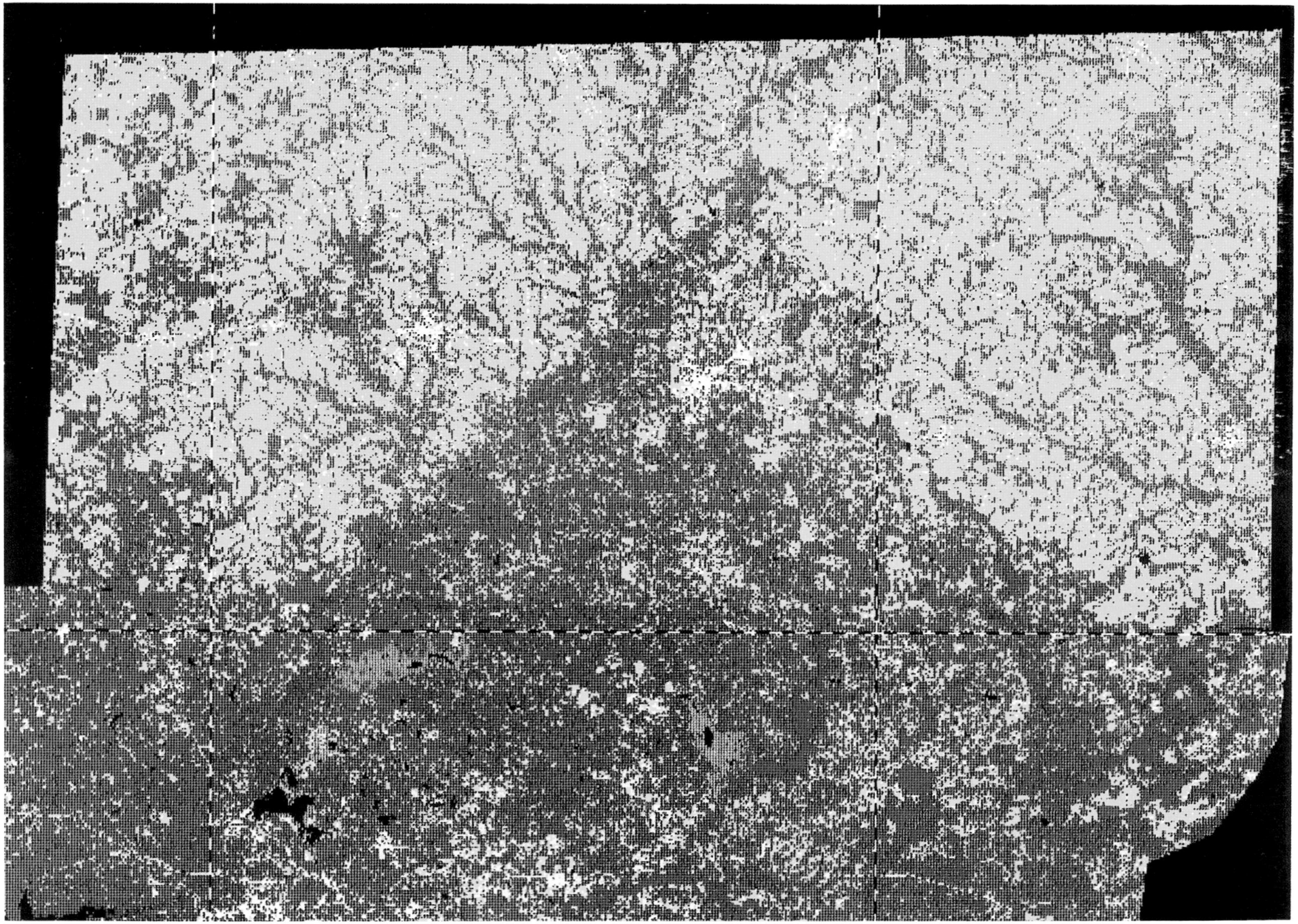

Figure 1.3A: Habitat Classification Map and Legend Based on Satellite Imagery. (Source: Florida Game and Fresh Water Fish Commission)

Figure 1.3B: Habitat Classification Legend

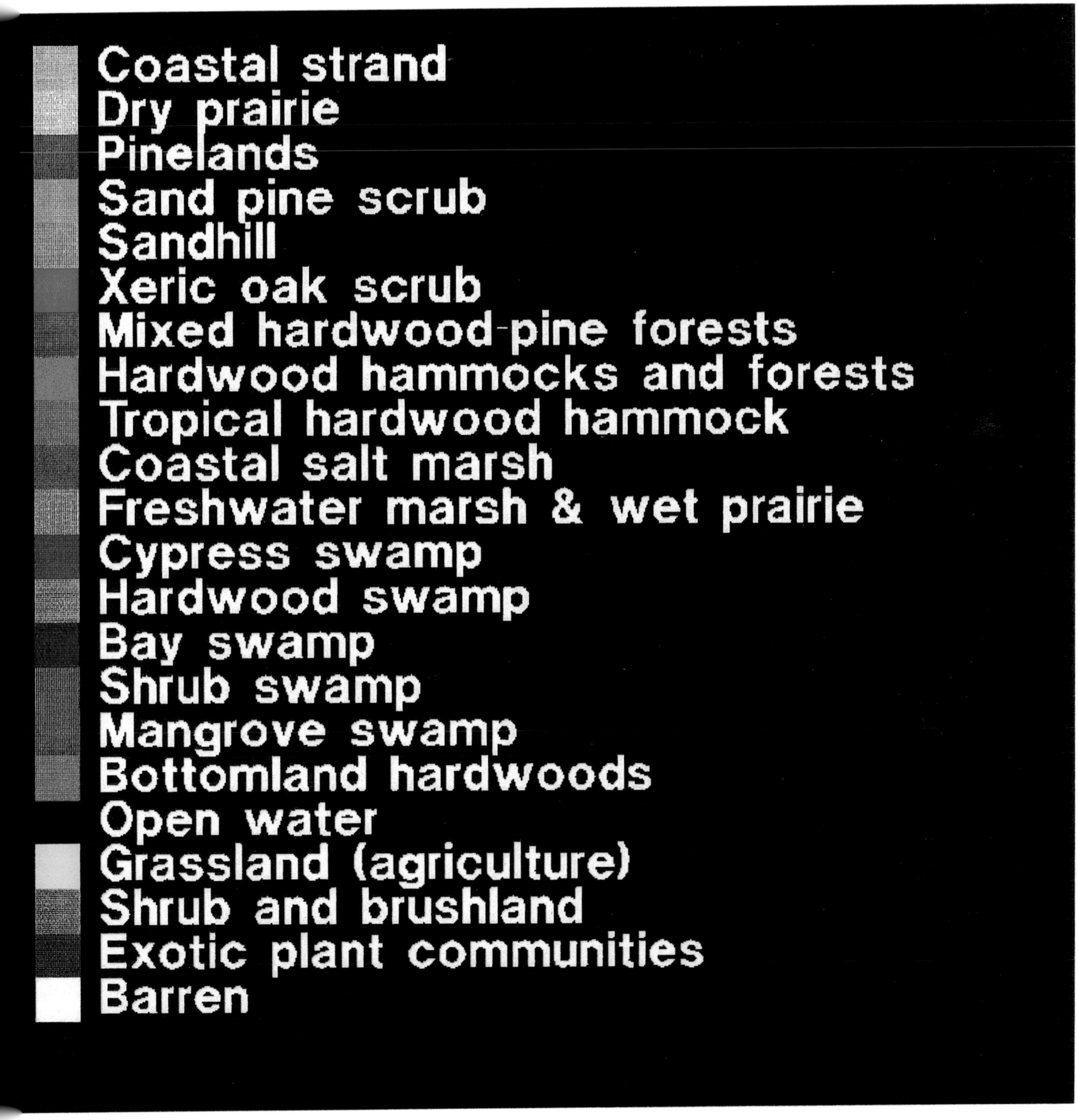
Coastal strand
Dry prairie
Pinelands
Sand pine scrub
Sandhill
Xeric oak scrub
Mixed hardwood-pine forests
Hardwood hammocks and forests
Tropical hardwood hammock
Coastal salt marsh
Freshwater marsh & wet prairie
Cypress swamp
Hardwood swamp
Bay swamp
Shrub swamp
Mangrove swamp
Bottomland hardwoods
Open water
Grassland (agriculture)
Shrub and brushland
Exotic plant communities
Barren

Table 1.1 Endangered and Potentially Endangered Fauna and Flora Indigenous to the Red Hills Region.

Global Rank	State Rank	Fed. Stat.	Georgia State	Name	Common Name
				FISH	
G3	S2			Ictalurus serracanthus	Spotted bullhead
G2	S1	C2		Notropis callitaenia	Bluestripe shiner
G4				Ictalurus brunneus	Snail bullhead
G2	S1			Micropterus sp. (undescribed)	Shoal bass
				Moxostoma sp. (undescribed)	Sucker
G2	S2			Moxostoma sp. (undescribed)	Greyfin redhorse
G3	S2			Notropis zonistius	Bandfin shiner
				AMPHIBIANS AND REPTILES	
G5				Ambystona tigrinum	Tiger salamander
G3	S1		R	Amphiuma pholeter	One-toed amphiuma
G4T3	S3	LT	T	Drymarchon corais couperi	Eastern indigo snake
G2	S2	LTC2	T	Gopherus polyphemus	Gopher tortoise
G2	S2	C2	V	Graptemys barbouri	Barbour's map turtle
G2	S1	C2	T	Haideotrion wallacei	Georgia blind salamander
G5	S2			Hemidactylium scutatum	Four-toed salamander
G5				Lampropeltis calligaster	Mole snake
G3	S3	C2	T	Macroclemys temminckii	Alligator snapping turtle
G3	S2		R	Notophthalmus perstriatus	Striped newt
G5	S3			Pituophis melanoleucus mugitus	Florida pine snake
G4	S3	C2	V	Rana areolata	Gopher frog (crawfish frog)
G5	S4	LTSA		Alligator mississippiensis	American alligator
				Chrysemys concinna suwanniensis	Suwannee cooter
				BIRDS	
G3	S3	C2		Aimophila aestivalis	Bachman's sparrow
G5	S2			Elanoides forficatus	Swallow-tailed kite
G3TU	S2	LE		Haliaeetus leucocephalus	Bald eagle
G4T2	S?	C2		Lanius ludovicianus migrans	Loggerhead shrike
G5	S2	LE		Mycteria americana	Wood stork
G5	S3S4			Nycticorax	Black-crowed night-heron
G5	S3S4			Mycticorax violaceus	Yellow-crowed night-heron
G2	S3S3	LE	E	Picoides borealis	Red-cockaded woodpecker
G5	S3			Casmerodius albus	Great egret
G5	S4			Egretta caerulea	Little blue heron
G5	S4			Egretta thula	Snowy egret
				Egretta tricolor	Tricolored heron
G5	S4			Eudocimus albus	White ibis
G5	S4			Falco sparverius palus	Southeastern American kestrel
G5	S4			Ixobrychus exillis	Least bittern
G5	S3			Seriurus motacilla	Louisiana waterthrush

Table 1.1   (Continued)

Global Rank	State Rank	Fed. Stat.	Georgia State	Name	Common Name
				MAMMALS	
G3?	S3S4	C2		Neofiber alleni	Round-tailed muskrat
G4	S3?	C2		Plecotus rafinesquii	Southeastern big-eared bat
G5T3		C2	LT*	Ursus americanus floridanus	Florida black bear
G5T4	S3			Mustela frenata olivacea	Southeastern weasel
G5T5	S2	C2		Mustela vison mink	Southern mink
G5T4	S4			Sorex longirostris longirostris	Southeastern shrew
				PLANTS	
G3	S2?	C2		Agrimonia incisa	Incised groove bur
G2	S1	C2	T	Asplenium heteroresiliens	Wagner's spleenwort
G2G3	S1	C2	PE	Brikellia cordifolia	Flyr's brickell-bush
G1Q	S1	C2	E	Bumelia thornei	Buckthorn
G2G3	S2	3C		Croton elliottii	Elliott's croton
G3G4	S3		PU	Epidendrum canopseum	Greenfly orchid
G2	S1	C2	E	Fimbristylis perpusilla	Harper fimbristylis
G4G5T?	S1			Habernaria quinqueseta	Michaux's orchid
G2		LE	PE	Lindera melissifolia	Swamp spicebush
G2	S2	C2		Lobelia boykinii	Boykin's lobelia
G?	S2?			Matelea flavidula	Carolina milkvine
G3?	S3	3C		Pieris phillyraefolia	No common name
G3G5	S3	3C		Pinckneya pubens	Hairy fevertree
G5	S3?			Platanthera nivea	Snowy orchid
G4	S3	3C		Rhapidophyllum hystrix	Needle palm
G2	S1	C2		Phexia aristosa	Awned meadowbeauty
G3G4	S3	3C		Rhododendron austrinum	Orange azalea
G4G5	S4		T	Sarracenia minor	Hooded pitcherplant
G2	S1	C1		Schwalbea americana	Chaffseed
G3	S1			Spiranthes longilabris	Long-lip ladies' tresses
G2?	S2	C2		Sporobolus teretifolius	Wire-leaf dropseed
G3?	S3?			Uvularia floridana	Florida bellwort

Table 1.2 Listed Species Documented From Plantations In and Adjacent to the Study Area.

Common Name	Scientific Name	Global Rank	State Rank	Comments
PLANTS				
Cup-seed	Calycocarphon lyonii	G5	S2?	Few locations recorded in Georgia
Green fly orchid	Epidendrum canopseum	G3-4	S3	Epiphytic on Magnolia grandifolia
Carolina milkvine	Matelea flavidula	G4-5	S1	Few locations in Georgia
Hooded pitcher plant	Sarracenia minor	G?	S4	Spotty distribution, its habitat often disturbed
VERTEBRATES				
Blackbanded sunfish	Enneacanthus chaetodon	G5	S2?	Only (+) record for Red Hills region
American alligator	Alligator mississippiensis	G5	S?	Regular-common in region
Gopher tortoise	Gopherus polyphemus	G2	S2	Scattered locations within population
Bachman's Sparrow	Aimophila aestivalis	G3	S3	Common in open (burned) pine
Red-cockaded woodpecker	Picoides borealis	G2	S2	Very significant part of core population
Wood Stork	Mycteria americana	G5	S2	Seasonal foraging, potential future nesting area
Round-tailed muskrat	Neofiber alleni	G3	S3-4	First (only) record from Thomas County

Source: Wilson Baker

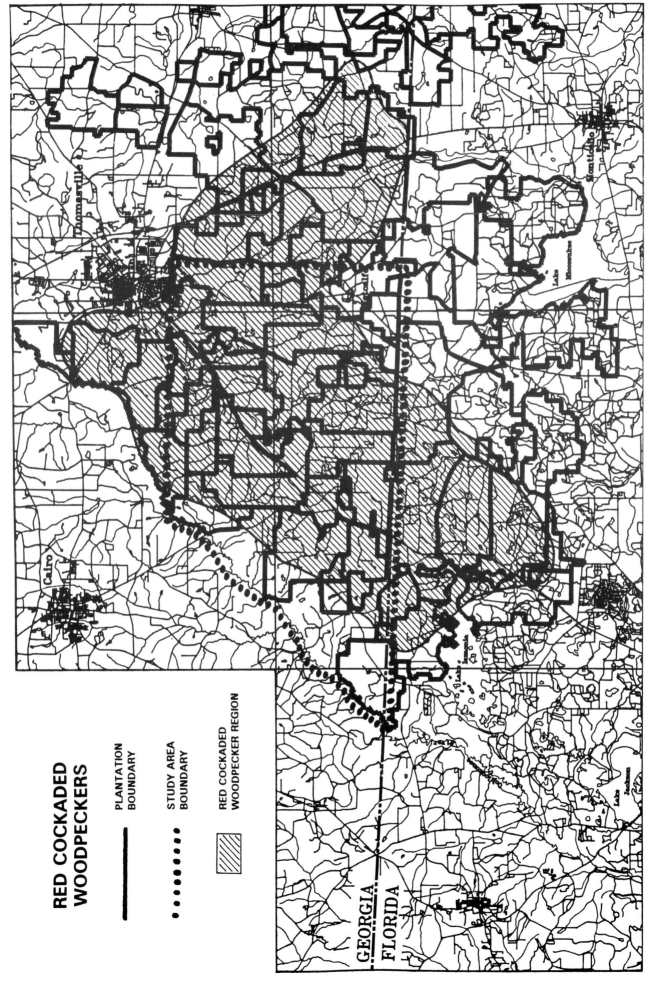

Figure 1.4: Distribution of the Red-Cockaded Woodpecker Within the Red Hills Region.

Significant Natural Areas

Although a field survey of the study area was not conducted for this project, certain types of natural areas can be identified and their occurrence classified as a significant natural area. These areas include virgin soils; old growth longleaf pine stands; mature hardwood forests, and other pine stands; wetlands; sinkholes; and habitat for endangered, threatened or rare species.

Virgin Soils. As discussed earlier, the presence of upland soils that have never been plowed or otherwise disturbed is considered by ecologists to characterize an important natural resource. The best are those that also support mature pine stands, especially if they are longleaf pine, and intact native ground cover. Such sites are the only locations that represent the true natural diversity of this region. Their value as baseline natural communities from which to compare the condition of successional communities is irreplaceable.

It is important to maintain as many patches of virgin soil as possible. Slight differences in soil type, moisture regime, topographic position, aspect, and surrounding habitat type may result in a high degree of biotic diversity among patches. Prior to extensive soil disturbance, these differences were expressed along a continuum of environmental gradients. All too often now, the patches are discreet units isolated by disturbed areas. The larger the area of virgin soil and the greater the degree of environmental variability within that area, the more significant the area becomes.

Old Growth Longleaf Pine Stands. Longleaf pine attains old growth characteristics after about 100 years of age. Many trees on the Wade Tract in the northeast corner of the study area exceed 225 years, and several trees in the Big Woods at Greenwood Plantation just northwest of the study area are over 400 years old. When uneven-aged stands of mature trees occupy relatively large (>40 acres) areas, that area would be considered significant. If the stand is near other old growth areas, is surrounded by other mature forest stands, has wetlands within or adjacent to it, or is on virgin soil, its significance increases.

Old longleaf is the primary refuge of the red-cockaded woodpecker. Gopher tortoises prefer the open, grassy groundcover vegetation of mature pine stands. Such stands also are more likely to support other critical species, especially groundcover plants.

Mature Hardwood Forests and Other Pine Stands. Just as with longleaf pine, areas of mature hardwood forest and other pine species are important natural areas. While groundcover species diversity is highest in longleaf pine forests, tree species diversity is greatest in hardwood forests. Animal species diversity is typically also greater here. Mature temperate hardwood forests are some of the most diverse and complex natural communities in the United States. In the study area this is especially true due to their close proximity to the subtropical forests of peninsular Florida.

Mature stands of other pine, including shortleaf, loblolly, and spruce pine, create important connections and bridge gaps between natural areas. As with most forest communities, the older the better. While diversity of species in mature pine stands on disturbed soil may be high, it typically is composed of weedy species or native species greatly out of proportion to natural conditions.

Wetlands. All lakes, ponds, rivers, streams, swamps and marshes are significant habitats. Again, the bigger the better, but even small wetlands may be important. For example, many amphibians need small, isolated wetlands devoid of aquatic predators in which to reproduce. A ¼ acre pool may be the only place over a large area where frogs can lay eggs safely. Most wetlands are protected to some degree by governmental regulation.

Floodplains provide many services, both to people and wildlife. Two important ones are storage of flood waters and movement corridors for wildlife. Wetlands increase habitat diversity in an area. They attract an entirely different suite of species. Headwater creeks and streams are the initial source of energy and materials to feed downstream riverine and estuarine systems. As discussed in the geology and groundwater assessment, many wetlands in the study area are connected to the aquifer. Thus their significance can extend well beyond the Red Hills region.

Wetlands of the study area as identified by the US Fish and Wildlife Service, National Wetlands Inventory (NWI) were summarized and mapped in Figure 1.5. This map shows the general location of wetland areas. Detailed classification of these wetlands is found on the following NWI 7.5 minute quadrangle maps:

Thomasville, GA
Pine Park, GA
Cairo South, GA
Metcalf, GA-FLA
Miccosukee Northeast, GA-FLA
Beachton, GA-FLA
Calvary, GA-FLA

The majority are palustrine forested swamps associated with the numerous creeks and basins of the area. Note how many wetland areas have inflows, but no outlets. This is the result of internal drainage into the aquifer.

Sinkholes. As just mentioned, many wetlands in the area are connected to the deep aquifer. Sinkholes provide the primary type of connection. Their significance to water resources can be added to their ecological significance.

The depressions formed by sinkholes represent a unique microhabitat in the area. They may be deep enough to expose limestone rock, creating a calcareous substrate. The sheltered microclimate within the depression supports an unusual flora, including a diverse fern assemblage. The occasional steep slopes are uncommon in the region and may exhibit rapid changes in moisture regime from top to bottom.

Endangered, Threatened or Rare Species Habitat. The sites and locations where critical species survive may be essential to the long term viability of that population. It is important in assessing the significance of species locations to understand the overall context into which that site fits. It may be the best location in the region, have the largest population, be a critical stepping stone for genetic exchange, or be an extension of the species range. Each factor must be weighed for that site and that taxa to determine relative significance.

The Red Hills Region. It must be pointed out that the study area and Red Hills region as a whole represent a significant natural area in and of themselves. The extensive forest cover, virgin soil areas, critical species, wetlands, aquifer connections, and proximity to urban populations for education purposes all contribute to a unique set of conditions probably found nowhere else. Figure 1.6 is a satellite image of the area. Although not interpreted to classify specific ground conditions, it graphically illustrates the acute difference between this area and surrounding developed land. This is especially evident in Georgia where the agricultural lands northeast, north and northwest of Thomasville stand out in sharp contrast to the forested mantle of the Red Hills plantations.

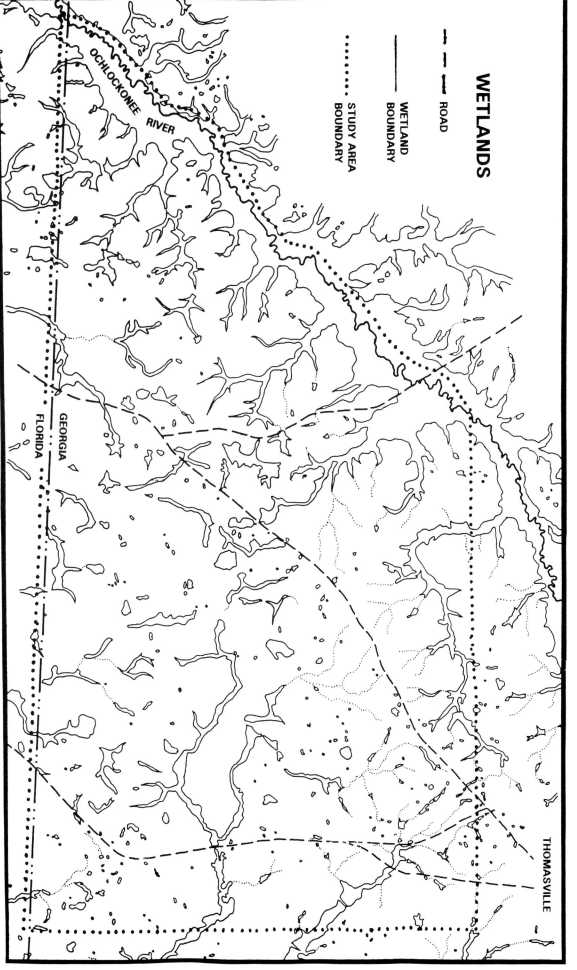

Figure 1.5: Location of Wetlands in the Study Area. (Source: National Wetlands Inventory, USFWS)

Figure 1.6: Unclassified Satellite Image of the Red Hills Region. (Source: Northwest Florida Water Management District)

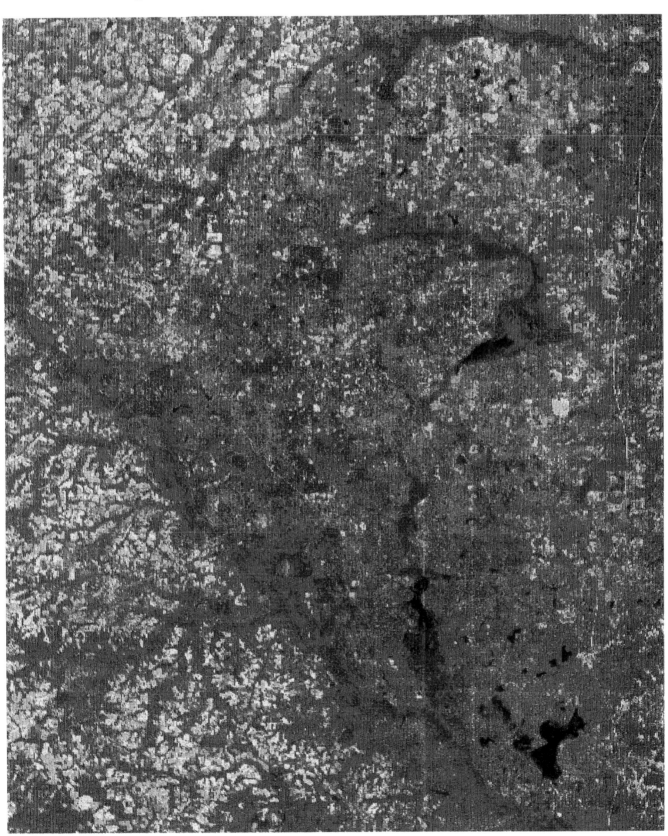

PAST, PRESENT, AND FUTURE

Historic Conditions/Future Trends

As discussed under settlement patterns, the study area has a long history of human use. As economic, political, and other conditions changed over time, the nature and intensity of use varied to reflect the new conditions. Today, the process continues and the future of the Red Hills region will be shaped by how the present generation deals with the elements of change.

Prior to major intrusion into the landscape by man several thousand years ago, the rich mosaic of pine and hardwood forests and wetlands interacted in a way that provided for a diverse mix of species. Major cataclysmic events such as storm, fire, flood, and drought, occasionally destroyed large areas of the landscape, but over time, natural systems recovered.

Native peoples introduced the first intrusions that did not result in the natural restoration of historic communities. Most of the Red Hills was cleared for agricultural production. The advent of European man brought a lull in intensive use as the native peoples died or were displaced. Intensive cotton farming with slave labor brought a renewal of large scale land clearing for agricultural production that lasted for several decades. When cotton declined, a lull in intensive use returned. This was followed by consolidation of the old cotton plantations into winter retreats and hunting plantations, the first time the region was purposely directed back toward the historic pattern of extensive forest cover. Agricultural use continued, but at a much lower level since bird hunting became the driving force behind most land management decisions.

While this type of land use could continue indefinitely, history tells us that change is likely. Furthermore, certain factors operating now frequently result in a diminishment of the positive landscape attributes that currently make the Red Hills area such a significant natural resource.

The urbanization and suburbanization of the Thomasville and Tallahassee metropolitan areas are a substantial threat. The pressure to develop rises as property taxes increase. As land is divided up among family members, fragmentation of large tracts into smaller parcels works against consistent application of current management philosophy. Tradition gives way to short term need. For very practical reasons, more and more land is devoted to more intensive use.

Another major threat is actually facilitated by the presence of large, single-owner tracts. Linear projects, like roads, pipelines, power lines, and the like, prefer to move through such areas because land acquisition is easier due to fewer owners, normally lower values associated with large verses small tracts, and the image of independent owners rather than a tightly woven community. The fragmentation impacts and large area impacted by linear facilities are threats in and of themselves.

Changes in timber management and harvest practices could have dramatic results. The dominant program, single tree or group selection of high value products from uneven aged stands, results in the type of mature, open forest valued as an ecological as well as economic resource. The trend toward pine plantations, whole tree chipping, mulch production, and higher returns from timber management programs drives the system away from the more natural structured forest that supports high natural biological diversity. The now-repealed "Timber Tax" in Georgia would have ushered in a new way of looking at standing timber value for the region. Adherence to silviculture best management practices (BMP's) in the harvesting and re-establishment of forest production areas is crucial to the long term protection of streams and aquatic resources.

Game bird population enhancement practices often are the overriding consideration when implementing on-the-land management actions. Many practices associated with quail production are compatible with protection of high ecological resource values - that is precisely why the region is like it is today. Refinement of two key techniques would go a long way toward increasing natural resource values: implementation of more growing-season prescribed burning and elimination of the creation of new food plots. If determined by research to be impractical throughout the region while still maintaining high game bird production, such management alterations should at a minimum be applied to all remaining virgin soils and high quality natural areas.

A difficult area to discuss, but one that must be addressed by the plantation owners themselves, is estate planning. Many of the original families that consolidated the cotton fields into game plantations still own them. As tax laws and inheritance laws have changed, it has become much more difficult to pass down appreciated real estate without intense pressure to sell off parcels, develop and intensify economic return, or otherwise drastically alter management of the land to accommodate federal and state governments. If the individual vision and plantation culture of these families are to be preserved over the generations, effective estate planning must be a high priority to protect the land from excessive development, the families from undue tax burden and the region from the continued unpredictable change that results in cycles of exploitation and conservation.

Resource Protection and Management Programs

The natural and cultural resource values of the area are being recognized locally, regionally, and nationwide. Locally, several programs have been put in place to address ecological and historic resource preservation and management.

The area landowners have helped found and support a conservation program at Tall Timbers Research Station, a local wildlife research organization with a long and credible history of affecting resource management and good land stewardship in the region. This association is dedicated to protecting the natural and cultural resources of the region through information exchange with and advocacy. This conservation program is strengthened by a strong coalition of consortium partners consisting of the

> Florida and Georgia Chapters of The Nature Conservancy
> Southeastern Offices of The Trust for Public Lands
> Historic Tallahassee Preservation Board
> Thomasville Landmarks, Inc.
> Joseph E. Jones Ecological Research Center.

Before this program was created, several individual landowners moved to protect key features of the natural landscape. Primarily through the efforts of Tall Timbers and The Nature Conservancy, a national non-profit conservation organization dedicated to preserving the earth's biological diversity, conservation easements were given over key tracts such as the Wade Tract, Titi Hammock, and the Mays Pond Miccosukee gooseberry (Ribes enchinellum) site. The first two listed are within the study area, while the third is southeast of the study area in Jefferson County, Florida. Since these easements over small tracts were established, a consortium of the Red Hills Conservation program, The Nature Conservancy (both Georgia and Florida Chapters) and Tall Timbers have funded detailed biological inventories of entire plantations in hopes of securing more comprehensive easements. Conducted at the request of individual plantation owners and with the data held confidentially until released by that owner, several easements over large tracts have been created. As an example, the easement for Sedgefield Plantation is included in the appendix, and all supporting documentation for that easement has been provided under separate cover for inclusion in the proposed Red Hills Regional Environmental Center at Thomas College. Additional surveys are underway and negotiations continue for specific easement language on several plantations with completed surveys.

From a regional perspective, The Apalachee Greenways Project of 1000 Friends of Florida seeks to establish an interconnected network of ecological, recreational, and cultural greenways from Thomasville to the Gulf coast of Florida. Working in partnership with the Red Hills Conservation program and Apalachee Land Conservancy, a local land trust in Tallahassee, Florida, several workshops have been held to identify existing trails, corridors, roads, and core areas. Proposed or desired linkages and core areas are also being identified, as well as existing and potential threats to the areas ecological and cultural integrity. The final result should be a conceptual plan and series of maps defining such a system. Background information on the Apalachee Greenways Project is included as an appendix.

Education and increasing the level of knowledge for the plantation owners and their managers is a critical area. Several landowners are trustees of national and local boards of key conservation and research groups, including Tall Timbers, The Nature Conservancy and others. They are committed to resource protection and management. Tall Timbers conducts field days and workshops for owners and managers covering subjects such as quail management, prescribed burning, conservation easements, and estate planning.

Information Gaps

Although the region has been studied for quite some time, no systematic survey or inventory of ecological resources has been completed. The biological surveys of plantations, conducted by the Red Hills Conservation program, Tall Timbers, and The Nature Conservancy, provide high quality data for limited areas. Extensive research is conducted on several of the conservation easement areas, especially Titi Hammock and the Wade tract. Each of these programs contributes to our current understanding of the region. However, there are several areas where information needs are acute. Development of this information would help fill in missing pieces of the regional landscape/biodiversity puzzle.

A regional vegetation or land cover map is essential to integrated planning and detailed assessment of historical, present, and potential future conditions. The vegetation map should include the entire Red Hills region and adjoining areas, and must be detailed enough to define habitats to the plant association level. Optimally, the map should be generated from satellite imagery and aerial photography, and ground-truthed sufficiently to allow a high level of accuracy. Processing with a Geographic Information System (GIS) would allow ease of data analysis and efficient update and comparison of data in the future. The Southwest Georgia Development Council reports that the Georgia Department of Transportation is developing land cover maps at the USGS 7.5 minute quad scale. These maps may be available soon.

A survey should be conducted to document the distribution of remaining virgin soil areas. Some data exists for a few plantations, but a systematic survey would provide a regional perspective. Commensurate with the virgin soil survey should be a survey for old growth forest communities.

Listed species surveys are needed to document the size and distribution of populations. The list of expected taxa is quite long compared to the observed list. Some work has been done, such as with the red-cockaded woodpecker, but the sensitive nature of the data precludes uncontrolled distribution and availability.

More technical assistance should be provided to facilitate development of long-range plans for large land holdings. This includes land management, estate, and strategic planning. Formulation and documentation of a long range vision for individual plantations and the region as a whole provides a yardstick by which resource protection or degradation can be measured. Just what should the study area and region look like in the year 2020?

A diverse but focused research effort is needed to assess existing and proposed land management techniques on resource attributes. Various techniques are being used or proposed to enhance a specific factor without a very good understanding of how it may affect other things. Growing season fire helps wiregrass propagation, but what does it do to quail production? Food plots enhance quail production, but how do they affect listed species populations? Protecting listed species habitat helps that species, but what does it do to economic return from the land? In short, research must help define a path that will integrate man's activities into the natural world while minimizing disruption and maintaining economic return or other desirable productivity.

REFERENCES

Avant, D.A. III. 1991. *Plantation management on a sharecropper's budget*. L'Avant Studios. Tallahassee.

Burleigh, T.D. 1958. *Georgia birds*. University of Oklahoma Press. Norman.

Clewell, A.F. 1978. *The natural setting and vegetation of the Florida panhandle — draft report*. US Army Corps of Engineers. Mobile, AL.

Cooke, C.W. 1939. *Scenery of Florida as interpreted by a geologist*. Florida Geological Survey — Bulletin No. 17. Tallahassee.

Duncan, W.H. and L.E. Foote. 1975. *Wildflowers of the Southeastern United States*. University of Georgia Press. Athens.

Florida Natural Areas Inventory. 1990. *Guide to the natural communities of Florida*. Florida Department of Natural Resources. Tallahassee.

Godfrey, R.K. and J.W. Wooten. 1979. *Aquatic and wetland plants of the Southeastern United States — monocotyledons*. University of Georgia Press. Athens.

_____. 1981. *Aquatic and wetland plants of the Southeastern United States — dicotyledons*. University of Georgia Press. Athens.

Golley, F.B. 1962. *Mammals of Georgia*. University of Georgia Press. Athens.

Harper, R.M. 1914. *Geography and vegetation of Northern Florida*. Florida Geological Survey — Sixth Annual Report. Tallahassee. 163-437.

Harris, J.L. 1972. *Butterflies of Georgia*. University of Oklahoma Press. Norman.

Harris, L.D. 1984. *The fragmented forest*. University of Chicago Press. Chicago.

Holder, T.W. and H.A. Schretter. 1986. *The atlas of Georgia*. Institute of Community and Area Development, University of Georgia. Athens.

Jones, S.B. Jr., and N.C. Cole. 1988. *The distribution of the vascular flora of Georgia*. University of Georgia. Athens.

Kral, R. 1983. *A report on some rare, threatened, or endangered forest—related vascular plants of the South — vols. I & II*. USDA Forest Service, Tech. Publication R8-TP2. Atlanta.

Landers, J.L. and B.S. Mueler. 1986. *Bobwhite quail management; a habitat approach*. Tall Timbers Station — Misc. Publication #6. Tallahassee.

Lynch, J.M., A.K. Gholson and W.W. Baker. 1986. *Natural features inventory of Ichauway Plantation, Georgia — vols. I & II*. The Nature Conservancy — SE Regional Office. Chapel Hill, NC.

Martof, B.S. 1956. *Amphibians and reptiles of Georgia*. University of Georgia Press. Athens.

McVaugh, R. and J.H. Pyron, 1951. *Ferns of Georgia*. University of Georgia Press. Athens.

Muller, J.W., E.D. Hardin, D.R. Jackson, S.E. Gatewood and N. Caire. 1988. *Summary report on the vascular plants, animals and plant communities endemic to Florida*. Florida Game and Fresh Water Fish Commission, NGWP Tech. Report No. 7. Tallahassee.

Myers, R.L. and J.J. Ewel. 1990. *Ecosystems of Florida*. University of Central Florida Press. Orlando.

Paisley, C. 1968. From Cotton to Quail: *An agricultural chronicle of Leon County, Florida, 1860-1967*. University of Florida Press. Gainesville.

_____. 1989. *The Red Hills of Florida, 1528-1865*. University of AL Press. Tuscaloosa.

Puri, H.S. and R.O. Vernon. 1964. *Summary of the geology of Florida and a guidebook to the classic exposures*. Florida Geological Survey — Spec. Publication No. 5, Revised. Tallahassee.

Stoddard, H.L. Sr. 1987. *Birds of Grady County, Georgia*. Tall Timbers Research Station — Bulletin #21. Tallahassee.

Swift, C., R.W. Yeager and P.R. Parrish. 1977. *Distribution and natural history of the fresh and brackish water fishes of the Ochlocknee River, Florida and Georgia*. Tall Timbers Research Station — Bulletin #20. Tallahassee.

USDA-SCS. 1979. *Soil survey of Brooks and Thomas Counties, Georgia*. USDA, Soil Conservation Service and University of Georgia.

Wahlenberg, W.G. 1946. *Longleaf pine, its use, ecology, regeneration, protection, growth and management*. Chs. Lathrop Pack. Forestry Foundation. Washington, DC.

Wharton, C.H. Undated. *The natural environments of Georgia*. Georgia Department of Natural Resources. Atlanta, GA.

CHAPTER 2: ECONOMICS AND DEMOGRAPHICS

Neil G. Sipe

This chapter establishes an economic and demographic database for a portion of the Red Hills region.

The chapter quantifies the role that plantations play in the local economy and examines the impact of economic and demographic trends on plantations. It then suggests areas requiring more further study and in-depth analysis.

INTRODUCTION

Project Description and Purpose

This chapter 1) establishes an economic and demographic database for a portion of the Red Hills region; 2) quantifies the role that plantations play in the local economy; 3) examines the impacts of economic and demographic trends on plantations; and 4) suggests areas requiring more in-depth analysis.

The Red Hills is a region between Thomasville, Georgia, and Tallahassee, Florida, dominated by plantations. Until 1963, the term "plantation" had not been well defined. Prunty (1963:1) provided some criteria for defining a "woodland plantation" which included: (1) a large land holding; (2) a division of labor and management functions; (3) specialized production; (4) distinctive spatial organizations of settlements and land use; (5) large input of cultivating power per unit of area; and (6) location in the South with a plantation tradition. The Red Hills plantations meet the criteria established by Prunty (1963:2) as being "woodland plantations." However most of the Red Hills plantations are used for quail hunting. Brueckheimer (1985) argues that quail plantations are a special type of "woodland plantation." He defines a quail plantation as "a large property whose most important product over the years has been quail for the hunting pleasure of northern owners and their guests. In modern times, the sale of timber and cash crops has grown in importance as the plantations have come to be operated as businesses" (Brueckheimer, 1985:45).

Figure 2.1 shows the Red Hills region with plantation boundaries delineated in thin black lines and the study area outlined with thick black lines. The Red Hills region is located in five counties in two states: the northern portions of Leon and Jefferson Counties in Florida, and southeastern Grady County, southern Thomas County and the extreme western portion of Brooks County in Georgia. The map shows the plantation boundaries as they existed in 1991. At that time there were approximately 73 plantations covering more than 263,000 acres. The study area encompasses 27 plantations covering more than 57,700 acres. The study area is generally defined by the Florida-Georgia border on the south, the city of Thomasville on the north, Old Metcalf Road on the east, and the Ochlocknee River on the west. Because the unit of analysis for this study was the plantation, plantation boundaries were used to delineate the exact boundaries of the study area. An enlarged map of the study area is shown in Figure 2.2.

Structure

This chapter contains five sections. The first contains the introduction. The second section provides population/demographic trends and projections. The third section contains an economic overview, analysis of the impact of plantations on the local economy and a discussion of the economic benefits attributable to the environmental management of the plantations. The fourth section provides the summary, conclusions and recommendations for further research.

POPULATION TRENDS AND PROJECTIONS

Population trends and projections have been analyzed at the county level. While the study area encompasses only portions of Thomas and Grady Counties, it is important to look at a region larger than the study area, particularly when examining population and economic trends. The region selected for the population analysis consists of four counties: Thomas and Grady Counties in Georgia, and Leon and Jefferson Counties in Florida.

County Population Trends 1970-1990

The population trends for the four-county region for the period from 1970 to 1990 are shown in Table 2.1. The table shows both absolute growth in terms of numbers of new residents as well as annual percentage growth rates. This table supports the following conclusions. First, Leon County is by far the most populous county in the region with more than two and one-half times the population of the other counties, combined. Second, over the 1970-1990 period, Leon County grew at an annual rate of 3.2 percent, which is more than double the rate of any other county. In terms of absolute growth, Leon County added almost 90,000 new residents over the 1970-1990 period or 4,500 per year. This amount of growth is almost 20 times that of Thomas County, which grew by 4,524 over the twenty-year period. Third, taking the four counties as a region, the 1990 population totaled a little more than 263,000 with almost 99,000 people added over the past twenty years. The annual rate of population growth for the region was 2.4 percent.

Figure 2.1

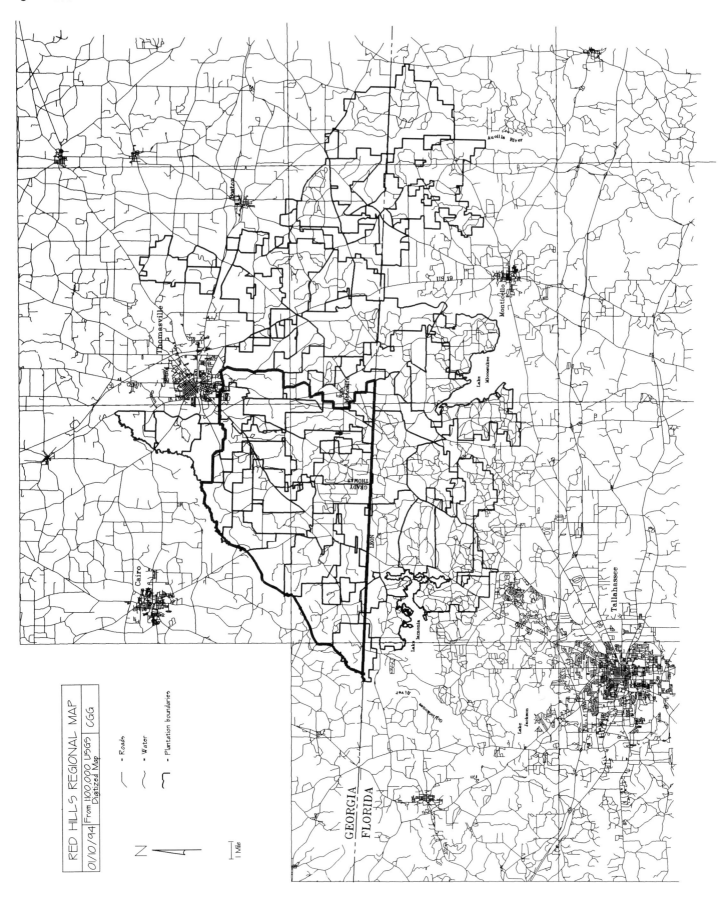

Figure 2.2

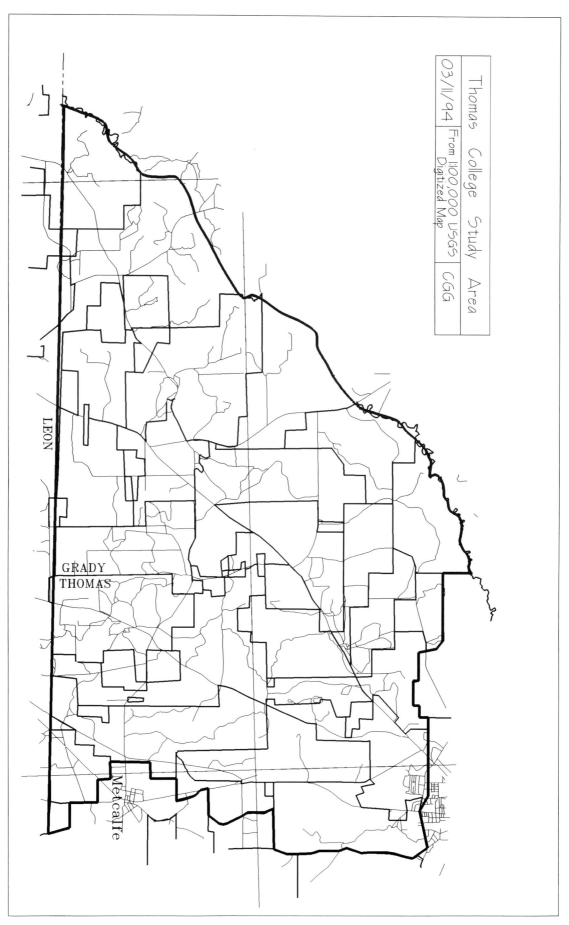

Table 2.1
Red Hills Economic Study
Population 1970-1990

	1970	1980	1970-1980 Growth	1970-1980 Annual Growth Rate	1990	1980-1990 Growth	1980-1990 Annual Growth Rate	1970-1990 Growth	1970-1990 Annual Growth Rate
Georgia Counties									
Grady	17,826	19,845	2,019	1.1%	20,279	434	0.2%	2,453	0.6%
Thomas	34,462	38,098	3,636	1.0%	38,986	888	0.2%	4,524	0.6%
Subtotal	52,288	57,943	5,655	1.0%	59,265	1,322	0.2%	6,977	0.6%
Florida Counties									
Jefferson	8,778	10,703	1,925	2.0%	11,296	593	0.5%	2,518	1.3%
Leon	103,047	148,655	45,608	3.7%	192,493	43,838	2.6%	89,446	3.2%
Subtotal	111,825	159,358	47,533	3.6%	203,789	44,431	2.5%	91,964	3.0%
Red Hills Region	164,113	217,301	53,188	2.8%	263,054	45,753	1.9%	98,941	2.4%

County Population Projections 1990-2010

Population projections for the four counties are provided in Table 2.2. The projections for the four counties were made at different times by different organizations. The Grady County projections were made in 1990, and the Thomas, Leon and Jefferson County projections in 1991. The projections for Grady and Thomas Counties were made jointly by the Southwest Georgia Regional Development Center and Woods and Poole Economics, Inc., while the Jefferson and Leon County projections were made by the Bureau of Economic and Business Research at the University of Florida which makes the official projections for Florida counties. Three different projections are made for Florida counties: high; medium and low. The projections shown in Table 2.2 are medium projections.

Between 1990 and 2010 the four-county region is projected to grow at an annual rate of 1.3 percent and gain almost 75,000 new persons. Both the percentage growth rate and the population gain are less than what was experienced between 1970 and 1990. However, population projections are based on past trends. If other factors come into play, these population projections could increase or decline. For example, the medium 2010 projection for Leon County is 258,500; however it could range from a low of 186,000 to a high of 345,500. If Leon County follows the trends of other state capitals in large states, such as Austin, Texas and Sacramento, California, the 2010 population could be closer to the high projection of 345,500 rather than the medium projection of 258,500. If Leon County does grow faster than expected between 1990 and 2010, the region's population could increase by 161,640 rather than 74,640 as shown in Table 2.2. This would give the region a 2010 population of almost 425,000.

Leon County Tract-Level Trends 1970-1990

Because Leon County is the most populous county and fastest growing county in the region, it is important to take a closer look at where this population growth is occurring. Figure 2.3 shows a map of the Leon County census tracts. Five of the county's ten fastest growing census tracts between 1970 and 1990 were located north of Interstate 10. Table 2.3 shows the population trends from 1970 to 1990 for those census tracts north of Interstate 10. Over the twenty years from 1970 to 1990 this area grew to 44,984 from 9,772. This represents growth of more than 35,000 or 1,760 persons per year. Stated another way, 40 percent of Leon County's growth between 1970 and 1990 occurred north of Interstate 10.

Leon County Tract-Level Projections 1990-2010

Based on projections made by Leon County, the area north of Interstate 10 will have a population of more than 67,000 by 2010 as shown in Table 2.4. This represents an increase of more than 22,000 or 1,100 per year. This is approximately 60 percent less than the growth experienced between 1970 and 1990. However, the tract-level projections are based the medium county projection.

Table 2.2
Red Hills Economic Study
Population Projections

	1990	1990-2000		2000	2000-2010		2010	1990-2010	
		Growth	Annual Growth Rate		Growth	Annual Growth Rate		Growth	Annual Growth Rate
Georgia Counties									
Grady	20,279	1,100	0.5%	21,379	1,700	0.8%	23,079	2,800	0.6%
Thomas	38,986	2,380	0.6%	41,366	2,549	0.6%	43,915	4,929	0.6%
Subtotal	59,265	3,480	0.6%	62,745	4,249	0.7%	66,994	7,729	0.6%
Florida Counties									
Jefferson	11,296	504	0.4%	11,800	400	0.3%	12,200	904	0.4%
Leon	192,493	35,707	1.7%	228,200	30,300	1.3%	258,500	66,007	1.5%
Subtotal	203,789	36,211	1.6%	240,000	30,700	1.2%	270,700	66,911	1.4%
Red Hills Region	263,054	39,691	1.4%	302,745	34,949	1.1%	337,694	74,640	1.3%

Table 2.3
Red Hills Economic Study
Population 1970-1990: Leon County Census Tracts

Census Tract	1970	1980	1970-1980 change	1970-1980 annual growth rate	1990	1980-1990 change	1980-1990 annual growth rate	1970-1990 change	1970-1990 annual growth rate
16.02	1,226	2,072	846	5.4%	2,912	840	3.5%	1,686	4.4%
22.03	347	1,226	879	13.5%	4,115	2,889	12.9%	3,768	13.2%
22.04	2,787	5,442	2,655	6.9%	6,150	708	1.2%	3,363	4.0%
23.02	343	1,729	1,386	17.6%	2,455	726	3.6%	2,112	10.3%
24.02	1,195	2,178	983	6.2%	6,270	4,092	11.2%	5,075	8.6%
24.04	1,516	8,820	7,304	19.3%	17,613	8,793	7.2%	16,097	13.0%
25.02	2,358	3,919	1,561	5.2%	5,469	1,550	3.4%	3,111	4.3%
Subtotal	9,772	25,386	15,614	10.0%	44,984	19,598	5.9%	35,212	7.9%
Remainder	93,275	123,269	29,994	2.8%	147,509	24,240	1.8%	54,234	2.3%
Co. Total	103,047	148,655	45,608	3.7%	192,493	43,838	2.6%	89,446	3.2%

Table 2.4
Red Hills Economic Study
Population Projections: Leon County Census Tracts

Census Tract	1990	2000	1990-2000 change	1990-2000 annual growth rate	2010	2000-2010 change	2000-2010 annual growth rate	1990-2010 change	1990-2010 annual growth rate
16.02	2,912	3,218	306	1.0%	3,480	262	0.8%	568	1.8%
22.03	4,115	5,156	1,041	2.3%	6,178	1,022	1.8%	2,063	4.1%
22.04	6,150	6,750	600	0.9%	7,178	428	0.6%	1,028	1.6%
23.02	2,455	3,140	685	2.5%	3,705	565	1.7%	1,250	4.2%
24.02	6,270	10,578	4,308	5.4%	14,109	3,531	2.9%	7,839	8.4%
24.04	17,613	20,716	3,103	1.6%	23,006	2,290	1.1%	5,393	2.7%
25.02	5,469	7,068	1,599	2.6%	9,700	2,632	3.2%	4,231	5.9%
Subtotal	44,984	56,626	11,642	2.3%	67,356	10,730	1.8%	22,372	4.1%
Remainder	147,509	178,493	30,984	1.9%	205,714	27,221	1.4%	58,205	3.4%
Co. Total	192,493	235,119	42,626	2.0%	273,070	37,951	1.5%	80,577	3.6%

Implications for the Future

Based on population growth since 1970 and expected future growth to 2010, it is clear that study area is in the direct path of growth. The northern portions of Leon County have been and will continue to be desirable locations for residential development. The main limiting factor to growth in this area is the availability of land. Much of the desirable land is currently held as quail plantations. The degree to which these plantations are converted into residential developments will dictate the rate and amount of growth in the study area. No precise estimate exists of the amount of plantation land that has been converted into residential development over the past 20-30 years; however a general estimate of the loss can be made from the data in Table 2.5. The table is taken from Brueckheimer (1985:59) with the addition of 1991 data by the author.

Table 2.5
Plantations in the Thomasville-Tallahassee Region

	1910	1930	1950	1976	1991
Number of owners	21	32	52	50	56
Total acreage	48,870	200,960	292,140	298,840	263,800
Average acreage	2,327	6,280	5,618	5,977	4,710

Sources: 1910, 1930, 1950 and 1976 data from Brueckheimer (1985:59); 1991 data derived by author from a digitized plantation map.

The table reveals that peak plantation acreage of 298,840 occurred in 1976. By 1991 this acreage had declined by 35,040 acres to 263,800 acres. A visual examination of the maps from which these data were taken shows that most of the acreage lost was in Leon County, as many plantations were converted into residential subdivisions.

Another factor that makes the study area attractive for development is the fact that Grady and Thomas Counties have less stringent development regulations than does Leon County. Less stringent regulations mean that land development is quicker and cheaper in Georgia. There have been discussions about developing an industrial park in Beachton, Georgia, which would service high-tech spin-offs from the National High Magnetic Lab at Florida State University in Tallahassee.

The combination of less stringent development regulations in Georgia combined with the fact growth is moving north from Tallahassee at a rapid rate means that the study area specifically and the Red Hills generally will be subject to increasing development pressures over the next several decades.

1990 RURAL AREA
CENSUS TRACTS
TALLAHASSEE / LEON COUNTY, FLORIDA

Tallahassee-Leon County Planning Department

ECONOMIC OVERVIEW AND ANALYSIS

The four-county region (Grady, Thomas, Leon and Jefferson) used for the population analysis is also used for the economic analysis.

Employment Trends 1970-1990

The first part of this analysis involves an examination of employment trends by industry between 1970 and 1990.

Grady County

Economic trends for Grady County are shown in Table 2.6. As of 1990 total employment was 8,468. The main economic activity was manufacturing, accounting for more than 27 percent of total employment. The top four industries, manufacturing, services, retail trade and government account for almost three-quarters of all employment in the county.

Between 1970 and 1990 employment grew at an annual rate of 1.6 percent, which amounted to an increase of 2,251 jobs. Those industries with the most growth over this twenty-year period were manufacturing (1,056 jobs), retail trade (654 jobs), services (493 jobs) and government (407 jobs). The only economic activities losing jobs over this period were farming which lost 1,062 jobs and federal government — civilian employment, which lost eight jobs. The decline of farming in the county is dramatic — in 1970 farming accounted for more than 30 percent of all jobs while in 1990 it accounted for only ten percent. Of equal importance, however, it that the loss of 1,062 farming jobs between 1970 and 1990 was replaced by 1,056 manufacturing jobs. Another interesting point is that while farming employment plummeted by more than half that agricultural services actually increased by more than three times from 31 jobs in 1970 to more than 100 in 1990. This is most likely the influence of the large number of plantations in the area that require various forms of agricultural services.

Thomas County

Employment trends for the county are shown in Table 2.7. Total employment for 1990 in Thomas County exceeded 22,500. The main economic activities in the county were manufacturing (23.8 percent), services (23.1 percent), government (16.2 percent) and retail trade (14.2 percent). Together these four industry groups account for more than three-quarters of all jobs in the county.

Between 1970 and 1990, the county's economy grew at an annual rate of 2.0 percent. All economic sectors grew except for farming (-2.6 percent) and transportation, communication and utilities (-0.6 percent). During these twenty years more than 7,300 jobs were added to the job base with 1,838 new jobs in service-related industries, 1,760 in government (mostly at the state and local level), 1,611 in manufacturing, and 1,000 in retail trade. Similar to the trends in Grady County, farming lost 595 jobs between 1970 and 1990 while agricultural services gained 38 new jobs. Again, one explanation for this trend is the large number of plantations that require agricultural services.

Jefferson County

Table 2.8 shows the employment trends for Jefferson County between 1970 and 1990. Total employment in 1990 was 3,593. Employment activity is concentrated in four sectors: state and local government (21.8 percent); farming (19.9 percent); services (13.4 percent); and retail trade (13.0 percent). Together these sectors account for more than 68 percent of total employment.

Between 1970 and 1990 employment grew at an annual rate of 2.7 percent. Total employment increased by 1,482. The largest increases were in the services (352), agricultural services (301), retail trade (294), and government (281). The farming and construction sectors experienced small losses over the twenty-year period. Similar to the trend in Grady and Thomas Counties was the decrease in farming employment by 26 and an increase of 301 jobs in agricultural services. Again this appears counterintuitive; however the large amount of acreage in plantations may help explain this trend.

Leon County

Employment statistics for Leon County are provided in Table 2.9. Total employment for 1990 was 11,467. Those sectors with the largest share of employment were government (41.0 percent), services (22.1 percent) and retail trade (19.0). These three sectors account for more than 82 percent of total employment.

Between 1970 and 1990 employment grew from a little less than 40,000 to more than 111,000, for an increase of almost 72,000 new jobs. New jobs in the government sector accounted for more than one-third of the increase. The two fastest growing sectors were agricultural services at an annual rate of 11.5 percent and services at a 10.6 percent annual rate. Again the trend of declining farm employment and an increase in agricultural services in present. Farming employment dropped by 136 jobs while agricultural services increased by 499 jobs.

Four-County Summary

A summary of 1990 employment by economic sector is shown in Table 2.10. The economies of the four counties are similar is some respects and different in others. Some important observations include the following. First, the size of the Leon County economy dwarfs the other three counties. Total employment in Leon County is more than three times greater than that in the other three counties combined. Second, manufacturing is the most important economic activity in Grady and Thomas Counties. In fact, total manufacturing employment in Thomas County is almost 70 percent greater than that of Leon County even though Leon's total employment is more than five times larger. Third, farming which was once important in all four counties is now significant in only one — Jefferson. Fourth, there are three economic activities that are important to all counties: retail trade, services and government.

Table 2.6
Red Hills Economic Study
Employment: Grady Co.

	1970	percent of total	1980	percent of total	1970-1980 Change	Annual Growth Rate	1990	percent of total	1980-1990 Change	Annual Growth Rate	1970-1990 Change	Annual Growth Rate
Farming	1,908	30.7%	1,348	18.7%	-560	-3.4%	846	10.0%	-502	-4.6%	-1,062	-4.0%
Agricultural Services	31	0.5%	70	1.0%	39	8.5%	105	1.2%	35	4.1%	74	6.3%
Mining	0	0.0%	0	0.0%	0	0.0%	0	0.0%	0	0.0%	0	0.0%
Construction	128	2.1%	221	3.1%	93	5.6%	313	3.7%	92	3.5%	185	4.6%
Manufacturing	1,256	20.2%	1,894	26.3%	638	4.2%	2,312	27.3%	418	2.0%	1,056	3.1%
Trans., Comm & Utilities	117	1.9%	150	2.1%	33	2.5%	191	2.3%	41	2.4%	74	2.5%
Wholesale Trade	226	3.6%	312	4.3%	86	3.3%	432	5.1%	120	3.3%	206	3.3%
Retail Trade	685	11.0%	860	11.9%	175	2.3%	1,339	15.8%	479	4.5%	654	3.4%
Finance, Ins & Real Estate	150	2.4%	216	3.0%	66	3.7%	314	3.7%	98	3.8%	164	3.8%
Services	945	15.2%	994	13.8%	49	0.5%	1,438	17.0%	444	3.8%	493	2.1%
Government	771	12.4%	1,136	15.8%	365	4.0%	1,178	13.9%	42	0.4%	407	2.1%
Federal Govt - Civilian	57	0.9%	53	0.7%	-4	-0.7%	49	0.6%	-4	-0.8%	-8	-0.8%
Federal Govt - Military	122	2.0%	78	1.1%	-44	-4.4%	218	2.6%	140	10.8%	96	2.9%
State & Local Govt	592	9.5%	1,005	14.0%	413	5.4%	911	10.8%	-94	-1.0%	319	2.2%
Total Employment	6,217	100.0%	7,201	100.0%	984	1.5%	8,468	100.0%	1,267	1.6%	2,251	1.6%

Table 2.7
Red Hills Economic Study
Employment: Thomas Co.

	1970	percent of total	1980	percent of total	1970-1980 Change	1970-1980 Annual Growth Rate	1990	percent of total	1980-1990 Change	1980-1990 Annual Growth Rate	1970-1990 Change	1970-1990 Annual Growth Rate
Farming	1,450	9.5%	1,317	6.9%	-133	-1.0%	855	3.8%	-462	-4.2%	-595	-2.6%
Agricultural Services	83	0.5%	162	0.8%	79	6.9%	121	0.5%	-41	-2.9%	38	1.9%
Mining	74	0.5%	239	1.3%	165	0.0%	420	1.9%	181	0.0%	346	0.0%
Construction	643	4.2%	725	3.8%	82	1.2%	1,024	4.5%	299	3.5%	381	2.4%
Manufacturing	3,766	24.7%	4,984	26.1%	1,218	2.8%	5,377	23.8%	393	0.8%	1,611	1.8%
Trans., Comm & Utilities	601	3.9%	477	2.5%	-124	-2.3%	534	2.4%	57	1.1%	-67	-0.6%
Wholesale Trade	644	4.2%	829	4.3%	185	2.6%	1,131	5.0%	302	3.2%	487	2.9%
Retail Trade	2,207	14.5%	2,999	15.7%	792	3.1%	3,207	14.2%	208	0.7%	1,000	1.9%
Finance, Ins & Real Esta	508	3.3%	797	4.2%	289	4.6%	1,044	4.6%	247	2.7%	536	3.7%
Services	3,373	22.1%	3,721	19.5%	348	1.0%	5,211	23.1%	1,490	3.4%	1,838	2.2%
Government	1,894	12.4%	2,846	14.9%	952	4.2%	3,654	16.2%	808	2.5%	1,760	3.3%
Federal Govt - Civilian	143	0.9%	134	0.7%	-9	-0.6%	213	0.9%	79	4.7%	70	2.0%
Federal Govt - Military	231	1.5%	151	0.8%	-80	-4.2%	365	1.6%	214	9.2%	134	2.3%
State & Local Govt	1,520	10.0%	2,561	13.4%	1,041	5.4%	3,076	13.6%	515	1.8%	1,556	3.6%
Total Employment	15,243	100.0%	19,096	100.0%	3,853	2.3%	22,578	100.0%	3,482	1.7%	7,335	2.0%

Table 2.8
Red Hills Economic Study
Employment: Jefferson Co.

	1970	percent of total	1980	percent of total	1970-1980 Change	Annual Growth Rate	1990	percent of total	1980-1990 Change	Annual Growth Rate	1970-1990 Change	Annual Growth Rate
Farming	740	35.1%	556	18.3%	-184	-2.8%	714	19.9%	158	2.5%	-26	-0.2%
Agricultural Services	51	2.4%	398	13.1%	347	22.8%	352	9.8%	-46	-1.2%	301	10.1%
Mining	0	0.0%	6	0.2%	6	0.0%	0	0.0%	-6	0.0%	0	0.0%
Construction	121	5.7%	47	1.5%	-74	-9.0%	118	3.3%	71	9.6%	-3	-0.1%
Manufacturing	199	9.4%	347	11.4%	148	5.7%	334	9.3%	-13	-0.4%	135	2.6%
Trans., Comm & Utilities	80	3.8%	111	3.7%	31	3.3%	144	4.0%	33	2.6%	64	3.0%
Wholesale Trade	16	0.8%	71	2.3%	55	16.1%	53	1.5%	-18	-2.9%	37	6.2%
Retail Trade	172	8.1%	376	12.4%	204	8.1%	466	13.0%	90	2.2%	294	5.1%
Finance, Ins & Real Estat	26	1.2%	70	2.3%	44	10.4%	110	3.1%	40	4.6%	84	7.5%
Services	129	6.1%	294	9.7%	165	8.6%	481	13.4%	187	5.0%	352	6.8%
Government	540	25.6%	601	19.8%	61	1.1%	821	22.8%	220	3.2%	281	2.1%
Federal Govt - Civilian			35	1.2%			36	1.0%	1	0.3%	36	
Federal Govt - Military			0	0.0%			0	0.0%	0	0.0%	0	
State & Local Govt			566	18.7%			785	21.8%	219	3.3%	785	
Other	37	1.8%	156	5.1%	119	15.5%	0	0.0%	-156	-100.0%	-37	-100.0%
Total Employment	2,111	100.0%	3,033	100.0%	922	3.7%	3,593	100.0%	780	1.7%	1,482	2.7%

Table 2.9
Red Hills Economic Study
Employment:Leon Co.

	1970	percent of total	1980	percent of total	1970-1980 Change	1970-1980 Annual Growth Rate	1990	percent of total	1980-1990 Change	1980-1990 Annual Growth Rate	1970-1990 Change	1970-1990 Annual Growth Rate
Farming	600	1.5%	848	1.2%	248	3.5%	464	0.4%	-384	-5.9%	-136	-1.3%
Agricultural Services	64	0.2%	329	0.5%	265	17.8%	563	0.5%	234	5.5%	499	11.5%
Mining	0	0.0%	0	0.0%	0	0.0%	0	0.0%	0	0.0%	0	0.0%
Construction	2,262	5.7%	3,496	4.9%	1,234	4.4%	5,236	4.7%	1,740	4.1%	2,974	4.3%
Manufacturing	1,925	4.9%	2,221	3.1%	296	1.4%	3,117	2.8%	896	3.4%	1,192	2.4%
Trans., Comm & Utilities	870	2.2%	2,606	3.6%	1,736	11.6%	2,794	2.5%	188	0.7%	1,924	6.0%
Wholesale Trade	1,264	3.2%	2,119	2.9%	855	5.3%	3,052	2.7%	933	3.7%	1,788	4.5%
Retail Trade	6,500	16.4%	12,599	17.5%	6,099	6.8%	21,196	19.0%	8,597	5.3%	14,696	6.1%
Finance, Ins & Real Esta	1,480	3.7%	3,257	4.5%	1,777	8.2%	4,766	4.3%	1,509	3.9%	3,286	6.0%
Services	3,284	8.3%	11,519	16.0%	8,235	13.4%	24,588	22.1%	13,069	7.9%	21,304	10.6%
Government	21,300	53.9%	32,920	45.8%	11,620	4.4%	45,691	41.0%	12,771	3.3%	24,391	3.9%
Federal Govt - Civilian	610	1.5%	1,209	1.7%	599	7.1%	1,603	1.4%	394	2.9%	993	4.9%
Federal Govt - Military	0	0.0%	0	0.0%		0.0%	0	0.0%	0	0.0%	0	0.0%
State & Local Govt	20,690	52.3%	31,711	44.1%	11,021	4.4%	44,088	39.6%	12,377	3.4%	23,398	3.9%
Total Employment	39,549	100.0%	71,914	100.0%	32,365	6.2%	111,467	100.0%	52,324	4.5%	71,918	5.3%

Table 2.10
Red Hills Economic Study
1990 Employment: Region

	Grady County	percent of total	Thomas County	percent of total	Jefferson County	percent of total	Leon County	percent of total
Farming	846	10.0%	855	3.8%	714	19.9%	464	0.4%
Agricultural Services	105	1.2%	121	0.5%	352	9.8%	563	0.5%
Mining	0	0.0%	420	1.9%	0	0.0%	0	0.0%
Construction	313	3.7%	1,024	4.5%	118	3.3%	5,236	4.7%
Manufacturing	2,312	27.3%	5,377	23.8%	334	9.3%	3,117	2.8%
Trans., Comm & Utilities	191	2.3%	534	2.4%	144	4.0%	2,794	2.5%
Wholesale Trade	432	5.1%	1,131	5.0%	53	1.5%	3,052	2.7%
Retail Trade	1,339	15.8%	3,207	14.2%	466	13.0%	21,196	19.0%
Finance, Ins & Real Estat	314	3.7%	1,044	4.6%	110	3.1%	4,766	4.3%
Services	1,438	17.0%	5,211	23.1%	481	13.4%	24,588	22.1%
Government	1,178	13.9%	3,654	16.2%	821	22.8%	45,691	41.0%
Federal Govt - Civilian	49	0.6%	213	0.9%	36	1.0%	1,603	1.4%
Federal Govt - Military	218	2.6%	365	1.6%	0	0.0%	0	0.0%
State & Local Govt	911	10.8%	3,076	13.6%	785	21.8%	44,088	39.6%
Total Employment	8,468	100.0%	22,578	100.0%	3,593	100.0%	111,467	100.0%

Location Quotient Analysis

Location quotient analysis is a statistical method that uses employment characteristics to analyze and determine the diversity of a community's economic base. Location quotient analysis provides a framework for understanding the community's economic stability and resilience to changing conditions by looking at the degree to which selected industries are located in a community (Heilbrun, 1987:143).

The location quotient is used to estimate the amount of export or "basic" industry employment. Industrial activities that bring dollars into the community through exports of goods and services are considered "basic" industries. Industries that supply goods and services for local consumption are designated as "non-basic" industries. Economic base theory asserts that "basic" industries drive the economy and that local economic activity depends on export activity and grows or declines proportionately with it.

In determining the amount of export activity, location quotient analysis also provides a measure of the amount of stability in the economic base. The stability is associated with diversity in the economic base. If economic base activities are spread over a range of goods and services the overall economy will be more stable than if the base activities are concentrated in a few industries. Therefore, changes in one industry will not greatly impact the overall economy. However if a community has only one or two export industries, the overall economy could be severely impacted during periods of change.

Location quotient analysis compares an industry's share of total local employment with that industry's share of total national employment. When an industry's local share exceeds the national, a portion of the industry's employment is considered export employment. See Galambos and Schreiber (1978) and Tiebout (1962) for more details on the location quotient technique.

Location quotient analysis is based on the following assumptions that should be considered when interpreting the results:

1. productivity per employee ratios are the same between the local government and the nation;
2. per capita consumption of products of industrial outputs is the same between the local government and the nation;
3. a region will not import and export the same product;
4. no net export by any industry in the nation (Isserman, 1977:35).

Because of time and budget limitations, location quotients were calculated for only those counties making up the pilot study area — Grady and Thomas Counties, rather than the expanded four-county region.

Grady County Location Quotients

Location quotients, based on 1992 employment data, were calculated for Grady County. As Table 2.11 shows, export or basic employment was estimated to be 1,117. Four sectors had export employment: apparel manufacturing with 770 export jobs, lumber and wood product manufacturing with 119 export jobs, government with 226 export jobs, and wholesale trade with two export jobs. As discussed above, diversity in export employment is important; however, in Grady County most of the export employment is engaged in apparel manufacturing. Should there be a decline in this industry, the economy of the county could be significantly impacted.

Table 2.11
Red Hills Economic Study
1992 Location Quotients:
Grady County

Industry	United States 1992	%	Grady County 1992	%	Local Employment	Export Employment
Mining	721	0.7%				
Construction	5,125	4.9%	141	2.6%	260	0
Manufacturing	19,403	18.4%	1,981	37.0%		
Food & kindred products	1,636	1.5%				
Textiles	729	0.7%				
Apparel	1,092	1.0%	825	15.4%	55	770
Lumber & wood products	765	0.7%	158	3.0%	39	119
Furniture & fixtures	530	0.5%				
Paper & allied products	693	0.7%				
Printing & Publishing	1,561	1.5%				
Chemicals & allied products	1,065	1.0%				
Rubber & misc. plastic products	829	0.8%				
Stone, clay, glass & concrete	600	0.6%				
Primary metal	774	0.7%				
Fabricated metal products	1,431	1.4%				
Computer equip; ind & comm ma	2,070	2.0%				
Transportation equipment	2,051	1.9%				
Instruments & related products	749	0.7%				
Transportation & public utilities	5,548	5.3%	156	2.9%	281	0
Wholesale trade	6,029	5.7%	308	5.8%	306	2
Wholesale trade - durable goods			86	1.6%		
Wholesale trade - nondurable goods			222	4.1%		
Retail trade	19,110	18.1%	875	16.4%	968	0
Finance, insurance & real estate	6,676	6.3%	144	2.7%	338	0
Services	25,600	24.2%	640	12.0%		
Hotels, other lodging places	1,550	1.5%		0.0%	79	0
Personal services	1,175	1.1%	37	0.7%	60	0
Business services	5,571	5.3%	42	0.8%	282	0
Auto repair, services, garages	837	0.8%	33	0.6%	42	0
Miscellaneous repair services			7	0.1%		
Motion pictures	241	0.2%		0.0%	12	0
Amusement & recreation service	918	0.9%		0.0%	47	0
Health services	7,144	6.8%	360	6.7%	362	0
Legal services	852	0.8%	12	0.2%	43	0
Educational services	1,557	1.5%		0.0%	79	0
Social services	1,611	1.5%		0.0%	82	0
Museums, botanical, zoos						
Membership organizations	1,731	1.6%				
Engineering & management services			27	0.5%		
Private households			48	0.9%		
Miscellaneous Services						
Government	17,372	16.5%	1,106	20.7%	880	226
Federal Government	2,971	2.8%	48			
State Government	4,063	3.8%	980			
Local Government	10,339	9.8%	78			
Not Elsewhere classified						
All Industries	105,584	100.0%	5,351	100.0%		1,117

Because employment varies from year to year, location quotients should be calculated over several years. Table 2.12 shows location quotients for Grady County from 1988 through 1992.

Table 2.12
Red Hills Economic Study
1988-1992 Location Quotients
Grady County

	1988	1989	1990	1991	1992
Total employment	5,788	5,990	6,000	5,770	5,991
Ag employment	686	677	697	642	635
Total-Ag employment	5,102	5,313	5,303	5,128	5,356
Base employment	733	889	938	996	1,116
Local employment	4,369	4,424	4,365	4,132	4,240
Local/Base ratio	5.96	4.98	4.65	4.15	3.80
Average 1988-1992	4.71				

Agricultural employment is not included in the analysis because most agricultural employees are not covered by the Employment Security Law and thus do not report data to the Georgia Department of Labor. Export employment increased from 733 jobs in 1988 to 1,116 in 1992. An important economic measurement is the ratio of local to export jobs. For Grady County this ratio ranges from a high of 5.96 in 1988 to a low of 3.80 in 1992, with an average of 4.71 for the five-year period. This ratio indicates the number of local jobs that are supported by each export job. Thus in Grady County, on average, each export job supports 4.71 local jobs. This is based on the assumption that as export activities expand, requirements for local activities increase by some multiple of the initial increase in export jobs. This ratio is also known as an employment multiplier and is useful in evaluating the impact of new or existing export employers. For this study, the employment multiplier will be used as one method of estimating the impact of plantation operations and management on the economies of Grady and Thomas Counties.

Thomas County Location Quotients

Location quotient analysis was used to estimate 1992 base employment as shown in Table 2.13. Total base employment totaled 4,518 and was distributed in a diverse range of economic activities. The largest base employers were in: state government (1,232 jobs); apparel manufacturing (885 jobs); health services (771 jobs); food manufacturing (587 jobs); and lumber and wood manufacturing (590 jobs). Unlike Grady County, Thomas County has a diverse group of base industries so that a change in one will not have such a severe impact on the overall county economy.

The trends in base employment over the past five years are shown in Table 2.14. Base employment dropped significantly from 5,525 in 1988 to 4,555 in 1989; however it has remained fairly stable since that time. The average local to base employment ratio is 2.58. Thus each base job results in 2.58 local jobs.

Economic Impact of the Plantations

The economic impact of the plantation on the local economy was first documented by Prunty (1963) to plantations in the South and by Komarek (1979:185) specifically to the Thomasville-Tallahassee region. Komarek argued that the economic effect of the hunting plantation of the local economy was important, but not recognized. He suggested that the average quail plantation had "a winter home, a resident manager, a staff of servants for the house, a staff of employees for the farm and quail work, for the dog kennels, and the dog men" (Komarek, 1979:185). In 1979 he estimated that costs for operating and maintaining a quail plantation could average $15 per acre, but that they could go as high as $40-50 per acre. An up-to-date picture of plantation operations budgets was obtained from an interview with an experienced plantation manager (Neel, 1994); the figures appear in Table 2.15. Annual expenditures for 1993 are shown for 17 plantations in the Thomasville-Tallahassee region. Annual operating expenditures range from a low of $20 per acre to a high of $171 per acre with an average of $55.41 per acre. Another economic impact of the plantations is timber production. The values shown in Table 2.15 are annual sustained timber harvests and range between $5 per acre and $23 per acre with an average of $12.69.

To obtain an estimate of the amount of money going into the local economies by plantations, the average operations expenditure per acre and average timber harvest per acre are applied to the amount of plantation acreage in the study area. The calculation is shown below:

57,704 (plantation acres in study area) X $55.41 (average expenditure/acre) = $3,197,378

Thus on an annual basis, the plantations spend almost $3.2 million for operations and maintenance. Most of this money is spent in the local economy. While plantations were not identified as a base industry in the location quotient analysis, they have the same characteristics of a base industry because they bring money into the local economy from outside the region. In addition to the operations expenditures is the timber harvest. The calculation of this impact is shown below:

57,704 (plantation acres in study area) X $12.69 (average timber production /acre) = $732,264

Thus between plantation operation and timber harvest, the plantations in the study area contribute more than $3.9 million to the local economy. Bear in mind that the plantations in the study area represent only about 20 percent of the total plantation acreage in the Thomasville-Tallahassee region.

What impact does this $3.9-million expenditure have on the local economies of Grady and Thomas Counties? If the number of jobs attributable to the plantations was available, the employment multiplier calculated from the location quotients could be used to determine the overall impact. However the U.S. Department of Commerce (1992:13) has developed multipliers that can be used based on expenditure levels. These multipliers are available at the state, regional or county level.

Table 2.13
Red Hills Economic Study
1992 Location Quotients:
Thomas County

Industry	United States 1992	%	Thomas County 1992	%	Local Employment	Export Employment
Mining	635	0.6%				
Construction	4,595	4.2%	544	3.3%	693	0
Manufacturing	18,190	16.8%	4,485	27.4%		
Food & kindred products	1,670	1.5%	839	5.1%	252	587
Textiles	678	0.6%				
Apparel	1,018	0.9%	1,039	6.4%	154	885
Lumber & wood products	687	0.6%	694	4.2%	104	590
Furniture & fixtures	465	0.4%	250	1.5%	70	180
Paper & allied products	688	0.6%				
Printing & Publishing	1,521	1.4%	105	0.6%	229	0
Chemicals & allied products	1,071	1.0%				
Rubber & misc. plastic products	879	0.8%	205	1.3%	133	72
Stone, clay, glass & concrete	519	0.5%				
Primary metal	703	0.6%				
Fabricated metal products	1,335	1.2%	310	1.9%	201	109
Computer equip; ind & comm ma	1,946	1.8%	321	2.0%	294	27
Transportation equipment	1,827	1.7%				
Instruments & related products	943	0.9%				
Transportation & public utilities	5,742	5.3%	253	1.5%	866	0
Wholesale trade	5,983	5.5%	966	5.9%	902	64
Wholesale trade - durable goods			422	2.6%		
Wholesale trade - nondurable goods			544	3.3%		
Retail trade	19,138	17.6%	2,700	16.5%	2,887	0
Finance, insurance & real estate	6,672	6.2%	476	2.9%	1,006	0
Services	28,903	26.7%	3,586	21.9%		
Hotels, other lodging places	1,597	1.5%	118	0.7%	241	0
Personal services	1,107	1.0%	138	0.8%	167	0
Business services	5,290	4.9%	256	1.6%	798	0
Auto repair, services, garages	878	0.8%	93	0.6%	132	0
Miscellaneous repair services			70	0.4%		
Motion pictures	395	0.4%	30	0.2%	60	0
Amusement & recreation service	1,116	1.0%	59	0.4%	168	0
Health services	8,464	7.8%	2,048	12.5%	1,277	771
Legal services	906	0.8%	50	0.3%	137	0
Educational services	1,716	1.6%		0.0%	259	0
Social services	1,950	1.8%	124	0.8%	294	0
Museums, botanical, zoos						
Membership organizations	2,005	1.8%	77	0.5%	302	0
Engineering & management servi	2,431	2.2%	124	0.8%	367	0
Private households			249	1.5%		
Miscellaneous Services						
Government	18,579	17.1%				
Federal Government	2,969	2.7%	202	1.2%	448	0
State Government	4,371	4.0%	1,891	11.6%	659	1,232
Local Government	11,239	10.4%	1,253	7.7%	1,695	0
Not Elsewhere classified						
All Industries	108,437	100.0%	16,356	100.0%		4,518

Table 2.14
Red Hills Economic Study
1988-1992 Location Quotients
Thomas County

	1988	1989	1990	1991	1992
Total employment	17,117	17,051	17,127	17,137	16,655
Ag employment	266	242	263	310	299
Total-Ag employment	16,851	16,809	16,864	16,827	16,356
Base employment	5,525	4,555	4,350	4,564	4,518
Local employment	11,326	12,254	12,514	12,263	11,838
Local/Base ratio	2.05	2.69	2.88	2.69	2.62
Average 1988-1992	2.58				

Table 2.15
Red Hills Economic Study
Plantation Budgets: 1993

Plantation	Size (acres)	Annual Operations Expenditures	$/acre	Sustained Timber Harvest	$ /acre
1	2,000	125,000	62.50	30,000	15.00
2	4,000	130,000	32.50	20,000	5.00
3	3,000	125,000	41.67	40,000	13.33
4	3,500	150,000	42.86	40,000	11.43
5	3,200	75,000	23.44	75,000	23.44
6	1,300	150,000	115.38	20,000	15.38
7	3,500	125,000	35.71	70,000	20.00
8	3,200	550,000	171.88	75,000	23.44
9	18,000	1,500,000	83.33	400,000	22.22
10	3,000	100,000	33.33	30,000	10.00
11	2,250	45,000	20.00	30,000	13.33
12	7,250	250,000	34.48	60,000	8.28
13	7,000	250,000	35.71	75,000	10.71
14	1,200	80,000	66.67	20,000	16.67
15	28,000	1,400,000	50.00	150,000	5.36
16	1,000	20,000	20.00	20,000	20.00
17	2,000	100,000	50.00	30,000	15.00
Totals	93,400	5,175,000	55.41	1,185,000	12.69

Due to budget restraints, only the state level multipliers were available for Georgia[1]. Using the multipliers for "agricultural products and agricultural, forestry and fishery services" the impact of plantations on the local economy amounts to 1) an additional 102 jobs; 2) increased earnings of $1.9 million; and 3) increased output for all economic activities of $8.4 million. These impacts are in addition to the $3.9 million of direct expenditures.

Another aspect of the plantations is the amount of property taxes paid. Table 2.16 shows property tax statistics for the plantations in the study area. The values include land and buildings/improvements. The plantations in Grady County paid a total of $112,196 in property taxes while those in Thomas County paid $170,771. Grady County plantations paid an average of $3.94 in property taxes per acre compared to $5.96 per acre in Thomas County. As Brueckheimer (1985:60) has shown, before 1970 plantations were assessed at a higher rate and paid more property taxes per acre than comparable large parcels and land held for forestry or farming. The bottom portion of Table 2.16 shows comparable values for large parcels in Grady and Thomas Counties. In both counties, plantations are assessed at higher levels and pay more property taxes per acre than comparable large parcels. In Thomas County, plantations are assessed at $384 per acre compared to $344 for other large parcels. In terms of property taxes paid, Thomas County plantations pay $5.96 per acre compared to $5.26 per acre for other large parcels. Grady County plantations are assessed at $197 per acre and pay property taxes of $3.94 per acre compared to other large parcels that are assessed at $167 per acre and pay property taxes of $3.33 per acre. In summary, plantations in the study area paid property taxes that, on average, are greater than those property taxes paid by similar large parcels used for forestry and farming.

While paying significant amounts of property taxes, plantations require little in terms of governmental services. They maintain most of their own roads, provide their own security and have low population concentrations so that the demand for schools and other public services is low. From a fiscal impact point of view they are desirable because they pay taxes in excess of their demand for governmental services. Contrast a plantation with a residential subdivision; a subdivision on a per acre basis may pay more property taxes. However, it will require a great deal more government-provided services such as public safety (police, rescue and fire), schools, water and wastewater, roads, etc.

Quantifying Environmental Aspects of the Plantations

The task of quantifying and placing a dollar value on the environmental benefits provided by plantations is difficult, and in some cases, impossible. However, before quantifying these benefits they must be identified. The first benefit provided by the plantations is ground-water recharge. Approximately half of the study area[2] is in a zone where 15 to 20 inches of the annual rainfall goes into the ground-water aquifer and the other half is in a 5-to-10 inch zone (Bush and Johnston, 1988). McWilliams and Trimble (1994) provide more details on the hydrogeology of the study area.

---

[1] The U.S. Department of Commerce will calculate multipliers at regional or county levels; however, there is a charge of $1500. The cost is substantially reduced if the multipliers have been previously calculated for another party.

[2] US 319 (Thomasville Road/Tallahassee Road) splits the study area approximately in half. The area to the east of US 319 is in the 15-20 inch recharge area, while the area to the west is in the 5-10 inch recharge area.

Table 2.16
Red Hills Economic Study
Property Tax Statistics:
Grady and Thomas Cos.

Plantation	County	Size	Net Taxable Value	1993 Exemptions	Taxes Paid	Taxable Value per Acre	Taxes Paid per Acre
1	Grady	3,120	634,747	0	13,728	203	4.40
2	Grady	564	68,612	22,566	1,483	162	2.63
4	Grady	3,237	478,370	0	10,347	148	3.20
7	Grady	2,343	392,348	0	8,486	167	3.62
8	Grady	4,994	670,161	156,352	14,279	166	2.86
11	Grady	1,983	727,367	2,000	15,732	368	7.93
12	Grady	1,586	410,032	0	8,868	259	5.59
15	Grady	2,700	569,994	0	12,328	211	4.57
16	Grady	2,325	286,923	80,294	6,205	158	2.67
17	Grady	960	103,368	61,508	2,235	172	2.33
20	Grady	115	168,669	2,000	3,648	1,484	31.72
21	Grady	1,793	201,355	86,355	4,355	160	2.43
22	Grady	2,459	342,077	0	7,398	139	3.01
23	Grady	175	41,156	0	890	235	5.09
26	Grady	100	102,392	2,000	2,214	1,044	22.14
Subtotal		28,454	5,197,571	413,075	112,196	197	3.94
Grady Co.		298,304					
3	Thomas	218	95,487	0	1,881	438	8.63
5	Thomas	5,411	1,444,475	375,681	25,335	336	4.68
9	Thomas	1,211	262,932	265,742	4,610	437	3.81
10	Thomas	5,248	1,655,542	0	32,614	315	6.21
12	Thomas	363	106,961	0	1,876	295	5.17
13	Thomas	1,119	248,784	224,386	4,363	423	3.90
14	Thomas	3,356	1,159,473	0	23,836	345	7.10
16	Thomas	631	797,749	0	15,532	1,264	24.61
18	Thomas	3,492	813,877	484,048	14,891	372	4.26
19	Thomas	1,453	454,845	168,751	7,975	429	5.49
23	Thomas	1,739	695,479	0	12,495	400	7.19
24	Thomas	2,925	526,043	379,039	9,771	309	3.34
25	Thomas	288	109,035	0	1,912	379	6.64
27	Thomas	992	707,256	0	13,173	713	13.28
28	Thomas	207	26,884	0	507	130	2.45
Subtotal		28,653	9,104,822	1,897,647	170,771	384	5.96
Thomas Co		338,735	254,035,158	14,524,728	2,207,567		
Totals		57,107	14,302,393	2,310,722	282,967	291	4.96
Comparable Parcels							
1	Thomas	4,153	1,238,531	0	21,723	298	5.23
2	Thomas	2,229	728,486	0	14,351	327	6.44
3	Thomas	2,000	277,335	426,003	4,864	352	2.43
4	Thomas	380	83,279	0	1,460	219	3.84
5	Thomas	2000	789750	208715	13852	499	6.93
6	Thomas	1640	511551	0	8972	312	5.47
Subtotal		12,402	3,628,932	634,718	65,222	344	5.26
7	Grady	2,013	357,860	0	7,740	178	3.85
8	Grady	3,597	532,618	0	11,520	148	3.20
9	Grady	1,007	145,458	39,695	3,146	184	3.12
10	Grady	490	64,346	21,449	1,391	175	2.84
11	Grady	467	76,839	23,116	1,662	214	3.56
12	Grady	346	43,179	14,393	933	166	2.70
Subtotal		7,920	1,220,300	98,653	26,392	167	3.33
Total		20,322	4,849,232	733,371	91,614	275	4.51

Using the following assumptions, the amount of water recharge from the study area can be estimated. First, the amount of plantation acreage in the study area is approximately 57,000; however, this does not include non-plantation ownership. For the sake of this example only plantation acreage will be used. Second, 50 percent of the acreage, or 28,500 acres are assumed to be in the 15-to-20 inch per year recharge area while the remaining 28,500 will be assigned to the 5-to-10 inch zone. Third, the mid-point of these recharge estimates will be used — 17.5 inches for the 15-to-20 inch zone and 7.5 inches for the 5-10 inch zone. These assumptions result in the following annual recharge:

$$
\begin{aligned}
&= (28,500 \text{ acres @ } 17.5\text{"/yr/acre}) + (28,500 \text{ acres @ } 7.5\text{"/yr/acre}) \\
&= 41,562 \text{ acre-ft/yr} + 17,813 \text{ acre-ft/yr} \\
&= 59,375 \text{ acre-ft/yr} \\
&= (59,375 \text{ acre-ft}) * (325,851 \text{ gals/acre-ft}) \\
&= 19,347,400,000 \text{ gallons/yr or} \\
&= 53 \text{ mgd (million gallons/day)}
\end{aligned}
$$

Thus the study area provides for an average daily recharge of 53 million gallons. To give some meaning to this number it is 45 percent more water than was used by all of Leon County in 1990 (Bureau of Economic and Business Research, 1991:222).

A second benefit is the wildlife habitat that the plantations provide. The study area provides more than 57,000 acres of nearly contiguous habitat which is many cases is professionally managed for wildlife. In many urbanizing regions, the preservation of wildlife habitat is the critical factor in protecting endangered species.

A third environmental benefit provided by the plantations is the small amount of impervious surface, resulting in reduced amounts of storm water runoff. Storm water runoff is one of the main sources of water pollution and once created is difficult to control. Storm water runoff becomes an even greater problems in areas with intensive agriculture due to leaching of pesticides and herbicides.

For many of these environmental benefits, quantification is not possible. One way to examine these benefits provided by the plantations is to evaluate them along with possible alternative uses. It the Red Hills were developed as intensive agriculture, there would be increased use of herbicides, pesticides and fertilizers. The use of these materials would not be desirable in areas of high aquifer recharge because of possible groundwater contamination. If the plantations were converted into residential subdivisions, the amount of impervious surface would increase along with the amount of runoff. While this runoff would not contain the amounts of herbicides, pesticides and fertilizers found in agricultural runoff, these substances would still be present. Again in an area with significant aquifer recharge such development would be undesirable. A third alternative to the plantations would be large-scale timber harvesting. While the amount of impervious surface would not be decreased, clear-cutting would increase the amount of soil erosion.

While this discussion has not provided dollars values for the environmental benefits provided by the current land use pattern, it has questioned whether any alternative land use pattern could provide the same or better environmental quality.

Conclusions

This economic overview and analysis shows clearly that the plantations have a significant role in the region's economy. They contribute $3.9 million to the region's economy through their operations budgets and timber production. These expenditures in turn result in multiplier effects in Grady and Thomas Counties, where plantations increase economic output by $8.4 million, employment by 102 jobs, and earnings by $1.9 million. These impacts result from only those plantations in the study area, a group that represents approximately 20 percent of all plantations in the Thomasville-Tallahassee region. The plantations also pay property taxes totaling more than $280,000 per year. From a fiscal impact viewpoint, the plantations provide more taxes than they require in terms of governmental services. From an environmental perspective, the plantations provide prime aquifer recharge areas, significant amounts of quality wildlife habitat, and low levels of impervious surfaces and the associated storm water runoff. While many people know that the region has numerous plantations, few recognize the economic, fiscal and environmental benefits that these plantations provide to the region.

SUMMARY AND CONCLUSIONS

The purpose of this pilot study is to establish an economic and demographic database for the study area; to quantify the role that plantations play in the local economy; and to examine the impacts of economic and demographic trends on the future of plantations.

Demographic Summary

The region selected for this analysis comprised four counties: Thomas and Grady Counties in Georgia and Leon and Jefferson Counties in Florida. Leon County is the most populous county in the region with more than two and one-half times the population of the other three counties, combined. In terms of population growth, Leon County grew at a rate that was double that of any other county. During the 1970-1990 period, the county added almost 90,000 new residents. Almost half of this growth occurred in the area north of Interstate 10. Over the 1990-2010 period, Leon is expected to add another 66,000 new residents.

Demographic Conclusions

What can we conclude from these trends? First, the northern portions of Leon County have been and will continue to be the fastest growing areas in the region. The primary limiting factor to even more growth in this region is the availability of land. The degree to which plantation land is converted to residential development will dictate the rate and amount of growth in the region. Between 1976 and 1991 more than 35,000 acres of plantations were converted into subdivisions — with most of this conversion taking place in northern Leon County.

As growth continues to move closer to the state line, land development regulations will come into play. The time and money required to obtain development approval in Leon County is substantial. Grady and Thomas Counties have less stringent development regulations; therefore, land development is quicker and cheaper. The northward movement of growth from Tallahassee combined with the fact the land development is cheaper and quicker in Georgia means that the study area will be subject to significant development pressures over the next several decades.

Economic Summary

The economic analysis used the same four-county study area. The economies of the four counties are similar in some respects and different in others. First, Leon County is the employment center for the region with more than three times the employment of the other counties, combined. Second, manufacturing is the most important employment sector in the Grady and Thomas Counties. Thomas County has 70 percent more manufacturing jobs than Leon County despite the fact that Leon County's total employment is five times greater than that of Thomas County. Third, farming which was once important in all counties is now only significant in Jefferson County. Fourth, retail trade, services and governmental employment are important to the economies of all four counties.

Economic Impact of the Plantations

Plantations contribute to the local economy through expenditures for operations and maintenance activities as well as timber harvesting. On an annual basis, the plantations in the study area spend almost $3.2 million for operations and maintenance in terms of salaries, supplies, etc. Timber production contributes another $.7 million per year. Therefore, the plantations in the study area directly contribute more than $3.9 million to the local economy. These expenditures, in turn, result in additional benefits to the economy. Using U.S. Department of Commerce multipliers developed for Georgia, the direct expenditure of $3.9 million by the plantations results in an additional 102 jobs, increased earnings of $1.9 million, and increased economic output of $8.4 million.

From a property tax perspective, plantations in the study area paid property taxes of more than $280,000. On average, plantations paid more taxes per acre than similar large parcels being used for forestry and/or farming. On a fiscal impact basis, plantations provide more taxes than they require in terms of governmental services.

From an environmental perspective, the plantations provide a number of benefits. First the study area provides for an average daily water recharge of 53 million gallons. Second, the plantations provide more than 57,000 acres of nearly contiguous wildlife habitat which in many cases is professionally managed. Third, the plantations have low amounts of impervious surfaces and thus low levels of storm water runoff.

RECOMMENDATIONS FOR FURTHER STUDY

Since this is a pilot study, the first recommendation for further study is to expand the study area to include all of the Red Hills region. This pilot study examined only 20 percent of the plantations in the region. Second, the study's scope should be expanded. This would involve obtaining an accurate picture of plantation acreage and location over the past 75 years. This study identified the existence of a series of plantation ownership maps beginning in 1924 with updates every ten to twenty years. These maps should be placed in a geographic information system (GIS) so that accurate estimates of plantation growth and decline as well as the location of this growth and decline can be made.

A third area of further study would involve a detailed survey of plantation economics including employment levels and details on the types of expenditures (e.g., supplies, salaries, etc.) made during an average year.

Lastly, further attention should be paid to factors that could impact the viability of the Red Hills. These factors include, but are not limited to 1) the encroachment of urban development from

Thomasville and Tallahassee; 2) the differential land use and development requirements between Florida and Georgia, as well as between Thomas, Grady and Brooks Counties; 3) the effect of utility (gas, oil and electric) corridors; 4) sales and division of plantations upon inheritance; and 5) the ability to obtain conservation easements from present plantation owners.

REFERENCES

Avant, David A. III. 1991. *Plantation management on a sharecropper's budget.* L'Avant Studios. Tallahassee.

Brueckheimer, William R. 1979. The quail plantations of the Thomasville-Tallahassee-Albany Regions. In *Proceedings Tall Timbers Ecology and Management Conference*, No. 16 (February 22-24). Tall Timbers Research Station. Tallahassee.

_____. 1985. The quail plantations of the Thomasville-Tallahassee-Albany Regions. *The Journal of Southwest Georgia History* 3, Fall 1985.

Bush, P.W. and R.H. Johnston. 1988. *Ground-water hydraulics, regional flow, and groundwater development of the Floridan aquifer system in Florida, and in part of Georgia, South Carolina, and Alabama.* U.S. Geological Survey Professional Paper 1403-C. U.S. Government Printing Office. Washington, DC.

Florida Plats. 1993. *Thomas County, Georgia plat directory.* Florida Plats. Clermont.

Galambos, E.C. and A.F. Schreiber. 1978. *Making sense out of dollars: economic analysis for local government.* U.S. League of Cities. Washington, DC.

Heilbrun, James. 1987. *Urban economics and public policy*, 3rd edition. St. Martin's Press. New York.

Isserman, Andrew. 1977. The location quotient approach to estimating regional economic impacts. *Journal of the American Planning Association* 43: 33-41.

Komarek, E.V. 1979. The role of the hunting plantation in the development of game, fire ecology and management. In *Proceedings Tall Timbers Ecology and Management Conference*, No. 16 (February 22-24). Tall Timbers Research Station. Tallahassee.

McWilliams, Richebourg G. and C.A. Trimble. 1994. *The Floridan aquifer and groundwater recharge in Thomas County, Georgia: a brief summary of current information.* Working paper February 7, 1994.

Neel, Leon. 1994. Personal communication on 13 January 1994.

Paisley, Clifton. 1981. *From cotton to quail: an agricultural chronicle of Leon County, Florida, 1980-1967.* University Presses of Florida. Tallahassee.

Prunty, Merle Jr. 1963. The woodland plantation as a contemporary occupance type in the South. *The Geographical Review* 53, 1.

Rogers, William Warren. 1989. *Foshalee: quail country plantation.* Sentry Press. Tallahassee.

Sipe, Neil and Robert Hopkins. 1984. *Microcomputer and economic analysis: spreadsheets for local governments*. University of Florida - Bureau of Economic and Business Research. Gainesville.

Southwest Georgia Regional Development Center. 1991. *The Cairo-Whigham-Grady County comprehensive land use plan*. Grady County. Cairo.

Thomas County Planning and Land Use Standards Commission and Thomas County/Thomasville Planning Department. 1992. *Thomas County unincorporated areas comprehensive plan*. Thomas County Planning Department. Thomasville.

Thomasville-Thomas County Chamber of Commerce. 1992. *Thomasville-Thomas County, Georgia market data*. Chamber of Commerce. Thomasville.

Tiebout, Charles M. 1962. *The community economic base study*. Supplementary Paper No. 16. Committee for Economic Development. New York.

U.S. Department of Commerce, Bureau of Economic Analysis. 1992. *Regional multipliers: a user handbook for the regional input-output modeling system (RIMS II)*. U.S. Government Printing Office. Washington, DC.

CHAPTER 3: ARCHAEOLOGY

Kenneth W.
Johnson, Ph.D.

This chapter examines
what is already known
about the archaeology
of the Red Hills region
and generates ques-
tions for future re-
search. It includes the
results of literature
searches and inter-
views. It summarizes
existing knowledge
and concludes with
research questions.

This chapter is not a
comprehensive survey
of archaeological sites
in the region, but a
preliminary statement
of existing knowledge
and future potentials.

INTRODUCTION

Project Description

Archaeological sites are finite, non-renewable resources (Crook,
1986), in some ways like endangered species. They are highly
sensitive and susceptible to destruction. Once disturbed and
destroyed, whether by construction activities or casual looting,
they can never be replaced, and the information they contain is
irretrievably lost. Large numbers of archaeological sites have
been destroyed in the twentieth century, highlighting the need to
preserve remaining significant sites.

This preliminary statement of existing knowledge and future
potentials involved only a small amount of field work as funding
levels were limited. Limited funding permitted only surface
reconnaissance in a few specific locales and excavation of a
small number of test pits with the assistance of Thomas College
students. This initial study needs to be followed by full-scale
archaeological survey in the Red Hills region.

The importance of archaeological sites is the information they
contain, not just the artifacts. The locations and relationships of
artifacts to each other, called "context," provide much
information. Each site is unique because each contains different
contexts and thus potentially different information. A site is
significant (or not significant) in relation to its potential to yield
information important to the understanding of history or
prehistory. An evaluation can be made only in relation to existing
knowledge. This chapter helps provide part of the framework for
evaluating the significance of individual sites within this region.

Sites on federal property, or sites threatened by construction
projects involving federal permits or funds or requiring environmental impact statements, are protected by the Antiquity Act of
1906, The Historic Sites Act of 1935, the Reservoir Salvage Act
of 1960, the Historic Preservation Act of 1966 (especially
Section 106), the National Environmental Policy Act of 1969,
Executive Order 11593, federal departmental regulations, and
state legislation. Sites on private lands have less protection,
unless federal permits or funds are involved. On these lands, it
is illegal to dig, disturb, or alter any archaeological, aboriginal,
prehistoric, or historic site for the purposes of investigating the
site or discovering artifacts without written permission from the
landowner, and the state Department of Natural Resources must
be notified five days in advance. State laws protect all human
burial remains of whatever age, modern or prehistoric, whether
buried in an Indian mound or modern cemetery or not (Official

Code of Georgia Annotated 12-3-620 to 12-3-622).

Purpose

This chapter is designed to 1) help educate the public of the value of cultural resources and the need for preservation; 2) provide an overview of regional culture history; 3) summarize previous research and the findings to date; 4) identify possible questions for further research; and 5) help provide a framework on which to base plans for future research and for evaluation of a site's significance.

The major themes in this approach include the Native American, African-American and European-American inhabitants of the region, their cultures and adaptations to local environments, subsistence patterns, technological developments (e.g., pottery, bow and arrow, plant domestication, etc.), architecture, sociopolitical organization, settlement patterns, demography and culture change. Data collected during the investigations helps provide important cultural and scientific information, and contributes to the understanding of regional and local prehistory and history. Information on these aspects of the prehistory and history is a benefit to the scientific community and interpretations for the public.

Structure

The study consists of four related sets of activities: 1) collection and assessment of existing information about known sites and artifacts in the region; 2) limited field investigations; 3) summary of information into an overview (or series of overviews), by culture period; 4) providing lists of possible research questions and making recommendations for further research. This project is intended to be the first of a series of projects, though no funds are available at present for continuing the work. Each of these sets of activities is described below.

Collection and Assessment of Existing Information

This activity determines what is already known about the region. One of the most important sources of information was interviews with local artifact collectors, landowners and managers, all of whom provided highly valuable information. Other information is found in published books, papers published in scholarly journals, technical reports, site forms for previously-recorded sites at the State of Georgia archaeological site files at the University of Georgia, Athens, and personal communication with other professional archaeologists. Very little professional research has been conducted within the Red Hills region of Georgia; consequently most of the professional literature deals with sites in related areas of South Georgia or North Florida, or with the Southeastern United States in general.

Limited Field Investigations

This chapter should not be treated as a comprehensive survey of the Red Hills region. Instead, it is a preliminary summary of existing knowledge and potential future research. The scope of the project involved little actual field work, as funding levels were limited. The contract called for the archaeologist to provide a total of 40 hours of professional services over a five-month period, thus averaging two hours per week. Actually, field investigations required approximately 70 hours in addition to many hours of background documentary research and report writing. Most of this field time was spent interviewing approximately three dozen local people (as referred to above). Field investigations included limited surface reconnaissance in a few specific areas, primarily at previously-known sites shown to me by landowners and managers. Other field work included excavation of a small number of test pits with the assistance of Thomas College students.

Summary of Information

This activity involves summarizing information into an overview, or actually a series of overviews by culture period. This information is tentative and partial because it is based primarily on informant reports and information from adjacent regions, and includes very little actual research. This information is presented in this chapter as an overview of each culture recognized or likely to be present in the Red Hills region.

I viewed several local collections of artifacts to identify components present, but unfortunately precise information on locations (other than "somewhere on the farm") was usually unavailable. Local informants have been generally unable to provide the kinds of precise information needed for a more comprehensive overview. Most people could recognize "arrowheads" but seemed unable to provide precise information about the locations where the artifacts were found, and seemed to know little about other kinds of artifacts.

I have seen very few pottery sherds from the region because few people collect them, which is unfortunate because pottery is more informative than are projectile points. I suspect that sizable village site are perhaps more common in the region than many people recognize, but surveys are needed to find sites. No major village areas have been identified during this study, though a number of smaller sites have been identified.

Questions for Future Research

A list of potential questions for future research is included with the overview for each culture period. The chapter concludes with recommendations for archaeological and historical surveys to determine the locations and distribution of sites, by period, and their condition and potential to yield further information. These questions and recommendations may be the most important part of the entire chapter.

A series of overviews describes each culture period, based on previous existing information. If little is known about that period in Thomas or Grady counties or Southwest Georgia, then the discussion takes the perspective of the Southeastern United States in general. Details about known artifacts and sites in the Red Hills region are inserted into the discussion whenever such information is available. Each overview concludes with a list of questions for future research.

PREHISTORIC AND HISTORIC OVERVIEWS, BY CULTURE PERIOD

Paleo-Indian Period, 12,000-9500 B.P.

The Paleo-Indian period, lasting from approximately 12,000 to 9500 years before present (B.P.), represents the first well-documented human occupation of the Southeastern United States (Anderson et al., 1990). Remains from this period are scarce with one exception: they are common in the rivers of North Florida and presumably South Georgia. These remains include stone projectile points (Simpson, Suwannee or Clovis), bone pins and other tools, and the bones of prey species. However, no undisturbed "kill site" site has been documented in the eastern United States due to disturbance by river currents or spring boil. Upland campsites also exist but are equally rare. Paleo-Indian artifacts have been reported previously in the Red Hills region around Lake Iamonia, just across the state line in Florida, but no major excavations have been conducted. Fewer than 100 Paleo-Indian sites are recorded in Florida, and even fewer in Georgia (Anderson et al., 1990: Figure 4).

One Simpson type projectile point, unfluted, basally ground, was examined. It is thought to have been found on the Sherwood Plantation in southeastern Grady County (in the Stoddard collection), though the location of the site from which it came is unknown. This placement may be significant, since this property is situated in the uplands rather than along the river. Another small Paleo-Indian projectile point was also examined (in Mr. Bolling Jones' collection), though it is said to have been found at Jacksonville Beach, Florida.

Wetlands, bogs and stratified floodplains in the Red Hills region have excellent potential to contain such deposits, and to be the first in the Southeastern United States to yield such information. For example, the University of Florida has been conducting underwater excavations of a 17,000 year old elephant skeleton in the Aucilla River, but evidence of human activity is lacking.

The Paleo-Indian period was within the time of the Wisconsin glaciation when ice sheets covered much of the North American continent. The mile-thick ice sheets locked up huge amounts of the earth's water, sea level was more than 200 feet lower, and the Atlantic and Gulf shores were much farther out. North Georgia was spruce/Jack pine forest (now retreated to New England), South Georgia was open pine or oak/hickory/southern pine forest, and peninsula Florida was patches of oak scrub and open savanna (Delcourt et al., 1980; Watts, 1970). Since there was less rainfall and sea level and aquifer levels were lower, most rivers, streams, springs, swamps and lakes were dry or smaller. Water for animals was available at sinkholes, which therefore became ambush places for hunters. Herds of large grazing animals such as elephants roamed South Georgia, along with other "megafauna" such as wild horses, long-horned bison, camels, giant ground sloths, giant land tortoises, and saber toothed tigers. These were the animals encountered by the first humans to reach America, the Paleo-Indians.

These foraging peoples were probably organized into mobile egalitarian bands each composed of a nuclear or extended family. They probably had social affiliations with other bands loosely aggregated into larger macrobands (Anderson et al., 1990).

General Research Themes

> Chronology
> Cultural adaptation to local environmental conditions
> Subsistence strategies and mobility
> Regional settlement patterns and local community patterns
> Demography

Specific Questions

Chronology:

> What artifact types and varieties are present?
>
> What chronological sub-phases are represented?
>
> Are deeply stratified sites present, such as on levee ridges?

<u>Subsistence strategies and mobility</u>:

Sites are situated in relation to what environmental features?

Are both wet sites and land sites present?

Are raw materials of local or exotic origin, showing mobility or relationships with other regions?

What plant and animal resources were procured?

Are organic materials present, such as bone or charcoal that can be identified?

<u>Regional settlement patterns and local community patterns</u>:

What is the distribution of Paleo-Indian sites across the Red Hills landscape?

What site types can be identified, based on site size, number of sites, artifact density tool types and diversity, and environmental setting?

How do these patterns differ from those of other regions and other culture periods?

Can any sites be identified which potentially are eligible for nomination to the National Register of Historic Places?

Archaic Period, 9500-3000 B.P.

For every Paleo-Indian artifact found, hundreds of Archaic artifacts are found. This is true at upland and riverine sites throughout South Georgia and North Florida, including several collections from Grady and Thomas Counties. Some of these collections have been examined, and others appear as photographs in published books (Balfour, 1975). Published photographs include the Ray Gainey collection from the Mistletoe Plantation in Grady County, the Mr. and Mrs. William D. Cox collection from the Merryway Plantation in Thomas County, the Bolling Jones III collection from the Myrtlewood Plantation and the Diston Place, and the Robert C. Balfour III collection (Balfour, 1975:14-17). Several other collections have also been examined. Frequent projectile points in these two counties include Early Archaic Arredondo, Kirk, Bolen Beveled/Hardaway Side Notched and other corner notched or side notched types (all 9500-7000 B.P.), and large stemmed points, many of which are probably Middle to Late Archaic (7000-3000 B.P.). Other types are also present, including small numbers of small triangular points (Pinellas, etc).

Two published photographs (Balfour, 1975:14, 16) were examined, resulting in the following list. However, more complete analysis would need to include additional details that cannot be seen in photographs, and thus the following classifications must be considered tentative. Classifications are based on Bullen (1975) or Cambron and Hulse (1973); also see Justice (1987).

Figure 3.1   Partial list of projectile points published in photograph (Balfour, 1975:14) of the Ray Gainey collection from Mistletoe Plantation, Southwestern Grady County, along the Ochlocknee River:

8	Arredondo	Early Archaic
9	Bolen, Kirk, Palmer, Hardaway, and other corner- notched and side-notched	Early Archaic
1	Lafayette	
8	Gilchrist (Bullen, 1975) or Elora (Cambron and Hulse, 1973:50)	
2	Hernando or Citrus (basally notched)	Middle Archaic
1	Morrow Mountain	Middle Archaic
5	Savannah River	Late Archaic
10	Other large Archaic stemmed	mostly Late Archaic?
?	Ledbetter, Limestone or McIntire? (Cambron and Hulse, 1973)	

44   Total classified
81   Others not classified (not counting others only partly visible in photo)

125   Total points in photo (but this is only part of the Gainey collection)

Figure 3.2   Partial list of projectile points in photograph (Balfour, 1975:16) of the Bolling Jones III collection from Myrtlewood Plantation and the Diston Place in southeastern Thomas County:

22   Bolen, Kirk, Palmer, Hardaway and other corner-notched and side notched Early Archaic points
1   Kirk Serrated
2   Gilchrist (Bullen, 1975) or Elora (Cambron and Hulse, 1973:50)
2   Hernando or Citrus (basally notched)
1   Abbey? (Cambron and Hulse, 1973:1)
3   Morrow Mountain
7 +   Large Archaic stemmed
?   Ledbetter, Limestone or McIntire? (Camabron and Hulse, 1973)
3   Pinellas

41   Total classified
75   Others not classified

116   Total visible in the photograph (excluding non-local black points)

Figure 3.3   A sample of artifacts from the Sonny Stoddard collection from the Sherwood Plantation included the following:

1	Simpson type Paleo-Indian projectile point (referred to above)
10	Bolen Beveled Early Archaic points
	Arredondo Early Archaic points
2	Savannah River stemmed Late Archaic points
	Other large stemmed points
7	Corner to basally notched, honey colored

Though abundant throughout the region, Archaic points are often described as isolated finds representing "campsites" or hunting camps. A typical view was that of Judge Hopkins, speaking about the Sherwood plantation:

> Evidently it was a favorite hunting ground of the Red Man, evidence of which was found in the unusual number of arrow heads found within its boundary, several hundred having been gathered by the "plow boys" of the writer (Hopkins, 1934).

However, it is possible that these casual impressions may not reflect a full picture of the area. Furthermore, even sites of low artifact density provide important data (Sullivan, 1992). At least 20 Archaic sites are recorded in extreme northern Leon County, Florida, within five miles of the Grady and Thomas Counties, Georgia (Tesar, 1980:Map 45). They indicate the likelihood that sites — more than just isolated artifact finds — are yet to be identified on the Georgia side of the boundary. Projectile points are said to be common around sinkholes in southeastern Thomas County (Jimmy Vaughn, personal communication, February 1994), but it is not clear if they are equally common around sinks in southwestern Thomas County. Points that may be Archaic have also been reported near Birdsong (Sonny Stoddard, personal communication). An Archaic site was tested in southern Thomas County by a student from Florida State University, but little was found (Calvin Jones, personal communication November 1994). The site is located near Saul Road approximately two miles east of U.S. 19 and 1/4 mile north of the state line.

Important changes occurred at the close of the Pleistocene and beginning of the Holocene period at 10,500 B.C. In eastern North America, the continental glaciers retreated, sea level rose, climate became warmer and wetter, rainfall increased, river and lake levels rose, strong seasonality began, forest openings closed in, forest types changed, herds of megafauna disappeared, and deer and elk (which are solitary animals) radiated across the Southeastern United States (Delcourt, 1979; Delcourt et al., 1980:112, 129; Watts, 1970:28; Watts and Struiver, 1980; Whitehead, 1964). The Early Archaic (or Transitional Paleo-Indian/Early Archaic) (9500 to 7000 B.P.) and the Middle Archaic (7000 to 5000 B.P.) periods are both within the Atlantic climatic episode. This is a time of cultural adaptation to changing environmental conditions. Paleo-Indian specialized hunting (to the extent that it existed) was replaced by Archaic generalized hunting, gathering, fishing and shell fishing. Subsistence strategies became more localized, more generalized, less selective (Neusius, 1986).

Few studies have been done in Southwest Georgia, but in many adjacent regions, such as North Florida, North Georgia, and North Alabama and other regions of the Southeast, Early Archaic traits included notched or stemmed points, unifacial flake tools, and much use of rock shelters (Chapman, 1977; Coe, 1964; DeJarnette et al., 1962; Griffin, 1974; Lewis and Lewis, 1961; Purdy, 1981; Walthall, 1980:38). In the Tennessee River valley in Alabama, Paleo-Indian and Early Archaic (e.g.,

Dalton) sites are most common on upper terraces above the river, and sites of later periods are most common on the lowlands and stream banks (Walthall, 1980:48).

In the Archaic, as in the Paleo-Indian period, social groups are thought (based on ethnographic analogy to living peoples) to have been small, autonomous bands of nuclear or extended families, migrating seasonally within a definite range of territory. There were no large permanent settled villages, no farming, no domesticated plants or animals (except possibly dogs, and squash toward the end of the period), no bows and arrows (spear thrower only), no pottery (except at the end of the period), no hereditary chiefs, no social stratification. Division of labor was based only on age and sex, not hereditary positions. Most such groups of hunter-gatherer-fishers throughout the world tend to be patrilineal and patrilocal, meaning that descent was determined through the male line, and after marriage the newly-wed couple would live with the husband's family rather than the wife's family. Such social patterns are optimal for a hunting society in which a successful hunt depends on the hunter having intimate knowledge of the local terrain and animal habits.

The Middle Archaic correlates with the Mid-Holocene Altithermal or Hypsithermal climactic episode, which was globally the warmest episode for tens of thousands of years, even warmer than now. Oak/hickory nut-bearing deciduous hardwood forests reached their peak and greatest extent in the eastern United States during this period (Watts and Stuiver, 1980:326; Whitehead, 1970:28). These optimal conditions no doubt contributed to the high number of artifacts in the region, not only in terms of increased human population density in times of abundance, but also in terms of the wide distribution of resources across the landscape.

Cultural adaptations during this period, called "primary forest efficiency" in Georgia (Caldwell, 1958, 1962), or the "broad spectrum revolution," epitomize the generalized subsistence pattern, in which a wide diversity of resources was exploited. In other regions such as Alabama, this pattern is seen in the equal numbers of different kinds of tools (weapons, fabricating tools, processing tools, domestic implements) (Griffin, 1974:107-108). Research at sites throughout the Southeast (e.g., Chapman and Shea, 1981) indicates that nuts, such as hickory and acorn, are heavily exploited during this period, along with the animals that subsist off the acorn mast including turkeys, squirrels and white-tail deer (Chapman and Shea, 1981; Asch, Ford and Asch, 1972). Nutting stones and woodworking implements (e.g., axes and adzes) first appear in significant numbers in this period. In Russell Cave in Alabama, the first pits appear in Middle Archaic times, indicating storage, which has long-range implications in terms of human mobility, subsistence, settlement patterns and social organization. These patterns established in the Archaic period result eventually in the first settled, sedentary villages in the following Woodland periods.

The Middle Archaic throughout the Southeastern United States includes the first known polished and ground stone tools, flexed burials (e.g., at Stanfield-Worley bluff shelter in Alabama [DeJarnette, Kurjack and Cambron, 1962]; Indian Knoll [Webb, 1946]), and riverine shell middens. This is a time of population increase, as shown by numbers of sites and artifacts, increased territoriality and regional stylistic diversity (Walthall, 1980:58). In contrast to the high percentage of unifacial tools in the Early Archaic level at Russell Cave, there is only a low percentage in the Middle Archaic Morrow Mountain levels, indicating changes in site function, technology, and settlement patterns that may have been widespread across the Southeast.

The Late Archaic period (3000 to 1000 B.C.) is a time of population growth, regional variations, and interregional trade or exchange in the Southeast (J.B. Griffin, 1967:178). The first domesticated plants (e.g., squash) are now present but not yet important in the economy; that importance will come later in the Woodland and Mississippi periods.

After 4000 B.C. and lasting into the Late Archaic period, which also corresponds to the Sub-Boreal climatic episode, environmental conditions became essentially modern, that is, increasingly moist, as sea level, rainfall, and water levels in springs, sinkholes and rivers reached generally current levels. Cypress swamps appeared. Since sea level rise had stabilized, vast salt marshes appeared along the Atlantic and Gulf coasts, and fish and shellfish production was stimulated. Humans lived along the coasts in higher population density and began building shell heaps (or shell "middens") composed of discarded foodstuffs, tools and other evidence of everyday life. Although upland areas such as Thomas and Grady County continue to be occupied, as shown by the occasional appearance of Savannah River type and other projectile points in collections, those sites are overshadowed by the more highly visible shell middens along the seacoasts.

Throughout the Southeastern United States steatite (soapstone) and sandstone bowls appeared in the Late Archaic period, though some are also found in the following Deptford and possibly Swift Creek periods. One steatite bowl fragment was found at the Diston Place in southern Thomas County (Bolling Jones), and whole steatite bowls and fragments have been found elsewhere in the county, though the locations are uncertain (see discussion of Deptford period.) Steatite is an exotic material in the Red Hills region because it was transported from the Piedmont region rock outcrops between Carrollton and Atlanta, 200 miles to the north.

Another time marker is the appearance of fiber tempered pottery. This oldest pottery in North America first appeared in South Georgia, Florida and Alabama (Phelps, 1965). Sites with this type of pottery are known from the Florida portion of the Red Hills zone, but none have yet been reported in the Georgia portion. Sites containing this pottery are generally more common in coastal zones but also occur in upland settings such as a site near Cuthbert, Georgia (Espenshade, 1993). The appearance of this pottery is sometimes used to distinguish the Gulf Formational Period, 2500-1200 B.C. (Walthall, 1980:77-103). There is little evidence that the invention of pottery had much effect (at first) on the human cultures, as the some foraging way of life seems to have continued, but this is an assumption needing further research (see below).

The Red Hills region has the potential to contain significant sites of the Early, Middle and Late Archaic period because of the great abundance of projectile points found, the special nature of the Red Hills soils, topography and environmental conditions in Southwest Georgia, and the possibility of addressing research questions concerning egalitarian hunter bands and their cultural adaptations to upland environments.

General Research Themes

> Chronology
> Subsistence strategies and mobility
> Cultural adaptation to local environmental conditions
> Regional settlement patterns and local community patterns
> Demography

Specific Questions

Chronology:

> What is the full range of projectile point types present in the region, and in what relative frequencies?

Are there types that are unique to the Red Hills region?

Are deeply buried, stratified sites present, such as on levee ridges?

Subsistence strategies and mobility:

Where are sites situated and in relation to what environmental features?

What diversity of tool types is present?

Are shell, wood or other tools present?

Are raw materials of local or exotic origin, showing mobility or relationships with other regions?

What were the Archaic people's seasonal movements and size of their territorial range — did they permanently occupy the uplands or did they seasonally migrate to the Gulf coast or Chattahoochee River or other zones?

What plant and animal resources were procured? Were they generalized foragers?

Are organic materials present, such as bone or charcoal, which can be identified?

Was cultural adaptation to the Red Hills environment any different from cultural adaptation to other, adjacent zones?

Regional settlement patterns, local community patterns, and demography:

What are the distributions of Early, Middle and Late Archaic sites across the Red Hills landscape?

What site types can be identified, such as base camps and short-term campsites, based on site size, number of sites, artifact density tool types and diversity, and environmental setting?

Why are Archaic artifacts so abundant, especially as contrasted with other periods?

How do these patterns differ from those of other regions and other culture periods?

Is there any difference between the Georgia and Florida portions of the Red Hills zone?

Is there any indication that the invention of pottery and the domestication of squash late in the Late Archaic had any effect on the economy, site settings or seasonal movements?

Can any sites be identified which potentially are eligible for nomination to the National Register of Historic Places?

Woodland Period, 1000 B.C. to A.D. 900

"Woodland" is a general term that includes the Deptford/Cartersville, Swift Creek and Weeden Island periods. The term is used to distinguish those cultures that post-dated the Archaic period and preceded the Mississippi period. Each of these periods will be discussed separately. This period is not well known in Southwest Georgia, though a moderate amount of research has been done on sites along the lower Chattahoochee and Flint Rivers (e.g., C.B.Moore, 1907; Bullen, 1950, 1958; DeJarnette, 1975; Kellar, Kelly and McMichael, 1962a,b; Kelly, 1950; Betty Smith, 1975a,b, 1977).

The Neolithic Revolution, referring to the domestication of plants and animals, was one of the most important events in human history globally. The Neolithic Revolution led to the establishment of permanent sedentary villages and ultimately the appearance of civilizations. The Woodland period cultures in Georgia are good examples of these processes of cultural evolution. These examples are important in understanding similar processes that occurred globally.

Throughout the eastern United States (or "Eastern Woodlands"), the first large, sedentary villages appeared during the Woodland period. They were based on horticulture (gardening, not full-scale agriculture), using domesticated native plants, and storage techniques not previously available. Cultigens include Amaranthus (pigweed), Chenopodium (lamb's quarters) (Griffin, 1974), Polygonum (knotweed), Iva (marsh elder), Ambrosia trifida (giant ragweed), Phalaris carolinia (may grass), Helianthus annua (sunflower) (Walthall, 1980:108) and varieties of squash and gourds. This horticultural complex was based on native plants before corn and beans were introduced. Hunting and gathering of such things as acorns and hickory nuts also remained major subsistence activities. Bows and arrows appeared in this period, along with new storage techniques. The development of storage capacities has important implications for changes in annual subsistence activities, seasonality and scheduling, seasonal migration patterns and the appearance of sedentary villages.

Woodland period villages in the Eastern Woodlands were generally lineage based, economically self-sufficient and politically independent, in contrast to the more hierarchial settlement patterns in the following Mississippi period. Woodland societies were not true chiefdoms; there was no hereditary status. Village head men had influence, but not true power. This period includes manifestations such as the Hopewell Cult, seen in exotic goods and raw materials; the cult was centered in Ohio and Illinois, but influences extended into Georgia. Evidence for horticulture, hunting and gathering may be seen in site settings, soil types, artifacts, and organic remains.

In artifact collections examined from the Red Hills region, check stamped and plain sherds were the most common pottery type present. However, the total number of specimens seen to date is small. A ground stone celt ("hoe") from Myrtlewood (Bolling Jones collection) may date to this or a later period.

Deptford Period, 500 B.C.- 100 A.D. ("Early Woodland")

The Deptford period was first identified by Waring and Holder (Williams, 1977) on the Georgia Atlantic coast, and later investigated by many others (Milanich, 1973; Milanich and Fairbanks, 1980; Willey, 1982:353-4). This is the period during which the first burial mounds were constructed and in which there was presumably increased use of domesticated plants, increasing sedentism, and population growth. It was a period of large, highly visible shell middens along the Gulf and Atlantic coasts, but it was not exclusively a coastal culture. Deptford sites are also found in the interior on lakes and rivers in the Tallahassee Hills region (Tesar, 1980:77). At least 12 Deptford sites are recorded in northern Leon County, Florida, within 4½ miles of Thomas and Grady Counties, Georgia (Tesar, 1980:Map 46). This period is known as the Shorter Phase in the Walter F. George Lake survey along the Chattahoochee River (Knight and Mistovich, 1984:217-218, 245), where an increase in the number of sites but decrease in site size was noted in this period. Zooarchaeological and botanical data are badly needed for inland sites (see list of questions below).

The "check stamped" pattern on pottery was created by carving lines into a wooden paddle and then pressing it into the wet clay pot before firing. This was a common technique in many time periods. The size of the checks and other technological details, as well as the presence of other artifact types found together in context, is used to distinguish Deptford check stamped from other types such as Wakulla or Leon Check Stamped.

Small amounts of Deptford Check Stamped pottery sherds have been observed in several collections from various plantations in southeast Grady County and southwest Thomas County. However, the specific site locations from which they came are uncertain. Lacking data on the density or distribution on artifacts and sites, it is impossible to say how many settlements were present, what were the specific ecological niches, what was the relative importance of various plants and animals in the local economy, which plants and animals were in the process of becoming domesticated and how the native cultures adapted to changing environmental conditions. Answers to such questions must await future research and better data.

Two sites are described below. First, a large mound on the Mistletoe Plantation along the Ochlocknee River may be a Deptford/Swift Creek period burial mound (Calvin Jones, Florida Bureau of Archeological Research, personal communication, December, 1993). It is 15 to 25 feet tall, and conical rather than flat-topped (Ray Gainey, personal communication; Sonny Stoddard, personal communication). Excavations were reportedly carried out at this mound by Dr. David Phelps at Florida State University in the 1960's. Mr. Ross Morrell, formerly archaeologist with the State of Florida, reportedly conducted additional excavations years ago, and the test pits are said to be still open and visible. More recently, Dr. Karl Steinen of West Georgia visited the mound eight or so years ago (Mr. Ray Gainey, personal communication; Mr. Calvin Jones, personal communication; Dr. Karl Steinen, personal communication). The official Archaeological Site Files for the State of Georgia record the existence of this mound, though little other information is available in those files. The land manager says that pottery is common around the mound, indicating that a village area may also be present (Ray Gainey, personal communication October 7, 1994). Another site on a hilltop, the Willow Oak site, has objects that superficially looked like pottery sherds until cleaned, revealing they were actually rocks.

Another site was destroyed by road construction:

> Many of the artifacts...were found on the Springhill Road when a bulldozer blade uncovered an old Indian Mound while making a new right-of-way and are of prehistoric age. (Balfour, 1975:18)

At least two collections exist from this same stretch of road, called "the cache." They were made by two people working together who later split the collection. Part of the problem in analyzing these collections is that artifacts from different sites are mixed together. The following list includes only those artifacts which are definitely thought to have come from this stretch of road, excluding those artifacts from elsewhere. These artifacts from the Bolling Jones collection were examined:

Deptford check stamped pottery sherds
Steatite stone bowls, unbroken
Steatite stone bowl fragments
Tubular stone pipe, unbroken
Tubular stone pipe fragment
Stone gorget fragments, two holes, drilled
Large stone blades or blanks

The Balfour collection from this roadbed is said to contain additional unbroken tubular stone pipes and unbroken stone gorgets (Mr. Bolling Jones, personal communication). A published photograph (Balfour, 1975) may depict part of this collection, but the artifacts are mixed with others from elsewhere.

Despite the problems with point of origin and context, the two individuals who made these collections are to be commended for preserving the only collections and information available about these sites. Without their efforts, all information would have been lost. The artifacts indicate a Deptford period occupation of the uplands, well away from major rivers. This assemblage may represent a ceremonial context. At other Southeastern sites the most common Deptford assemblage of artifacts represents ordinary, "secular" village life, whereas the ceremonial complex is found only at "sacred" locations such as mounds. The Deptford ceremonial complex is called Yent (Sears, 1962), though few data are available. Few such sites have been investigated (Sears, 1962; Tesar, 1980:75; Morrell, 1960), making the Springhill Road site/collection that much more important.

Swift Creek Period, A.D. 100-300 ("Middle Woodland")

Swift Creek, a culture of the upland forests as well as rivers and coasts, is distinguished by its pottery decorated with curvilinear complicated stamped designs (Willey, 1982:366-396; Snow, 1977; Saunders, 1986; Phelps, 1969; Penton, 1970; Bullen, 1958). Sites are found from the Atlantic and Gulf coasts to middle Georgia at Macon, but the largest number of Swift Creek sites may be in the upland forests of the Red Hills region (Milanich and Fairbanks, 1980:117), though more surveys are needed. These are presumed to be horticultural sites but no evidence of cultigens has been found, primarily because of the lack of research. At least five Swift Creek sites are recorded within 4½ miles of Thomas and Grady Counties, Georgia, in northern Leon County, Florida (Tesar, 1980:Map 47).

The best known Swift Creek site in Southwest Georgia is Mandeville in Clay County along the Chattahoochee River (Kellar, Kelly and McMichael, 1962a,b; Betty Smith, 1975a,b), west of the Red Hills region. Hopewell-affiliated items were found at the site, indicating connections with a cultural tradition that was widespread across the eastern United States. Swift Creek sites are also found in other areas of central to south to Southeast Georgia (e.g., Kelly, 1938; DesJean, Quitmeyer and Walker, 1985; Espenshade, 1993).

In the collections from the Red Hills region seen by the author, only one Swift Creek type sherd was observed (in the Bolling Jones collection), though it seems likely that many more are present in the region since few people bother to collect pottery. The mound reported along the Ochlocknee (see above) may contain Swift Creek components (Mr. Calvin Jones, personal communication, December 1993). Within the Red Hills region, Swift Creek ceramics are also reported from a sand burial mound and village area (9GR50) on the Melrose Plantation in Grady County (Dan Penton, personal communication to Betty Smith [1977:68]).

Weeden Island Period, A.D. 300-900

Weeden Island was a period of elaboration of ceremonial complexes, increased sociopolitical complexity, emphasis on status as seen in exotic pottery, population growth, and continued development of domesticated plants. The Weeden Island cult or culture was first identified by Willey (1982:396-452) based on Gulf Coast sites. At least 16 Weeden Island sites are recorded within 4½ miles of Grady and Thomas Counties, Georgia, found in northern Leon County, Florida (Tesar, 1980:Map 48). Other sites are also found in Southwest Georgia, such as at Bainbridge (Kelly, 1960). Kolomoki, near Blakely in Southwest Georgia, is the largest and most complex Weeden Island site (Sears, 1959). McKeithen, a site in North Florida, has yielded evidence for the emergence of incipient chiefdoms, prior to the appearance of true chiefs (Milanich et al., 1984). Southwest Georgia, North Florida and Southeast Alabama is the Weeden Island "heartland" (Sears, 1959; Steinen, 1976, 1977, 1986, 1989; Milanich, 1974; Milanich et al., 1984; Milanich and Fairbanks, 1980). Many of these sites have been listed on the National Register of Historic Places. Milanich described major Weeden Island site distributions:

> Not all Weeden Island cultures inhabited the coastal strand. In fact, the major Weeden Island developments were probably centered at inland sites in southwestern Georgia, northern Florida, and southeastern Alabama (Milanich and Fairbanks, 1980:91-92).

The most prominent Weeden Island site in southeast Grady County is the Balfour Mound (listed as site #GR-12 in the official State of Georgia site files at the University of Georgia in Athens). The site was discovered by Mr. Sonny Lee and subsequently excavated by Dr. Karl Steinen, West Georgia College, in Summer 1985 (Steinen, 1989). It was 6 meters in diameter and 0.6 meters tall. Most of the 60 whole or partial pots were Wakulla Check Stamped, Weeden Island Plain, Carrabelle Punctated, Weeden Island Incised, Weeden Island Punctated, sand tempered plain (which may be body sherds from Weeden Island Plain pots), simple stamped (Thomas Simple Stamped?), Crooked River Complicated Stamped, and a "carpet" of plain and Kolomoki Complicated Stamped and Swift Creek Complicated Stamped sherds. Red painting, lattice cut-outs and effigies are missing. Steinen discusses the mound in relation to interpretations of Weeden Island chronology and society by Sears (1968:144-146), Percy and Brose (1974:20-21; Brose, 1984:175), White (1981:651-2) and Milanich (Milanich et al., 1984). The Sonny Lee Site (GR-11 in site files at the University of Georgia) is an apparent habitation area approximately one kilometer from the mound, located in a field on a bluff over the Ochlocknee River, Grady County (Steinen, 1986). Plans to excavate this habitation site never materialized.

Two test pits were excavated by the author with the assistance of Thomas College students at a small site that may have been related to the Balfour occupation. The Turkey Creek Plantation Site #1 is situated on a bluff above Tired Creek, a tributary of the Ochlocknee River, in southeastern Grady County. Only a few check stamped and plain sherds were encountered, but the paste does not appear to be Deptford and the size of the checks is too small for Leon. A report is in preparation.

General Research Themes

Chronology
Subsistence strategies, mobility and sedentism
Cultural adaptation to local environmental conditions
Domestication of plants, and its consequences
Regional settlement pattern and local community pattern changes
Demography

Specific Questions

Chronology:

What pottery types and varieties phases are present, and what phases can be identified from them?

Are "pure" Swift Creek sites present?

Was there an indigenous Weeden Island to Fort Walton development?

Which chronological scheme works best here (e.g., 2-part vs. 3-part division of Deptford, and how does it relate to Cartersvile)?

Subsistence strategies and mobility/sedentism:

What and where is the evidence for domesticates, storage of surplus, the establishment of permanent settlements, and correlation with increased sociopolitical complexity and ceremonialism?

Are there features (e.g., firepits, trashpits, postmolds) with ethnobotanical remains?

What species are represented, and do the grain sizes and other morphological features indicate that domestication was in progress?

Regional settlement patterns, local community patterns, and demography:

What is the distribution of sites across the Red Hills landscape, by culture period?

What site types can be identified, based on site size, number of sites, artifact density tool types and diversity, and environmental setting?

How did these patterns change from the Deptford through the Weeden Island periods?

What were the relationships with coastal sites?

Were there population shifts? External contacts?

Are marine shells found inland?

Are there other exotic materials, and from where?

What is the evidence for Woodland period traditions extending into the Mississippi period?

What is the local nature of the Woodland-Mississippian interface?

Can any sites be identified which potentially are eligible for nomination to the National Register of Historic Places?

Mississippi Period Fort Walton Culture, A.D. 900-1600

Fort Walton was the local variant of the Mississippian culture (Willey, 1982:452-475;Scarry, 1980, 1981, 1984; Jones, 1982; Milanich and Fairbanks, 190; Payne, 1981; Tesar, 1976, 1980; Marrinan and Bryne, 1986; Bryne, 1986). More than 200 Fort Walton sites are recorded in the Tallahassee Red Hills between the Ochlocknee and Aucilla Rivers (Payne, 1981), and a large number — at least 40 sites — are known within only 4½ miles of Grady and Thomas Counties, found in northern Leon County, Florida. It is not clear how far this culture extended into the Georgia portion of the Red Hills.

One Fort Walton rim sherd, two zoned punctate sherds, and plain sherds were found by the landowner on the Sherwood Plantation in southeastern Grady County (in the Stoddard collection). However, the location(s) of the site(s) from which the sherds came is uncertain. The importance of the Fort Walton sherds is that they verify the extension of the Fort Walton culture into the area, which would not be surprising since large numbers of such sites are known on the Florida side of the state line (Florida Master Site Files; Payne, 1993:24).

Another Fort Walton site is also reported in southern Thomas County. Mr. Calvin Jones examined a small collection of Fort Walton sherds, some with lugged handles. They were reportedly recovered from a plowed field, but he did not visit the site. The collection also included several Hernando type projectile points (Calvin Jones, personal communication, November, 1994).

The Mississippi period in the Southeastern United States began around A.D. 900, and reaching its peak about A.D. 1300 and lasting until European contact around A.D. 1500-1600. The period was a time of cultural innovation, population increase, increased energy input from agriculture, permanent towns, ceremonial centers with large platform mounds, outlying support villages and farmsteads, hierarchial socio-politico-religious structure, participation in a common belief system, and widespread trade (J. B. Griffin, 1967, 1985:63). The economy was generally based on full-scale agriculture of corn, beans, squash and other domesticates, imported and native, on alluvial river bottomlands (B. Smith, 1978). The societies were hierarchically-organized, densely populated, powerful, warlike chiefdoms, with hereditary priests/chiefs who controlled redistribution, access to scarce resources and control of ritual and agricultural cycles. Common traits at Mississippian sites include certain pottery types and small triangular projectile points (often improperly called "bird points").

It is not clear to what degree the above description applies to southwest Georgia. A moderate amount of research has been undertaken on the lower Chattahoochee and Flint Rivers, but not in Grady or Thomas Counties. Different archaeologists use two different schemes for sites along those two rivers. In one scheme, the sequence of archaeological phases is Standley (early Mississippian), Rood (mature Mississippian), Singer, Bull Creek, Stewart, Abercrombie (A.D. 1550-1650, the time of the first European contacts), Blackmon (A.D. 1650-1715?;English traders arrive) and Lawson Field (lower Creek, ending at 1836 (Schnell and Wright, 1993; Caldwell, 1955, 1957; Kellar et al., 1961; Knight, 1979; Knight and Mistovich, 1984; Kurjack and Pearson, 1975; McMichael and Kellar, 1960; Schnell, Knight and Schnell, 1981; Schnell, 1986; Sears, 1956; Willey and Sears, 1952). The other scheme includes the archaeological phases called Chattahoochee Landing (analogous to Standley), Bristol (analogous to Rood), Cayson, Sneads and Yon (to 1500 A.D.) (Scarry, 1980, 1981, 1985; White, 1981). The relationship between Fort Walton in Florida and the Rood Phase along the lower Chattahoochee River in Georgia, two counties west of Grady County, is uncertain (Schnell, Knight and Schnell, 1981:243). All phases are distinguished primarily by differences in pottery.

In historic times the Apalachee Indians were the bearers of the Fort Walton culture. They were the group encountered by the Narvaez and de Soto expeditions (see below) in the early 16th century, when they were one of the most powerful chiefdoms in Florida and Georgia. The names of the Appalachian Mountains and Apalachicola Bay are derived from their name.

Fort Walton research is needed in general to increase our understanding of the Fort Walton way of life, excavations are needed in Tallahassee Hills hamlet and dispersed village sites, east Tallahassee Hills mound sites, dispersed villages, hamlet and farmstead sites, Apalachicola River valley farmstead and village sites and "paired" mounds, Marianna Lowlands mound and farmstead sites, coastal shell middens and mounds, and pine flatwoods camp sites. A clear understanding of chronology is a necessary element in constructing a picture of Fort Walton life. Another issue...is correlations between Fort Walton cultural assemblages and the historic groups of the region. (Payne, 1993:28)

General Research Themes

> Chronology
> Subsistence strategies, mobility and sedentism
> Cultural adaptation to local environmental conditions
> Domestication of plants, and its consequences
> Regional settlement patterns and local community patterns
> Demography

Specific Questions

Chronology:

> What pottery types and varieties are present, and which archaeological phases can be identified from them?

> Do they show closer affinities with the Tallahassee variant of Fort Walton, as expected, rather than with lower Chattahoochee River, Fall Line, Okeefenokee Swamp or other Fort Walton variants?

Regional settlement patterns, local community patterns, and demography:

> What is the distribution of sites across the Red Hills landscape?

> What site types can be identified, based on site size, number of sites, artifact density tool types and diversity, and environmental setting?

> Are large Fort Walton village sites present in Thomas and Grady County? Or outlying villages or farmsteads? Or was this simply hunting territory and a buffer zone between warring chiefdoms?

> Were the subsistence and settlement patterns different here from those at current Tallahassee?

> Where was the boundary and what were the differences between this and other variants of the Mississippi culture, such as Cemochechobee/Rood Phase on the Chattahoochee River, or other variants in Georgia, Florida and Alabama (Schnell, Knight and Schnell, 1981:233-246)?

Can any sites be identified which potentially are eligible for nomination to the National Register of Historic Places?

European Contact: The Hernando de Soto Entrada, A.D. 1539-1540

The Hernando de Soto expedition is historically important because this was the first major European exploration into the interior of North America (Milanich and Hudson, 1993; Hudson, DePratter and Smith, 1984, 1989; Milanich and Milbrath, 1989; Swanton, 1985). It is historically important because this was the first stage in the European colonization of the America and ultimately the founding of the United States of America. The expedition is important in anthropology because the chroniclers of the expedition provide the first and sometimes the only information on the native cultures and environmental conditions of the Americas before disrupted by European contact and colonization. Many of these peoples soon disappeared in epidemics of introduced European and African diseases (Crosby, 1972; Dobyns, 1983; Ramenofsky, 1982; M. Smith, 1987; Hassan, 1981). The de Soto expedition is also important in archaeology because the presence Spanish trade goods on Indian village sites provide an excellent time marker for the study of culture change.

Hernando de Soto's army of 600 Spanish soldiers and 250 horses invaded Florida in 1539. Travelling along established trails up the Florida peninsula (Johnson, 1991), they fought their way from Indian town to Indian town, while searching for gold, slaves, and food. They spent the winter of 1539-1540 at current Tallahassee, at a site found by Mr. Calvin Jones of the Florida Bureau of Archaeological Research.

Hernando de Soto sent explorers northward from the Indian town of Apalache at current Tallahassee into what is now Georgia:

> Although the enemy continued their alarms and sudden attacks day and night, the army rested a few days and recuperated somewhat from the great toils of the past. Meanwhile the Governor [de Soto] sent out chosen officers with soldiers on horseback and afoot to penetrate inland for fifteen or twenty leagues to see what there was to be found in the surrounding country. Two of these officers, Captain Arias Tinoco and Andres de Vasconselos, took different routes toward the north, but returned without having experienced anything worthy of note, one of them eight days and the other nine.... The reports of both were almost identical, for each said that he had found many populous villages as well as land that was abundant in food and clear of swamps and extensive forests (Varner and Varner, 1962:185).

Milanich and Hudson believe that these two explorers penetrated into Decatur, Grady, or Thomas Counties, and possibly as far as Mitchell or Colquitt counties, Georgia (Milanich and Hudson, 1993:218-219). In Spring 1540 the army marched northward into Georgia, possibly through current Grady or Thomas County, though the route is uncertain because no archaeological sites have been reported:

> [H]aving commanded that food supplies and other necessities be made ready for leaving Apalache now that it was time to go, the Governor and Adelantado Hernando de Soto led his army out of the encampment during the closing days of March in the year fifteen hundred and forty. He traveled three days toward the north in that same province without encountering any enemies; had he done so, he might have been

molested because the Indians of that land were both hostile and warlike. (Varner and Varner, 1962:263)

Since the army ordinarily spent each night in an Indian village they had conquered that day, it is possible that there may be at least one de Soto encampment in Grady or Thomas County. Evidence could be in the form of Spanish artifacts such as chain mail or other armor, cross bow points, iron lance points, iron horseshoes (wide widths), wrought iron nails, dated coins, glass trade beads, Spanish ceramics, found undisturbed in association with Fort Walton Indian artifacts — most of which have been recovered at the winter camp.

They were probably following established trails, especially since they had horses and were seeking Indian towns. Reconstruction of the routes of Indian trails identifies possible routes of these explorers and may lead to Spanish and Indian archaeological sites. The Hawthorn Trail (Hemperley, 1989:12) is a possible de Soto route into current Grady County, and the Miccosukee Trail (Hemperley, 1989:21) is a possible de Soto route into current Thomas County. Other routes are also possible (McGorty, 1992). No de Soto era artifacts or sites are known from Thomas or Grady County, or anywhere else in South Georgia. Such a site would be highly informative, and it would almost certainly be eligible for nomination to the National Register of Historic Places.

Spanish Mission Period, 1633-1704 A.D.

Beginning several decades after the de Soto entrada, Spain established a permanent settlement at St. Augustine in 1565 and from there began extending a chain of religious mission stations westward across North Florida, reaching the Apalachee at current Tallahassee by A.D. 1633 (Hann, 1988). Many additional missions were added throughout the rest of the 17th century (Hann, 1990), but the system was destroyed by attack from South Carolina between 1702 and 1704 (Gannon, 1965; Hann, 1988).

Much is known about the Apalachee in North Florida (e.g., Boyd et al., 1951; Deagan, 1987; Jones, 1970, 1971, 1972, 1973; Jones and Shapiro, 1990; Marrinan, 1985, 1993; Marrinan and Bryne, 1986; McEwan, 1991, 1993; Mitchem, 1993; Morrell and Jones, 1970; Reitz, 1993; Ruhl, 1990; Shapiro and McEwan, 1992; Scarry, 1984; M.Scarry, 1993; Swanton, 1979:89-93; Tesar, 1980, 1981; Vernon, 1988; Vernon and Cordell, 1993). But, in contrast, almost nothing is known about any Apalachee sites one step across the state line in Georgia. The locations of dozens of Spanish period sites, marked by the presence of Lamar/Leon-Jefferson pottery and/or Spanish artifacts, have been found in the Tallahassee area. At least eleven Leon-Jefferson sites are known within only 4½ miles of Thomas and Grady Counties, Georgia, in northern Leon County, Florida (Tesar, 1980:Map 50). However, the distribution north of the state line is unknown.

At least one collection from Grady County (the Bolling Jones collection) contains one Miller Plain pottery sherd. Miller Plain pottery was made with aboriginal technology but copying European vessel forms, in this case probably a plate. It is often black in color, as is this specimen.

It is possible that only scattered farmstead or small village sites are present for the Georgia area in this period. However, just because they are small does not mean they are not significant. Such sites may have the potential to yield important information. Future surveys should attempt to locate large and small sites in Georgia.

Specific Questions

Are Native American sites of the Spanish Mission Period present in Thomas and Grady County in significant numbers?

Regional settlement patterns and local community patterns: How are sites distributed, and in what numbers and site sizes?

Were there missions, visitas, rancherias or "heathen" villages, and how can these be distinguished archaeologically?

Was the area of Thomas and Grady Counties peripheral to the main centers of Spanish/Indian occupation at current Tallahassee, as many suspect?

Peripheral areas offer special research opportunities. What were the environmental settings, ecological adaptations, subsistence strategies, and diets of common people in isolated communities remote from the main ceremonial and civic centers?

When and in what sequence do European-introduced plant and animal species (such as wheat, peaches, oranges, cattle, horses and pigs) appear in the zooarchaeological and ethnobotanical record? In what archaeological contexts? What changes in environmental relations, seasonality and scheduling, subsistence and economy, tool types and material culture, settlement patterns and social organization accompanied these new traits?

After the missions were established at Apalachee settlements in the current Tallahassee area, were non-missionized groups found in peripheral areas such as current Thomas and Grady counties? Were the earlier mission sites situated in different settings and associated with different aboriginal pottery types than the later missions?

Early Nineteenth-Century Native Americans, European-Americans and African-Americans

Southwest Georgia offers outstanding opportunities for the study of interactions between three ethnic groups — Native Americans, African-Americans, and European-Americans. The processes of culture change — acculturation, innovation and diffusion — can all be seen in the interactions among the two minority groups and one dominant group. By the Treaty of Fort Jackson in 1814, the Lower Creek Indians gave up control of lands in Southwest Georgia, including the area of Thomas and Grady counties (Rogers, 1963:3-4, 34). By the 1820's, land-hungry settlers were moving into the area, the first of whom were often "cattle rangers, wood rangers or farmers" (Rogers, 1963:6). By the late 1820's, farms and plantations had been established, and by 1840 the number of black slaves outnumbered whites. Officially and legally, there were no native Americans remaining in Southwest Georgia after the Treaty of Fort Jackson in 1814 and the "Removal" of the 1830's (Coleman, 1960:34). In South Georgia in general (not just Thomas and Grady counties), pioneer and Indian occupation has been characterized as follows after the Treaty of Fort Jackson in 1814:

> Pioneer settlers had already moved into these areas [after 1818]. Many were without proper land title and at first settled close to the rivers but gradually began to move into the lonely stretches of longleaf pine and wiregrass. Here, too, the Indians continued to live despite relinquishment of their land titles.... Although there were no major villages, settlers...migrated to the area. The newcomers...first located on the rich

hammock lands near the Florida line. ...once the importance of South Georgia was realized, the region was cleared and occupied by large planters.... In 1830, only five years after Thomas County was created, over one third of the population of 3,299 was slave. (Rogers, 1963:6)

Some early settlers included Thomas Hill Bryan about 1819, Thomas J. Johnson at Pebble Hill by 1825 (Rogers, 1963:10-11), Paul Coalson in 1825 (Thomasville Landmarks, 1986:10), and many others. Archaeological data could be found at the sites of each of these settlers, and also at sites such as a small settlement out from Glasgow in southeast Thomas County. This village was first settled in 1823-25 and occupied continuously until destroyed by fire in 1941 (Jimmy Vaughn, personal communication).

General Questions

How many native Americans remained after 1814? How many today?

How did they interact with the new arrivals in the 1820's?

To what degree have each group preserved their cultural heritage and identify?

How is today's society a blend of these different cultural traditions?

How did their interactions produce modern Thomas and Grady counties?

Specific Questions: Native Americans

Regional settlement patterns and local community patterns — Are there native American archaeological sites in Thomas and Grady Counties that post-date 1814, and white settler's sites that pre-date 1814?

What was their distribution?

Do they represent nucleated settlements, dispersed communities, isolated farmsteads, temporary camps? How many and what sizes of each type?

Adaptation, subsistence and economy — Sites are distributed in relation to what natural environments and resources?

What is the material culture assemblage, including tool types, datable artifacts and prestige goods?

How far can these and other cultural traditions be traced into the historic and prehistoric past?

How did the number, size and distribution of native American sites change after 1814? Was there a shift from nucleated to dispersed settlements or to isolated family farmsteads?

Are there archaeological sites with stratified undisturbed deposits that would show long-term, continuous occupation?

Specific Questions: European-Americans

How many whites were present when the region was still under native American control?

How different were the lifestyles of the earliest white settlers and native Americans?

Are there differences in material culture assemblages (tools, houses, clothing, etc.)?

Are there differences in percentages of wild versus domesticated food remains in the zooarchaeological and ethnobotanical record?

Are there features or midden deposits present at the sites?

Is it possible to distinguish European-American from native American sites at that time?

Can ethnic identity be identified archaeologically?

Specific Questions: African-Americans

(Also see section on Ante-bellum Plantation Period Archaeology.)

As minorities under the control of a dominant culture, were there similarities in African-American slave and Native American material culture?

Were status and prestige indicators (e.g., expensive or inexpensive ceramics or other goods) in the archaeological record different for these two groups?

Did any native Americans become slaves?

As on coastal Georgia plantations, did the slaves provide a significant proportion of their own subsistence in wild and collected foods? If so, then were slave and native American subsistence patterns similar?

Ante-Bellum Plantation Period Archaeology

The significant forces during the ante-bellum period have been summarized by Rogers:

> The invention of the cotton gin, the potential of a textile industry, the development of upland cotton that could be grown all over the South, and the pattern of plantation economy based on Negro slavery, all combined to create an insatiable demand for land. (Rogers, 1963:5)

There are direct connections between Southwest Georgia and coastal Southeast Georgia, South Carolina, and Louisiana. Some plantations in the Red Hills were established by planters such as the Jones family (Rogers, 1963:6) directly from Southeast Georgia and South Carolina plantations. Hardy Bryan, the prominent planter whose home in Thomasville is the current headquarters for Thomasville Landmarks, Inc., died while taking a group of slaves from Brunswick, Georgia, to Louisiana. A comparison of the coastal versus upland plantation systems would be fruitful. Archaeological research has already been undertaken on some of the Georgia tidewater plantations.

A significant amount of research has been conducted on the tidewater plantations, but little on the upland plantations. The late Dr. Charles Fairbanks, Distinguished Research Professor Emeritus at the University of Florida, was the first archaeologist to excavate slave cabin sites, along with other plantation structures (Fairbanks, 1972,, 1976; Ascher and Fairbanks, 1971). He examined the material aspects of slave life, housing, diet, and lifestyle at Kingsley Plantation near Jacksonville, at Cannon's Point (owned by the Coupers) near Brunswick, at Lawrence (both of which were long-staple cotton plantations), briefly at Ryefield on Cumberland Island, at Butler Point or Hampton Plantation (Mullins-Moore, 1980), and Butler Island (Singleton, 1980, 1985; Fairbanks, 1984). Various Fairbanks students conducted additional slave and plantation studies (Hamilton, 1980; McFarlane, 1975; Otto, 1975, 1979).

Evidence from the slave cabins was compared with that from the overseers' houses and planters' mansions. Excavated food remains and evidence for status and wealth was found in the broken and discarded flatware and hollowware, stemware, and other artifacts from the kitchens of the main houses. Fairbanks summarized the kinds of information recovered archaeologically:

> At the Couper house, behind what had been the most elaborate kitchen on the Georgia coasts, we recovered ceramics, glass, and food bones that represented the daily discards of an elite household that entertained widely and richly. These materials were abundantly informative about the lifestyle of the Coupers and their guests. Beef, pork, and venison were eaten in the form of roasts served from platters onto transfer-printed pearlware plates in matching sets. Fish taken from the deep sounds, as well as the adjacent Hampton River, were frequently eaten. Game and fish were evidently procured by slaves specifically assigned to those tasks. French wines were regularly enjoyed, and shellfish were a common feature of the diet. At the opposite end of the scale, the food and artifact evidence from slave trash piles presented sharp contrasts. Beef and pork were still common but they were usually represented by head and foot bones. No steaks or roasts for these people! Opossum and raccoon were the most frequent wild animal bones identified.... (Fairbanks, 1984:3)

Much of this data is not available in written records. The overseers' economic standards did not match their social status. Their food bones and ceramics were closer to that of the slaves than to that of the planter.

Among other things, Fairbanks was surprised to discover the degree to which the slaves provided for their own subsistence, such as collecting fish and shellfish, trapping animals such as raccoons, and other wild foods. The evidence is in the form of food bones and other discards. Those plantations were on the task system, which allowed the slaves free time if they finished their assigned work for the day. But did this same task system and subsistence patterns exist in Southwest Georgia? The coastal regions are marked by their poor agricultural soils but abundance of food in tidal estuaries, in contrast to Southwest Georgia with good agricultural soils and less prolific aquatic resources. How did the different ecological potentials and limitations affect the plantation systems?

Another archaeological surprise from coastal Georgia plantations was the frequent evidence of firearms at slave cabins. The slaves were apparently much better armed than their masters realized. Was this also true in Southwest Georgia? Another surprise was the almost total lack of Africanisms in the archaeological deposits, such as decorative themes or ways of doing things, even among slaves recently arrived from Africa. One general question is, therefore, where are the beginnings of the Afro-American tradition in America?

Another question is relevant to Southwest Georgia. What evidence, if any, is there for any Indians included in the slave population, since they were landless and lacked political protection.

Local informants report that there may have been two different slave settlements on the Susina plantation (Jimmy Mason, personal communication 2/7/94). One settlement was presumably at the main house, and the other was among the fields more than a mile back from the main house. These reports have not yet been verified. Historic documents indicate that at least ten slave dwellings were located on Melrose and Sinkola plantation, but the locations are unknown (Thomasville Landmarks, 1986:6). Other plantations such as Pebble Hill would also have had slave cabins but little information is available on their locations or condition of subsurface archaeological deposits or potential to yield further information.

Though slaves were the greatest capital investment of the plantations, slave cabins are not the only source of information on plantation life. A variety of other structures and activities were also present, some lasting into the twentieth century. For example, the inventory of previous structures and features with archaeological potential at Birdsong includes the following: 1850's ginhouse; depression/well; road; nineteenth-century kitchen; late nineteenth-century school; syrup shed; pre-1912 kitchen and dining room; smokehouse; ironing house, a possible former slave house, near three others on 1871 map; cotton house; guano house; tenant houses; buggy house; privies; and stables (information on file at Thomasville Landmarks, Inc.). Building surveys are needed at all of the plantation complexes throughout the Red Hills region.

Specific Questions

Where are the slave cabin sites located, and how are they distributed across the landscape?

Where was the overseer's house located?

What other structures were present, how were they arranged, and what economic activities do they represent?

What are the differences in material culture for slaves vs. overseer vs. planter?

What were the differences in terms of status and prestige artifacts discarded, lifeways, and food and nutrition?

As on coastal Georgia plantations, were overseer and slave (surprisingly) similar in nutrition and diet?

What floral and faunal remains are present as discards in middens or features, representing which wild or domesticated foods? How many calories, such as meat weight represented by bone fragments? What proportion would have been gathered (such as raccoons), and what proportion provided (such as beef bones)?

Does the evidence indicate the task system or gang system of slave organization?

How do these patterns on Red Hills plantations differ from those on coastal plantations?

What evidence is there that slaves in Grady and Thomas counties possessed firearms?

Local Community History and Development: Nineteenth-Century Towns

The archaeology of early towns and their origins would potentially be very informative (also see above sections on settlers and plantations). Why did some frontier settlements or rural crossroads communities emerge and develop into towns, but others did not? What factors contributed to the growth and/or subsequent decline of communities such as Duncanville, Glasgow, Boston, Grooverville, Tatesville or Thomasville? Many Georgia towns developed "railroad towns" but Thomasville prospered without benefit of a railroad, navigable river or port (Rogers, 1963:19). What factors are still relevant today to the continued economic prosperity of current Georgia cities?

Archaeological data may be found at many sites in Thomas and Grady counties, such as at the original post and stage coach stop near Twelve Mile Road in eastern Thomas County (McGorty, 1992:46). Early 1800's towns in Thomas County are listed below, excluding Metcalf, which was not founded until 1888 (Rogers, 1973:16). Grady County settlements are not included.

Boston (whose location moved)   (Rogers, 1973:14)
Duncanville [Beachton]   (Rogers, 1963:44 [map])
Eatwan   (Rogers, 1964:7 [map])
Glasgow   (Rogers, 1964:7 [map])
Grooverville   (Rogers, 1964:7 [map])
Tatesville   (Rogers, 1964:7 [map])
Thomasville (incorporated 1831)

Commercial stores were established in Thomas County by 1827 by E.J. Perkins, James Kirkey, and Simon A. Smith and son. Where are these sites and what is their condition and potential to yield further information? Are there archaeological deposits available for information on material culture, economy, technology, lifestyle and diet, interaction with other regions, population increase, and rapid culture change? What is the full range of different types of occupations and of structures — stores, residences, blacksmith shops, liveries, churches, stagecoach stops, taverns or hotels, etc., and how would each be distributed and represented archaeologically?

The Civil War, 1861-1865

A Civil War prison camp was constructed and occupied briefly in western Thomasville during the war. Union prisoners were transferred here from Andersonville when Sherman's army was cutting a swath to the sea.

The region may also contain other Civil War sites and earthworks. Another defensive ditch reportedly was dug in downtown Thomasville by local residents as Sherman approached central Georgia (Jimmy Vaughn, personal communication).

No professional-quality archaeological research has been reported, though there is of danger of looting and destruction of such sites through use of metal detectors. Much information is lost by casual, untrained digging. Preservation is a key concern.

Questions

How was the camp constructed? Was the ditch part of the prison stockade wall or defensive earthworks protecting the camp? Was the stockade wall constructed of vertical posts set in a trench, as at Andersonville?

Is there evidence for other structures such as hospital or barracks just outside the stockade walls?

Were the prisoners and guards provisioned and equipped by residents of Thomasville?

The Archaeology of Tenant Farms, Tourist Hotels and Hunting Plantations

Tenant farming, tourist hotels/winter resorts (Rogers, 1973:131f) and hunting plantations are historically important. They became the basis of the economic system by which Thomas and other counties survived in the decades after the Civil War (Rogers, 1973; Prunty, 1955).

The following description of tenant farming is summarized from Rogers (1973:26-31). Many of the large plantations were sold off in pieces, changing the county into an area of small to middle sized farms. Little cash was available after collapse of the Confederate currency, so tenant farmers paid rent with a share of their crops or with scarce cash from cash crops. They secured provisions from stores located at country crossroads or in Thomasville or Cairo. The store owners sometimes held liens against the crop to insure the investment. The store owners, themselves in debt, often forced the debt-ridden farmers to grow cash crops such as cotton despite low prices, a cycle seen throughout the South (Rogers, 1973:28). Tenant farming thus helped sustain the county economy.

The locations of several possible tenant farmer houses have recorded during the current survey. At these particular sites, no structures are standing, but artifacts were visible on the surface of the ground. Several such sites were recorded on the Hines Hill and Mandalay plantations with the assistance of the land managers.

With tourist hotels and hunting plantations, portions of the Red Hills region have achieved economic prosperity while other regions of Georgia were experiencing stagnation. What lessons can other regions of Georgia learn from this? What lessons for the economic future can modern Thomas and Grady Countians learn from the past?

RECOMMENDATIONS

The greatest archaeological needs in the Red Hills region are for 1) preservation of significant cultural resources, including significant archaeological sites and structures; and 2) archaeological and historic structure surveys throughout the Red Hills region. Surveys are needed to determine the locations of sites and structures, their time periods and components, condition and potential to yield further information. Many sites may be eligible for nomination to the National Register of Historic Places.

REFERENCES

Anderson, David G., R. Jerald Ledbetter and Lisa O'Steen. 1990. *Paleo-Indian period archaeology of Georgia*. University of Georgia Laboratory of Archaeology Series Report No. 28. Georgia Archaeological Research Design (GARD) Paper No. 6.

Asch, Nancy B., Richard I. Ford, and David L. Asch. 1972. *Paleoethnobotany of the Koster site: the archaic horizons*. Report of Investigations No. 24, Illinois State Museum, Springfield.

Ascher, Robert, and Charles H. Fairbanks. 1971. Excavation of a slave cabin: Georgia, U.S.A. *Historical Archaeology* 5: 3-17.

Balfour, Robert C., Jr. 1975. *This land I have loved*. Rose Printing Co., Tallahassee.

Boyd, Mark F., Hale G. Smith, and John W. Griffin. 1951. *Here they once stood; the tragic end of the Apalachee missions*. University of Florida Press, Gainesville.

Brose, David S. 1984. Mississippian cultures in Northwest Florida. In *Perspectives on Gulf Coast Prehistory*, edited by Dave D. Davis. University Presses of Florida, Gainesville.

Brose, David S., and George W. Percy. 1978. Fort Walton settlement patterns. In *Mississippian Settlement Patterns*, edited by Bruce D. Smith, pp. 81-114. Academic Press, New York.

Bullen, Ripley P. 1958. Six sites near the Chattahoochee River in the Jim Woodruff reservoir area, Florida. In *River Basin Survey Papers*, edited by Frank H. Roberts, Jr., pp. 315-357. *Bureau of American Ethnology, Bulletin* 169. Smithsonian Institution, Washington.

Bullen, Ripley P. 1975. *A guide to the identification of Florida projectile points*. Kendall Books, Gainesville, FL.

Caldwell, Joseph R. 1955. Investigations at Rood's Landing, Stewart County, Georgia. *Early Georgia* 2(1): 22-49.

_____. 1957. *Survey and excavations in the Allatoona Reservoir, Northern Georgia*. Manuscript on file, Department of Anthropology, University of Georgia.

_____. 1958. Trend and tradition in the prehistory of the Eastern United States. *Memoirs of the American Anthropological Association* No. 88.

Cambron, James W., and David C. Hulse. 1973. *Handbook of Alabama archaeology, part i: point types*. Revised edition. Edited by David L. DeJarnette. Alabama Archaeological Society, Huntsville, Alabama.

Chapman, Jefferson. 1977. *Archaic period research in the lower Little Tennessee River valley*. Report of Investigations No. 18, Department of Anthropology, University of Tennessee, Knoxville, and the Tennessee Valley Authority.

Chapman, Jefferson, and A.B. Shea. 1981. The archaeobotanical record: early archaic period to contact in the lower Little Tennessee River valley. *Tennessee Anthropologist* 6: 61-84.

Coe, Joffre. 1964. *The formative cultures of the Carolina piedmont.* Transactions of the American Philosophical Society 54(5).

Coleman, Kenneth. 1960. *Georgia history in outline.* University of Georgia, Athens.

Crook, Morgan R., Jr. 1986. *A strategy for cultural resource planning in Georgia.* Office of the State Archaeologist, West Georgia College. Georgia Department of Natural Resources, Parks and Historic Sites Division, Historic Preservation Section, Atlanta.

Crosby, Alfred W. Jr. 1972. *The Columbian exchange: biological and cultural consequences of 1492.* Westport: Greenwood.

Deagan, Kathleen. 1987. *Artifacts of the Spanish colonies of Florida and the Caribbean, 1500-1800. volume 1: ceramics, glassware and beads.* Smithsonian Institution Press, Washington, DC.

DeJarnette, David L. 1975. *Archaeological salvage in the Walter F. George basin of the Chattahoochee River in Alabama.* The University of Alabama Press, University, Alabama.

DeJarnette, David L., Edward Kurjack and James Cambron. 1962. Stanfield-Worley Bluff Shelter Excavations. *Journal of Alabama archaeology* 8(1 and 2).

Delcourt, Paul A., Hazel R. Delcourt, Ronald C. Brister, and Laurence E. Lackeys. 1980. Quaternary vegetation history of the Mississippi embayment. *Quaternary Research* 13: 111-132.

DePratter, Chester B. 1975. The archaic in Georgia. *Early Georgia* 3(1): 1-16.

DesJean, Thomas, Irvy R. Quitmyer, and Karen Jo Walker. 1985. A coastal Swift Creek community at Kings Bay, Georgia. In *Indians, Colonists and Slaves, Essays in Memory of Charles H. Fairbanks,* edited by Kenneth W. Johnson, Jonathan M. Leader and Robert C. Wilson. *Florida Journal of Anthropology Special Publication No. 4,* Florida Anthropology Student Association, University of Florida, Gainesville, pp. 155-177.

Dobyns, Henry F. 1983. *Their number become thinned: native American population dynamics in Eastern North America.* The University of Tennessee Press, Knoxville.

Espenshade, Christopher T. 1992. *A few visits in prehistory: data recovery excavations at 9Rh18, Randolph County, Georgia.* With contributions by Linda Kennedy and Eric C. Poplin. Brockington and Associates, Inc., Atlanta and Charleston. Prepared for the Georgia Department of Transportation, Office of Environment/Location, Occasional Papers in Cultural Resource Management #5. Atlanta.

Fairbanks, Charles H. 1972. The Kingsley slave cabins in Duval County, Florida, 1968. *The Conference on Historic Site Archaeology Papers* 7: 62-93.

_____. 1984. The Plantation archaeology of the Southeastern coast. *Historical Archaeology*. 18: 1-14.

Gannon, Michael V. 1965. *The cross in the sand: the early Catholic church in Florida, 1513-1870*. University Press of Florida, Gainesville.

Griffin, James B. 1967. Eastern North American archaeology: a summary. *Science* 156: 175-191.

_____. 1985. Changing concepts of the prehistoric Mississippian cultures of the Eastern United States. In *Alabama and the Borderlands: From Prehistory to Statehood*, edited by R. Reid Badger and Lawrence A. Clayton. University of Alabama Press, University, Alabama, pp.40-63.

Griffin, John W. 1974. *Investigations in Russell Cave*. Publications in Archeology 13. National Park Service, Department of the Interior, Washington.

Hamilton, Jennifer. 1980. *Early history and excavation of the Le Conte Woodmanston plantation*. M.A. thesis, Department of Anthropology, University of Florida, Gainesville.

Hann, John H. 1986. Demographic patterns and changes in mid-seventeenth century Timucua and Apalachee. *Florida Historical Quarterly* 64: 371-392.

_____. 1988. *Apalachee, the land between the rivers*. University of Florida Press/Florida State Museum, Gainesville.

_____. 1990. Summary guide to Spanish missions and visitas with churches in the sixteenth and seventeenth centuries. *The Americas* XLVI (4): 417-513.

Hassan, Fekri A. 1981. *Demographic archaeology*. Academic Press, New York.

Hemperley, Marion R. (former State Surveyor General). 1989. *Historic indian trails of Georgia*. The Garden Club of Georgia, Inc.

Hopkins, Judge. 1934. *Historical sketch of "Sherwood Plantation" from the red man 1814 to 1934; by a former owner*. Manuscript on file at Thomasville Landmarks, Inc. 3 pages.

Hudson, Charles, Marvin T. Smith and Chester B. DePratter. 1984. The Hernando de Soto expedition: From Apalachee to Cheaha. *Southeastern Archaeology*. 3: 65-76.

Johnson, Kenneth W. 1991a. *The Utina and the Potano Peoples of Northern Florida: changing settlement systems in the Spanish colonial period*. Ph.D. dissertation, Department of Anthropology, University of Florida, Gainesville.

Jones, B. Calvin. 1973. A Semi-subterranean structure at mission San Joseph de Ocuya, Jefferson County, Florida. *Bureau of Historic Sites and Properties, Division of Archives, History and Records Management, Bulletin* 3, pp. 1-50. Florida Department of State, Tallahassee.

Jones, B. Calvin, and Gary Shapiro. 1990. Nine mission sites in Apalachee. In *Columbian Consequences, Volume 2: Archaeological and Historical Perspectives on the Spanish Borderlands East*, edited by David Hurst Thomas, 491-509, Smithsonian Institution Press, Washington, DC.

Justice, Noel D. 1987. *Stone age spear and arrow points of the midcontinental and Eastern United States*. Indiana University Press, Bloomington.

Kellar, James H., A.R. Kelly, and E.V. McMichael. 1962a. The Mandeville site in Southwest Georgia. *American Antiquity* 27: 336-355.

_____. 1962b. Final report on archaeological explorations at the Mandeville Site, 9Cla1, Clay County, Georgia, seasons 1959, 1960, 1961. *University of Georgia Laboratory of Archaeology Series Report* No. 8, Athens.

Kelly, Arthur A. 1938. A preliminary report on archaeological explorations at Macon, Georgia. *Bureau of American Ethnology, Bulletin* 119: 1-68.

_____. 1950. Survey of the lower Flint and Chattahoochee Rivers. *Early Georgia* 1: 27-33.

_____. 1960. A Weeden Island burial mound in Decatur County, Georgia. *University of Georgia Laboratory of Archaeology Series Report* 1.

Knight, Vernon James, Jr., and Tim S. Mistovich. 1984. *Walter F. George Lake archaeological survey of fee owned lands, Alabama and Georgia*. Office of Archaeological Research, the University of Alabama, Report of Investigations 42. Submitted to United States Army Corps of Engineers, Mobile, Alabama.

Larson, Lewis H. 1980. *Aboriginal subsistence technology on the Southeastern coastal plain during the late prehistoric period*. University Presses of Florida, Gainesville.

Lewis, Thomas M.N., and Madeline Kneberg Lewis. 1961. *Eva, an archaic site*. University of Tennessee Press, Knoxville.

Marrinan, Rochelle A. 1985. The archaeology of the Spanish missions of Florida: 1565-1704. In *Indians, Colonists and Slaves, Essays in Memory of Charles H. Fairbanks,* edited by Kenneth W. Johnson, Jonathan M. Leader and Robert C. Wilson. *Florida Journal of Anthropology Special Publication No. 4*, Florida Anthropology Student Association, University of Florida, Gainesville, pp. 241-252.

_____. 1993. Archaeological investigations at Mission Patale, 1984-1992. In *The Spanish Missions of La Florida*, edited by Bonnie G. McEwan. University Press of Florida, Gainesville, pp.244-294.

McEwan, Bonnie G. 1991. San Luis de Talimali: the archaeology of Spanish-Indian relations at a Florida mission. *Historical Archaeology* 25(3): 36-60.

_____. 1993. Hispanic life on the seventeenth-century Florida frontier. In *The Spanish Missions of La Florida*, edited by Bonnie G. McEwan. University Press of Florida, Gainesville, pp.295-321.

McFarlane, Suzanne S. 1975. The ethnohistory of a slave community: the Couper plantation site. M.A. thesis, Department of Anthropology, University of Florida, Gainesville.

McGorty, Kevin. 1992. *Views from the road: a community guide for assessing rural historic landscapes*. Sponsored by the Trust for Public Land, the National Trust for Historic Preservation, and the Red Hills Conservation Association.

Milanich, Jerald T. 1973. *The Southeastern Deptford culture: a preliminary definition*. Bureau of Historic Sites and Properties, Division of Archives, History and Records Management, Bulletin 3, pp. 51-63. Florida Department of State, Tallahassee.

_____. 1974. *Life in a 9th century Indian household, a Weeden Island fall-winter site on the upper Apalachicola River, Florida*. Bureau of Historic Sites and Properties, Division of Archives, History and Records Management, Bulletin 4, pp. 1-44. Florida Department of State, Tallahassee.

Milanich, Jerald T., Ann S. Cordell, Vernon J. Knight, Jr., Timothy A. Kohler, and Brenda J. Sigler-Lavelle. 1984. *McKeithen Weeden Island, the culture of Northern Florida, A.D. 200-900*. Academic Press, Orlando.

Milanich, Jerald T., and Charles H. Fairbanks. 1980. *Florida archaeology*. Academic Press, New York.

Milanich, Jerald T., and Charles Hudson. 1993. *Hernando de Soto and the Indians of Florida*. University Press of Florida, Gainesville.

Milanich, Jerald T., and Susan Milbrath, Editors. 1989. *First encounters; Spanish exploration in the Caribbean and the United States, 1492-1570.* University of Florida Press and the Florida Museum of Natural History, Gainesville.

Mitchem, Jeffrey M. 1993. Beads and pendants from San Luis de Talimali: inferences from varying contexts. In *The Spanish Missions of La Florida*, edited by Bonnie G. McEwan. University Press of Florida, Gainesville, pp.399-417.

Moore, Clarence B. 1907. Mounds of the Lower Chattahoochee and Lower Flint Rivers. *Journal of the Academy of Natural Sciences* 13: 426-456. Philadelphia.

Morrell, L. Ross. 1960. Oakland Mound (Je58), Florida: a preliminary report. *The Florida Anthropologist* XIII(4): 101-108. Tallahassee.

Morrell, L. Ross, and Calvin B. Jones. 1970. San Juan de Aspalaga (a preliminary architectural study). *Bureau of Historic Sites and Properties, Division of Archives, History and Records Management, Bulletin* 1, pp. 25-43. Florida Department of State, Tallahassee.

Mullins-Moore, Sue A. 1980. *The antebellum plantation: in search of an archaeological pattern*. Ph.D. dissertation, Department of Anthropology, University of Florida, Gainesville.

Neusius, Sarah W., Editor. 1986. *Foraging, collecting and harvesting: archaic period subsistence and settlement in the Eastern Woodlands*. Southern Illinois University at Carbondale, Center for Archaeological Investigations, Occasional Paper No. 6.

Otto, John Solomon. 1975. *Status differences and the archaeological record: a comparison of planter, overseer, and slave sites from Cannon's Point Plantation (1794-1861), St. Simons Island, Georgia*. Ph.D. dissertation, Department of Anthropology, University of Florida, Gainesville.

_____. 1979. Slavery in a coastal slave community, Glynn County, 1790-1860. *Georgia Historical Quarterly* 64(4): 461-468.

Payne, Claudine. 1981. A preliminary investigation of Fort Walton settlement patterns in the Tallahassee Red Hills. *Southeastern Archaeological Conference Bulletin* 24: 29-31.

_____. 1993. Chapter 14. Fort Walton culture. In draft *Florida's Historic Contexts: A Framework for Management*, version of 9-23-93, edited by Louis Tesar. Bureau of Archaeological Research, Division of Historical Resources, Florida Department of State, Tallahassee.

Penton, Daniel T. 1970. *Excavations in the early Swift Creek component at Bird Hammock (8-Wa-30)*. M.A. thesis, Department of Anthropology, Florida State University.

Percy, George W., and David S. Brose. 1974. *Weeden Island ecology, subsistence and village life in Northwest Florida*. Paper presented at the 39th Annual Meeting of the Society for American Archaeology, Washington.

Phelps, David S. 1966. Deptford cross stamped: a preliminary statement. *Southeastern Archaeological Conference Newsletter* 10(1): 23-25.

Prunty, Merle, Jr. 1955. *The renaissance of the Southern plantation*. Bobbs-Merrill Reprint Series in Geography. Reprinted from the Geographical Review XLV(4): 459-491, October 1955.

Purdy, Barbara A. 1981. *Florida's prehistoric stone technology. A study of the flintworking technique of early Florida stone implement makers*. University Presses of Florida, Gainesville.

Ramenofsky, Ann. 1982. *The archaeology of population collapse: native American response to the introduction of infectious disease*. Ph.D. dissertation, University of Washington.

Reitz, Elizabeth J. 1993. Evidence for animal use at the missions of Spanish Florida. In *The Spanish Missions of La Florida*, edited by Bonnie G. McEwan. University Press of Florida, Gainesville, pp.376-398.

Ruhl, Donna L. 1990. Spanish mission paleoethnobotany and culture change: a survey of the archaeological data and some speculations on aboriginal and Spanish Agrarian interactions in La Florida. In *Columbian Consequences, Volume 2: Archaeological and Historical Perspectives on the Spanish Borderlands East*, edited by David Hurst Thomas, 555-580, Smithsonian Institution Press, Washington, DC.

Rogers, William Warren. 1963. *Ante-bellum Thomas County 1825-1861*. The Florida State University, Tallahassee.

_____. 1973. *Thomas County 1865-1900*. Florida State University Press, Tallahassee.

_____. 1979. *Pebble hill: the story of a plantation*. Sentry Press, Tallahassee.

Saunders, Rebecca. 1986. *Attribute variability in late Swift Creek phase ceramics from Kings Bay, Georgia*. M.A. thesis, Department of Anthropology, University of Florida, Gainesville.

_____. 1993. Architecture of the missions Santa Maria and Santa Catalina de Amelia. In *The Spanish Missions of La Florida*, edited by Bonnie G. McEwan. University Press of Florida, Gainesville, pp. 35-61.

Scarry, John F. 1980. The chronology of Fort Walton development in the upper Apalachicola Valley, Florida. *Southeastern Archaeological Conference Bulletin* 22: 38-45.

_____. 1981. Fort Walton culture: a redefinition. *Southeastern Archaeological Conference Bulletin* 24: 18-21.

_____. 1985. A proposed revision of the Fort Walton ceramic typology: a type-variety system. *The Florida Anthropologist* 38(3): 199-233.

Scarry, C. Margaret. 1993. Plant production and procurement in Apalachee province. In *The Spanish Missions of La Florida*, edited by Bonnie G. McEwan. University Press of Florida, Gainesville, 357-375.

Schnell, Frank T., Vernon J. Knight, Jr., and Gail S. Schnell. 1981. *Cemochechobee, archaeology of a Mississippian ceremonial center on the Chattahoochee River*. With contributions by Mary E. Dunn, Mary C. Hill-Clark, Barbara Ruff, and Gary Shapiro. University Presses of Florida, Gainesville.

Schnell, Frank T., and Newell O. Wright, Jr. 1993. *Mississippi period archaeology of the Georgia Coastal Plain*. University of Georgia Laboratory of Archaeology Series Report No. 26. Georgia Archaeological Research Design (GARD) Paper No. 3.

Sears, William H. 1952. An archaeological manifestation of a Natchez-Type mortuary ceremony. *The Florida Anthropologist* V: 1-7.

_____. 1956. Excavations at Kolomoki, Final Report. *University of Georgia Series in Anthropology* 5.

_____. 1959. Two Weeden Island period burial mounds, Florida. *Contributions of the Florida State Museum*, University of Florida, Gainesville.

_____. 1968. The state and settlement patterns in the New World. In *Settlement Archaeology*, edited by K.C. Chang. National Press Books, Palo Alto.

_____. 1973. The sacred and the secular in prehistoric ceramics. In *Variations in Anthropology*, edited by D.W. Lathrop and J. Douglas, Illinois Archaeological Survey, Urbana.

Shapiro, Gary, and Bonnie G. McEwan. 1992. *Archaeology at San Luis: the Apalachee council house*. Florida Archaeology no. 6, part 1. Bureau of Archaeological Research, Department of State, Tallahassee.

Singleton, Theresa A., editor. 1980 *The archaeology of Afro-American slavery in Coastal Georgia: A regional perception of slave household and community patterns*. Ph.D. dissertation, Department of Anthropology, University of Florida, Gainesville.

_____. 1985. *The archaeology of slavery and plantation life*. Academic Press, Orlando.

Smith, Betty A. 1975a. The relationship between Deptford and Swift Creek ceramics as evidenced at the Mandeville Site, 9Cla1. *Southeastern Archaeological Conference Bulletin* 18: 195-200.

_____. 1975b. *A Re-analysis of the Mandeville Site, 9Cla1, focusing on its internal history and external relations*. Ph.D. dissertation, Department of Anthropology, University of Georgia, Athens. University Microfilms, Ann Arbor, Michigan

_____. 1977. Southwest Georgia prehistory: an overview. *Early Georgia* 5(1,2): 61-72.

Smith, Bruce, editor. 1978. *Mississippian settlement patterns*. Academic Press, New York.

Smith, Marvin. 1987. *Archaeology and aboriginal culture change in the interior Southeast: depopulation during the early historic period*. University Presses of Florida, Gainesville.

Snow, Frank. 1977. A survey of the Ocmulgee big bend region. *Early Georgia* 5(1,2): 37-60.

Steinen, Karl. 1976. *The Weeden Island ceramic complex: an analysis of distribution*. Unpublished Ph.D. dissertation, Department of Anthropology, University of Florida, Gainesville.

_____. 1977. Weeden Island in Southwest Georgia. *Early Georgia* 5(1,2): 73-99.

_____. 1986. *Ochlocknee River Weeden Island project: phase ii*. Proposal submitted to the Tall Timbers Research Station, Tallahassee. Manuscript. West Georgia College, Carrollton.

_____. 1989. *The Balfour Mound and Weeden Island culture in South Georgia*. Manuscript. Department of Sociology and Anthropology, West Georgia College, Carrollton.

Swanton, John R. 1979. *The Indians of the Southeastern United States*. Bureau of American Ethnology, Smithsonian Institution Press, Washington DC. Bulletin 137. Originally published 1946.

_____. 1985. *Final report of the United States De Soto expedition commission*. Smithsonian Institution Press, Washington, DC.

Tesar, Louis Daniel. 1980. *The Leon County bicentennial survey report: an archaeological survey of selected portions of Leon County, Florida*. Performed for the Florida Bicentennial Commission, City of Tallahassee, and National Park Service, by the Bureau of Historic Sites and Properties, Division of Archives, History and Records Management, Florida Department of State, Tallahassee. Miscellaneous Project Report Series No. 49, Volumes 1 and 2. 1981. Fort Walton and Leon-Jefferson Cultural Development in the Tallahassee Red Hills Area of Florida: A Brief Summary. *Southeastern Archaeological Conference Bulletin* 25: 27-29.

Varner, John G., and Jeannette J. Varner. 1962. *The Florida of the Inca, a history of the Adelantado, Hernando de Soto, Governor and Captain General of the kingdom of Florida, and of heroic Spanish and Indian cavaliers, written by the Inca, Garcilaso de la Vega*. University of Texas Press, Austin.

Vernon, Richard. 1988. Seventeenth-century Apalachee Colono-ware as a reflection of demography, economics, and acculturation. *Historical Archaeology* 22(1): 76-82.

Vernon, Richard, and Ann S. Cordell. 1993. A distributional and technological study of Apalachee Colono-Ware from San Luis de Talimali. In *The Spanish Missions of La Florida*, edited by Bonnie G. McEwan. University Press of Florida, Gainesville, pp.418-442.

Walthall, John A. 1980. *Prehistoric Indians of the Southeast: archaeology of Alabama and the Middle South*. The University of Alabama Press, University, Alabama.

Watts, W.A. 1970. The full-glacial vegetation of Northwestern Georgia. *Ecology* 51(1): 17-33.

Watts, W.A., and M. Stuiver. 1980. Late Wisconsin climate of Northern Florida and the origin of species-rich deciduous forest. *Science* 210: 325-327.

Webb, William S. 1974. *Indian knoll*. The University of Tennessee Press, Knoxville. Originally published 1946.

White, Nancy Marie. 1981. *Archaeological survey of Lake Seminole*. Cleveland Museum of Natural History, Archaeological Research Report, No. 29.

_____. 1985. Archaeology of Northwest Florida and adjacent borderlands. Florida Anthropological Society Special Publications No. 11. *Florida Anthropologist* 38(2).

Whitehead, D.R. 1964. Palynology and pleistocene phytogeography of unglaciated Eastern North America. In *The Quaternary of the United States*, edited by H.E. Wright and D.G. Frey. Princeton University Press, Princeton, New Jersey.

Williams, Stephens, editor. 1977. *The Waring papers; the collected works of Antonio J. Waring, Jr.* Papers of the Peabody Museum of Archaeology and Ethnology, Harvard University, Cambridge, Massachusetts, Volume 58.

Willey, Gordon R. 1982. *Archeology of the Florida Gulf Coast*. Reprinted by Florida Book Store, Gainesville. Originally published in 1949, Bureau of American Ethnology, Smithsonian Institution, Smithsonian Miscellaneous Collections Volume 113.

CHAPTER 4: HISTORY

Nancy Tinker

This chapter reviews the nineteenth- and early twentieth-century history of Thomas and Grady Counties. It then discusses in detail some of the individual plantations of this unique region

INTRODUCTION

Hills region of Southwest Georgia and Northern Florida spans approximately 375,000 acres of managed wildlands. Lying broadly between Thomasville, Georgia, and Tallahassee, Florida, the region's land mass extends thirty miles north and south and forty miles east and west between these individual communities. Seventy-one quail hunting plantations are found in the region, an area whose landscape is hallmarked by park-like forest, unpaved canopied roads, and rolling, grassy plains.

The Red Hills region is remarkably lacking in residential and industrial development. Convenience markets, billboards, and multi-lane highways are few. The region also lacks extensive agricultural cultivation. There are no plantations immediately to the north of Thomasville and none to the south of Tallahassee. The concentration of quail hunting plantations, then, is as unique as it is surprising.

Questions abound as the curious examine the region's cultural and historic fabric. What fosters the plantation community's well-being, and what occasion prompted its inception during the closing years of the nineteenth century? Why are these plantations found precisely in this location, and what cultural and natural forces prompted some of the nation's wealthiest families to create winter homes and quail shooting estates in this corner of America?

What follows is not a definitive history on Southwest Georgia and Northern Florida's Red Hills region. The following pages and their addenda initiate the investigative process. For in investigating and correctly interpreting Red Hills' history, the region must be explored as a single piece, ignoring, as much as is possible, the state line that divides the region into parts of a greater whole. Much work remains to be done.

This chapter, then, serves as an introductory look at Georgia's Red Hills and the growth occurring in Thomas and Grady Counties during the closing days of the 19th century. The chapter discusses community leaders and the homes and cities they established. It presents the values that brought settlers into the region, and the values that continue to hold present-day land owners to the land. The region's land use patterns are unique, giving rise to a history that is equally remarkable.

THOMASVILLE AND THOMAS COUNTY

Overview

Thomas County is located in Georgia's southwestern coastal plain. The region has long been an agricultural leader in both state and national forums. Traditionally, major differences in agriculture and land use exist between the area north of Thomasville, the county seat, and the region located south of the city.

The southern part of Thomas County has long been known for its plantations — both nineteenth-century cotton plantations and the large hunting plantations prevalent in the twentieth century. The countryside is a rolling landscape of grassy park-like pine forest with few farm houses and a scattering of comparatively small cultivated fields. This area, along with the northern portion of adjacent Leon County, Florida, is known as the Tallahassee Red Hills. The exposed soils are noticeably redder than in areas to the north of Thomasville. Throughout its history, the region's land use, and thus its history, has been distinctive, and this distinction is directly due to the rich deposits of dehydrated iron compounds found in the region's subsoils (McGorty, 1992).

Forest, Springwood Plantation

Origins

The antebellum planters who settled Southwest Georgia and North Florida arrived searching for soils conducive to cotton production. Cotton planters, through previous experience, selected the region's heavier, redder soils while the county's northern sandy soil was cultivated by smaller land holders. The soil differences resulted in southern Thomas County and the Red Hills region containing large

Entrance, Borderline Plantation

cotton plantations with a substantial number of slaves while the region to the north of Thomasville had small farms and few slaves.

Thomas County was created on December 23, 1825, by an act of the Georgia General Assembly out of the larger counties of Irwin and Decatur. In 1826, a portion of Lowndes County, formed at the same time as Thomas, was incorporated into Thomas County. Settlers had begun arriving here as early as 1819, although they were few in number. By 1827, Thomasville had become an outpost in Southwest Georgia's pine barrens (Decatur County General Index to Deeds). Buildings were few although the settlement featured a rough-hewn log court-house and a small collection of homes and commercial businesses (Rogers, 1963).

History says that Thomasville and Thomas County were named after General Jett Thomas. General Thomas had fought in the battles of Autossee and Chalibbee in the War of 1812. He was a Virginian who migrated to Georgia and became famous for his architectural abilities. It was largely due to him that the first building at the University of Georgia was built, as well as the Old State House in Milledgeville. General Thomas died in 1817. Thomas Johnson and a relative of General Thomas decided to honor him by naming the newly formed county after him.[†] (This paragraph and others so marked have been taken from a thesis written by Adriane Lea Kelley entitled *The Plantation Homes of John Wind*.)

The town of Thomasville was formed by another legislative act on December 22, 1826. When the town was incorporated in 1831, it was the major town in Thomas County. The area was still a wilderness, with only sparse population, including Indians, but more and more people were moving to the region.[†]

New Hope Road, Thomas County, Georgia

The infant town was governed from its birth by a group of five commissioners whose duties included levying and overseeing the collection of taxes, maintaining roadways, and insuring the safety of the town. Elections were held each year and this was the form of the city's government until 1856 when it was changed to a mayor and council system.[†]

The first mayor, in 1856, was Robert Hardaway, who presided over the board of six aldermen. Their powers were much the same as those of the commissioners with such additions as the taxation of saloons, billiard tables, and other necessities in a frontier town. The town's law enforcement officers were also under the control of the aldermen and mayor.[†]

Agriculture and Economy

At this time, agriculture was the basis of the whole Southern economy, and Thomas County was no exception. Several of the original settlers in the area had acquired land in lotteries and amassed their holdings into sizeable plantations. Yet these were not the only farms in the area. Many men with much smaller farms contributed to the overall plan. The soil in the Thomas County area was ideal for farming. In 1840, the census records 2,330 people who supported themselves through farming as opposed to 40 in other professions.[†]

From the beginning, land and land prices were an intrinsic part of Thomas County's history. Land was easily acquired and could be purchased in small lots or extensive tracts. "This is a fine healthy country," wrote a settler in 1828 to friends living in Savannah. "Persons from all parts of the country (are) coming to settle, as fine land can be purchased at $1.50 per acre. The country offers many advantages to an industrious man, with a small capital to begin with" (Rogers, 1963).

By 1850, Thomas County contained 63,931 acres in improved farm land and 383,453 acres in unimproved land. The cash value of the county's farms was $1,104,240 while the value of farm implements and machinery was listed at $108,041. In 1860, the cash value of farms had grown to $1,530,540, giving Thomas County thirty-ninth place among Georgia's 132 counties (Rogers, 1963).

Cotton was the major crop, with corn being second. Sugar cane, from which molasses and sugar were made, was also a major crop. Tobacco, a valuable crop elsewhere in the South, was here less important. Livestock, including the pigs, cows, and chickens that most households kept, was a large part of the agricultural economy, and in 1840, Thomas County had the second largest number of cattle and the thirty-seventh largest number of horses, mules, and sheep in Georgia.[†]

In the nineteenth century, the county's growth was sustained primarily by the cotton trade, a commodity that gave life to the plantation economy and the institution of slavery. It was the cotton trade that allowed yeoman farmers to exist, and it was the sale of cotton that provided Thomasville's doctors, lawyers, and merchants with stable incomes. While Thomas County's agricultural economy was diversified, cotton production remained the county's premiere product in the years preceding the Civil War (Brooks, 1984).

In 1840, Thomas County produced 1,565,262 pounds of cotton and ranked thirty-fifth in the state. Ten years later, in 1850, Thomas County farmers ginned 7,667 bales of cotton, advancing the county's rank to twenty-ninth place. In 1860, having lost land to the newly formed Brooks County, Thomas County ginned 6,582 four-hundred pound bales. While Thomas County cotton planters and their counterparts in Leon and Jefferson Counties, Florida, faced few obstacles producing cotton, it was getting the product to market that created a multitude of problems for the region's planters (Rogers, 1973).

Until the Atlantic and Gulf Railroad reached Thomasville in 1861, South Georgia and North Florida farmers shipped their cotton from Florida ports located in the Gulf of Mexico. The St. Marks River communities of Magnolia and St. Marks were popular shipping centers, and throughout the 1840's and 50's, these communities vied for cotton shipments originating in South Georgia and Northern Florida. Thomas County farmers who preferred St. Marks delivered their cotton by mule team to Tallahassee and from there by rail to St. Marks. The community of Newport, Florida, anxious to gain a foothold in the shipping of cotton, constructed in 1855 a plank road that terminated at the Georgia line. This competition encouraged the Tallahassee Railroad, which hauled cotton from Tallahassee to St. Marks, to convert from horse pulled trains to locomotives driven by steam engines (Prisley, 1990).

The inconvenience and time spent in getting a mule team pulling a wagon load of cotton to a Florida port prompted a Madison County, Florida, planter to complain it took "a prime six-mule team a whole week to carry and return." The expense required in marketing cotton only reinforced public demand that a railroad beginning in Savannah and continuing through Thomasville be completed.

In 1845, Nathaniel R. Mitchell, a Thomas County planter, shipped his cotton crop from St. Marks to Boston, Massachusetts, and was paid $1,258.85 for the crop, but returned home with only $833.87.

The remaining $424.98 had been spent on the following costs:

Insurance	$ 22.50
Freight	179.28
Expenses in St. Marks	99.03
Primage	13.80
Fire Insurance	7.26
Weighing and Labor	10.00
Interest on Cash Charges	12.22
Wharfage	12.68
Trucking	2.68
Commission	32.44
Storage	42.88

Thomas County's isolation from the remainder of Georgia continued through the 1840's and 50's. Thomas County citizens were tied to Tallahassee through the shipment of cotton and banking needs. As late as 1860, business leaders in Thomas County had been unsuccessful in chartering a local banking house. In 1855, a Thomas County resident wrote, "We are compelled to go to Tallahassee, a two-days' absence, to purchase a check of any kind, and pay in addition to the regular per cent on exchange, the sum of eight dollars passage money, besides" (Prisley, 1990).

Dissatisfaction with existing commercial practices and a need for the railroad festered throughout the late 1850's. A public meeting protesting the exclusion of Southwestern and Southeastern Georgia from rail line construction was conducted in the Thomasville courtroom in February, 1856. A report, written by a previously appointed committee, was adopted and declared South Georgia had been "kept tributary to our young sister State of Florida in all its commerce..." and that South Georgia had received "denials, reproaches, and bitter taunts" in response to its economic and shipping needs. The report concluded with threats that South Georgia might secede from the state. Such threats were put aside as the railroad reached Thomasville in April, 1861. The year 1861 also witnessed the organization of the Cotton Planters Bank of Georgia, an institution created in response to the Civil War and the heightened fear of economic isolation (Prisley, 1990).

While the Atlantic and Gulf Railroad securely tied Thomas County to the port of Savannah, it was the county's system of roads that assured the railroad's success. The earliest roads were Indian trails that were succeeded by "roads" which were not ditched or graded. In 1833, Thomas County's roads were in such poor condition that Charles Joseph Latrobe, a visiting Englishman wrote, "The roads through the south of Georgia are in the roughest state." It was necessary, he wrote, "to wade many deep creeks, and swim one or two" (Latrobe, 1985).

Mail delivery was closely tied to the county's roadways and was a tool used in promoting county development. The federal government believed extending postal routes boosted population growth, and the agency was aggressive in spurring route expansion. Postal routes not only provided access to the outside world, but also brought letters and news of state and national importance that filled the pages of local newspapers. Thomas County possessed an abundance of post offices and postmasters. Between 1827 and 1860, the county boasted fourteen post offices and forty-six postmasters (Rogers, 1973).

Many of Thomas County's early roads were originally created as postal routes. The road connecting Thomasville and Albany is but one example.

Mayhaw Plantation Stage Stop

Constructed in 1842, this connector soon served military, social, and economic purposes. Mail was carried along this and other later routes. Despite impassable roads and swollen streams, the mail was eventually delivered (Rogers, 1973).

Thomas County's first post office was opened in the community of Duncanville on November 26, 1827 with William Coggins serving as postmaster. Isaac P. Brooks opened what could be Thomasville's first post office on March 12, 1832 in James Kirksey's store. Additional post offices were established in the following order: Grooverville, July 16, 1833; Tired Creek, July 19, 1833 (closed in 1837); Boston, April 29, 1847; Station, December 4, 1849 (closed in 1859); Ochlocknee, May 1, 1851; Glasgow, November 28, 1853; Denson, March 16, 1854 (closed 1860); Arabia, July 31, 1856 (closed 1860); Youngsville, February 17, 1857; and Dry Lake, January 22, 1857. Quite often, homes or stores housed postal services (Hopkins' Collection).

The Troupville stage left Thomasville every Monday and Thursday morning at 6:30 and returned to Thomasville every Tuesday and Friday morning. As the Thomasville stage entered the village of Troupville, a bugle was sounded, prompting citizens to gather to welcome passengers and receive news. In 1860, a stage passenger complained horses were not changed often enough for, "horses, if driven, cannot stand such heats, and if not driven, the journey becomes very tedious." By 1856, mail arrived once a week in Ochlocknee from Thomasville. This thirty-three-mile trip included stops in Tatesville and Greenfield.

On April 16, 1861, the first train arrived in Thomasville. On April 17, daily train service to Savannah began with the arrival of the 4:35 A.M. train. The Savannah-bound train departed Thomasville approximately eight hours later at 12:45 P.M. The thirteen-hour trip to Savannah featured scheduled stops that were coordinated with local stage lines (Rogers, 1964).

Mayhaw Plantation Stage Stop, Building's Interior

"Georgia's mode of thought, traditions, concepts, and behavior has been firmly molded by...agricultural influence." So wrote Georgia historian Willard Range (Rogers, 1964). The 1840 census confirmed this assertion by revealing that a total of forty Thomas County citizens worked in "manufacturing and trades" while 2,330 people identified agriculture as their vocation. Social distinctions were varied, with citizens divided into approximately four groups: large land and slave owners, smaller land owners who owned few slaves, towns people, and yeoman farmers (Rogers, 1963).

Slavery

For the ante-bellum farmer, the more agricultural an area, the more slaves were needed to work the farms. Even the small farmer had at least one slave, and a few of the largest planters had one hundred or more. The tax records of Thomas Jones of Thomas County for the years immediately preceding the War Between the States show him to have anywhere from eighty-nine to one hundred and ten slaves.[†]

In Thomas County by 1850, over half the population was black (United States Census, 1830-1860). Thomas County ranked fifty-eighth in the state in population in 1830 and by 1860 was thirty-first. The large number of slaves made it twenty-second in the number of slaves in 1860, and one of the forty-three counties with more slaves than whites. In 1860, Thomas County's population totaled 4,488 whites and 6,244 slaves (United States Census, 1860-1890). Out of the white population, 403, or one out of eleven Thomas County citizens, owned slaves.[†]

Records show that the slave population was not excessively abused in the community. Their needs were cared for in most aspects, including religion, which was a major part of the community as a whole. The Methodists, Baptists, and Presbyterians had all established churches in the area by 1860, and each group could count numerous slaves as members. For the most part, the slaves attended the churches of their masters, at special services, but often, as in the case of the Baptist Church, they had their own conferences, disciplinary measures, and even, a slave preacher.[†]

Churches[†]

The churches were a major part in the lives in the Thomas County citizenry during this time. The diaries of William Dickey, owner of a moderate-sized plantation, show that church was attended regularly on Sundays and, if possible, during the week. Often, if one church was not holding church service, the people would travel to the nearest one that was.

The Methodists built the first church in Thomasville. They had established conferences in South Georgia before 1825, and circuit riders preached along the frontiers of South Georgia and North Florida. In 1833, the Methodists were given land to build a church in Thomasville, and the church was completed in 1840. The Methodist Church had 381 white members and 278 black members in the 1850's.

The Baptists were among the first settlers to Thomas County. The Thomasville Baptist Church was officially established in 1849, and the building was completed in 1853. The Baptists exercised strict moral control over their members, black and white, and were a major part of the town.

The Presbyterians organized into a church in 1853. The church had a limited membership and no official building until 1858. Services were held the first three Sundays of each month, with weekly prayer meetings and Bible classes on Thursdays. Black members were allowed to hold services one afternoon per month.

The various denominations also established themselves around in the county. The oldest Presbyterian Church in the county, dating from 1836, was in Old Boston, a predominantly Scottish community.

Civil War and After

Thomasville was enjoying a booming economy when the Civil War began in 1861. The community had six lawyers, six doctors, two dentists, two hotels, an architect, and a thriving business district. A new courthouse had been completed in 1858. The railroad played an important role in Thomasville during the war years, as the town was the terminus of the Atlantic and Gulf Railroad that supplied Savannah during its defense against Union forces.

Slavery did not end in Thomasville until May 8, 1865, and during the Civil War life continued as before for most Thomas County slaves. Some free blacks as well as slaves were employed during the war in businesses left under-staffed due to white employees' service in the Confederate Army (Rogers, 1963).

The first several years following the Civil War were marked by uncertainty concerning many issues, including the future of Thomas County's black population. The county was placed under military rule on May 9, 1865, with Thomasville becoming the headquarters for the 12th Maine Volunteers, an action highly unpopular with white residents (Rogers, 1973).

Before long, it became clear to at least some white residents that blacks would have to play a role in the county's revitalization. Plantation owners lacked sufficient capital, and many Thomas County property owners found that they were unable to operate large tracts of farm land; out of desperation, some attempted to sell portions of their lands or even entire holdings. Moses W. Linton, owner of a 1,600 acre plantation near Grooverville, advertised his property in August of 1865. Linton's advertisement described cattle, frame slave quarters, wells, a fish pond, streams, fences, farm equipment, and "about seventy-five freed people who may be hired at moderate wages to do the labor." Linton's dilemma was that he could not afford to pay wages of any type, but his effort to sell the property failed, and he resorted to instituting the crop lien system of management. Linton wrote up contracts between himself and his workers outlining expectations of both land owner and tenant.

What came to be known as the tenant system dismantled many large land holdings and increased the availability of farm land. Thomas County thus became a region of small and medium-sized farms, with individual acreages typically in the range of 100 to 500 acres (Commission of Agriculture 1866). The county had 611 farms operating in 1870 and 1,588 by 1880. Large land owners, unable to resume their pre-war agricultural practices without slave labor, were forced to either sell portions of their lands or divide it into a series of tenant farms. The tenant, in turn, either paid cash for the land's use or gave the owner a share of the crop as rent. Merchants utilized this system as well, as tenant farmers were sometimes provided with dry good items on the condition that a portion of future crops be delivered to the merchant's establishments. By 1900, Thomas County had 3,183 farms, many operated by black tenant farmers and most fairly small. The presence of small farms was welcomed and, according to former Congressman James L. Seward, "The question of small farms is the salvation of our country, and the sooner the planters adopt it, the sooner will Thomas County be indeed, the banner county of Georgia" (Rogers, 1973).

An example of the sort of contractual agreements drawn up between Thomas County land owners and their tenants is that between P. N. Vickers and his laborers, dated June 1865. The tenants were to "work every day in the week beginning before sunup...and stopping at dusk." They would have two hours off at noon until October 1, after which they would have only one hour and a half. Workers agreed "to be respectful and obedient" to Vickers and to conduct themselves uprightly and honestly. Not only would they abstain from stealing, but they would report any thieves to Vickers or the proper authorities. If fences were blown down and stock got into a field on the Sabbath, the men and boys agreed to mend the fences and were to feed the stock on Sundays by turns. For their efforts, tenants were to receive one-fourth of the growing grain and potato crop. Each person was to be furnished with rations and three pounds of meat and one peck of meal for every seven days until January 1. Should a laborer violate the contract, he would be fired and would forfeit his wages "or agree for our employer to have us punished, which we agree to submit to, our employer being the judge whether we are to be punished or turned off" (Prisley, 1990).

The Bureau of Refugees, Freedmen and Abandoned Lands — commonly known as the Freedmen's Bureau — was signed into law by President Lincoln on March 3, 1865. Among many other responsibilities, this agency was charged with supervising work contracts drawn between whites and blacks. Captain C. C. Richardson, an army officer, arrived in Thomas County in the fall of 1865 to oversee the Thomasville District, serving under Major G. A. Hasting, the director of the Freedmen's Bureau for Southwest Georgia. Richardson soon organized a meeting at the Methodist church, where freedmen and whites gathered to hear him explain that work agreements, once fairly written, would be issued and supervised by the Bureau. In 1865, the *Southern Enterprise*, Thomasville's local newspaper at the time, quoted a white meeting attendant as stating, "Let all parties deal justly and forbearingly with each other, and all will move on smoothly." Many blacks were wary of the new system, some believing that if they signed they would be returned to slavery, but in only a year and a half, 202 contracts had been finalized for 1,259 employees (Rogers, 1973).

Besides supervising work contracts, the Freedmen's Bureau also authorized apprenticeships for black children who had been abandoned, orphaned, or who lived in abusive homes. On December 19, 1865, fourteen-year old Sally Capurs was apprenticed to Thomas W. Capurs for four years as a house servant. Sally's mother was living, but since she had been determined to be of "abandoned character and having so confessed it to the authorities," Sally was indentured to Capurs and remained with him until her eighteenth birthday. Capurs was obligated to clothe, feed, and educate his apprentice and at the end of Sally's apprenticeship provide her with $100 and two suits of clothing. This is but one example of many such apprenticeship arrangements in Thomas County (Register of Freed Persons 1865).

By the late 1870's, many blacks owned and managed their own properties in Thomas County. The Congressional Confiscation Acts of 1861 and 1863 had taken thousands of acres of Georgia farm land for future distribution to freed blacks, and the Freedmen's Bureau Act of March 3, 1865 provided for the dispersion of this land in 40-acre parcels. Whites generally opposed this plan, and the editor of the *Southern Enterprise* wrote in July of 1865 that

> they (freedmen) regard Southerners as their oppressors, and believing that they were held in slavery contrary to some natural right, they expect the South to be punished for the wrong, and reparation made to them by having all property of the South confiscated and distributed among them. They cannot see why this should not be done and to convince them that it will not be done, and, at the same time, show them that to live they must continue to labor, will be to convince the negro that he is not free.

Although blacks eventually received some land in Thomas County through the distribution program, nearly all of it later reverted to its original owners, as was generally the case throughout Georgia. Two blacks who did purchase land were Barry Mitchell and Martha Poe. Mitchell, a former Fair Oaks Plantation slave, purchased 100 acres of land for a dollar an acre in the late 1870's. Poe, a black laborer, purchased a log house and four acres of land for $24 (Thomas County General Index to Deeds 1826-1910).

By 1875, Thomas County had 2,155 black farmers and 562 white farmers who were not land owners; all these people either worked for wages, rented or sharecropped. By 1900, a significant change had occurred, for while there were 644 white tenant farmers in the county that year (a 14.6% increase), there were only 1,133 black tenant farmers, a decrease of 47.4%. A total of 277 blacks actually owned farm land in 1900, constituting 23% of the county's 1,202 land owners (Rogers, 1973).

Although Thomas County's white property owners depended on black labor to hold on to their properties, they nevertheless made efforts to "import" immigrant labor. Beginning in 1867, some white farmers began recruiting European families who had recently emigrated to the northeastern United States. The county had an immigration society in place in 1876, and this organization published pamphlets promoting Thomas County. The *Thomasville Times-Enterprise* was involved in this effort, as it encouraged land owners in 1873 to "cut up your large plantations into one hundred acre tracts or in lots to suit purchasers and offer proper inducements to white immigrants." As it turned out, however, relatively few white immigrants arrived in Thomas County. Most landowners were satisfied with their black tenants and considered immigrant labor to be inferior. Furthermore, Northern Europeans who did come to South Georgia had difficulties adjusting to the heat and unusual crops (primarily cotton) grown in the region (Spangle, 1977).

Education

Thomasville also provided for the educational needs of the area. On December 24, 1845, the day after the legislature passed the act forming Thomas County, it approved a bill to establish an academy in the county. Thomasville Academy received its charter in 1830. It was an all-white, sexually integrated school, serving as a primary and secondary institution.[†]

Other schools opened in the 1840's, both private and public. The literacy rate among Thomas County whites was high, with only slightly more than 300 people being unable to read and write. The school attendance was relatively high, with 36 students in the two academies and elementary schools, and 169 students attending the eight primary and common schools.[†]

In 1848, the Methodists established a school just outside the city limits. This school, Fletcher Institute, had one hundred and thirty-two students in 1850, from Thomas County and Thomasville plus Tallahassee and surrounding areas. The brick buildings housed the school on approximately six acres of land. Combined with the residents of "Fletcherville," it made an attractive community that Thomasville incorporated in 1856.[†]

The school contributed to the overall economy of Thomasville. It charged according to the courses a student enrolled in; tuition could be paid half in advance, with the balance being due March 1. The school year began the first Monday in October and ended the last Thursday in July, with one week at Christmas. A room, board, washing facilities, and lights were included in tuition, if desired, at ten dollars a month.[†]

Throughout the 1850's, many other schools were established around Thomasville. The Thomasville Female Seminary was established in 1859. In 1860, Young's Female College was established to offer more advanced courses to older girls, but it was put into operation until after the Civil War. Although the state had no comprehensive public school system until after the War, Thomasville and Thomas County tried to provide for the educational needs of the citizens.[†]

Prior to emancipation, it was illegal for blacks — whether enslaved or free — to read and write. Not surprisingly, many blacks viewed education as a symbol of true freedom and success. The Freedmen's Bureau was involved in efforts to educate blacks almost immediately after the Civil War, and perhaps as many as five black schools were in operation in the county by 1867. Many in the white community favored education for blacks, and the Episcopal church in Thomasville opened a school for blacks that enrolled more than 200 students of all ages. Some whites thought that educated blacks would be less likely to commit crimes, and the *Thomasville Times* commented in 1873 that

> Whilst we shall always unhesitatingly condemn and denounce the short-comings and petty crimes committed by many of the colored people..., the freedmen could be prosperous and useful...if they will educate their children and inculcate lessons of morality and integrity in them.

The American Missionary Association (AMA) played a key role in educating blacks in Southwest Georgia. In 1885, Mrs. F. L. Allen of Waterbury, Connecticut, gave a hotel she owned in Quitman to the AMA to serve as a school for blacks. The school opened in October of that year and soon had an enrollment of 140 day and 12 boarding students. The institution was not accepted by the white community, however, and teachers were badly treated. On the morning of November 17, 1885, the school was destroyed by fire; while the cause was never determined, some people speculated that it had been deliberately set (Rogers, 1973).

Faced with the problem of organizing a new school, the AMA began seeking an alternate location. The community of Thomasville and its black and white leadership worked toward bringing the school to Thomasville, and in January of 1886, black leaders William M. Henderson and Charles Rice began organizing plans. Their efforts were prompted by Rev. James Powell of New York, an AMA official who had toured Thomasville earlier that year. They reached agreement with the AMA to house the school temporarily in the former Negro Academy building on North Broad Street. The institution formally opened in the spring of 1886 as the Connecticut Industrial School and initially served only girls. It offered subjects such as nursing, cooking and dressmaking. The school was staffed by Northern white teachers and soon accepted girls as boarders and boys as day students (Niles, 1985).

A permanent building for the Connecticut Industrial School, later renamed the Allen Normal and Industrial School in honor of its original benefactor, Mrs. F. L. Allen, was constructed in 1887. Four acres of land on Lester Street, in the section of town known as Southside, were donated for the project by Judge H. W. Hopkins. The 32-room school was a three-story frame building built at a cost of $10,000. The Bethany Congregational Church was established in 1891 to meet the religious needs of children attending the Allen School and was constructed by the American Missionary Association. For black children from the county's rural areas as well as those from Thomasville, the opportunity to attend the Allen School was life-changing. As one AMA worker noted, "To those who have always lived in a one-room cabin, in crowded families and ignorant homes, it is like entering a new world to live in a large house, where one must learn how to walk up and down stairs, and how to go through the daily routine of boarding-school" (Rogers, 1973). Although the school is no longer standing, the Bethany Church still survives, as does a nearby house that was associated with some instructors at the Allen Normal School (Brooks, 1985).

Although education for blacks in Thomas County started out with considerable promise, the success of the Allen Normal School proved to be the exception rather than the rule. By 1900, only 11% of the county's 7,347 black residents could read or write, and the departure of the Freedmen's Bureau in 1869 meant an end to most of the educational opportunities for blacks (Spangle, 1977).

Political Life

Politically, ante-bellum Thomasville and Thomas County were not much different from the rest of Georgia. Whigs and Democrats were the major party decisions, and in state elections, the Whigs dominated until mid-century. Local elections were usually evenly divided between the two.[†]

The majority of the larger landowners were Whigs, although a few were Democrats. In Thomas County, the Democrats were an especially strong minority. In the 1850's, the local Know-Nothing Party and the national Republican Party entered the political scene. Both presented threats to the established parties, as some Thomas County politicians switched to the Know-Nothings. The Whig Party disintegrated, and by 1860, the Democrats were easily the majority party in Thomas County.[†]

In 1860, the problem of secession arose, and involved Thomas County in the number of debates over the question. Three delegates from Thomas County were sent to the state convention in Milledgeville on January 16, 1861. In the final vote, the Thomas County delegates, who had previously voted against secession, voted yes, and on January 19, 1861, Georgia seceded from the Union.[†]

Following the Civil War, blacks in Thomas County, and particularly in Thomasville, made efforts to become politically active during the first few years of Reconstruction. Many white residents believed that political equality was equivalent to social equality, and they were not prepared to grant either to the black population. Georgia rejected the Fourteenth Amendment (which granted blacks civil rights, citizenship and political rights) in November of 1866, but blacks gained the right to vote the following April after the military had taken over the state government a month earlier and established Boards of Registration to register blacks for the vote. Blacks in Thomasville formed a chapter of the Republican Party in the spring of 1867 and also held a large meeting in April of the same year to promote good relations between blacks and whites. Several prominent members of the white community spoke at the gathering, which went on without incident (Rogers, 1973).

The Georgia Constitution of 1868 granted blacks the vote and full civil rights, but in September of that year, black members of the state legislature were replaced by white conservatives on the rationale that while blacks had been granted the right to vote, they had not been given the right to hold office. Blacks were again given the right to serve in the legislature after the state again came under military rule. Several Thomas County blacks held office during the early 1870's, but gradually the conservative white Democrats gained strength. The election of 1876 proved to be a turning point, as Democrats outnumbered Republicans and continued to gain strength. Thomas County blacks continued to lose ground politically through the remaining years of the nineteenth century (Spangle, 1977).

Thomasville's black population benefitted considerably when, during the latter decades of the nineteenth century, the city achieved considerable acclaim as a winter destination for wealthy Northern tourists. Word spread of the region's mild, dry climate, opportunities for game hunting, and the receptiveness with which local residents welcomed visitors. Black agricultural laborers found seasonal employment of many kinds, not only in the hotels, but also as dog handlers and guides as well as in jobs related to various construction trades. Blacks in Thomasville were also employed — as gardeners, blacksmiths, livery workers, cobblers, teachers, domestics and railroad employees (Rogers, 1973).

The Hotel Era

As Thomas County became known for its healthy climate and later for shooting and social activities, the community entered into what has become known as the "Hotel Era." This period may be divided into two periods with the first spanning 1865 to 1883. The second begins in 1884 and ends roughly at 1900.

The Hotel Era's initial period witnessed the construction of boarding houses and hotels for the city's influx of winter visitors. In the years before 1883, Thomasville's most important hotels included the Waverly House, Gulf House, West End, and the Mitchell House. A fire that destroyed the Mitchell House in August, 1883 marked the end of the first era.

The second period marked the height of Thomasville's fame. The Piney Woods Hotel, a 160-room Queen Anne frame building, was constructed in response to the Mitchell House fire. Opened on

January 11, 1885, the Piney Woods' guest book revealed addresses from Wisconsin, Philadelphia, New York, Chicago, Louisville, Pittsburgh, and Nova Scotia. E. L. Youmans, a reporter for the magazine *Popular Science Monthly* wrote that the "Piney Woods is the best hotel in the South."

1885 Map of the City of Thomasville

Northern and Midwestern winter visitors became property owners as they purchased homes in town or acquired country estates. New York's S. R. Van Duzer purchased Greenwood Plantation while J. Wyman Jones acquired Elsoma. Howard Melville Hanna acquired Melrose Plantation in November, 1896 and Pebble Hill in 1897. By the turn of the century, Hanna had purchased adjoining tracts of land, converting farmland into wildlife preserves and shooting plantations. Hanna was joined by other Northern and Midwestern business associates who acquired large land holdings for hunting, timbering, and agricultural purposes (Rogers, 1973).

Plantations

Observers of the Red Hills' plantation history may believe the hunting preserves' existence to be unique to Southwest Georgia, an unusual fold in American history. But this phenomenon was not isolated. In the late years of the nineteenth century, the organization of large tracts of land for the purpose of quail propagation occurred throughout the Southeastern United States and came to encompass 390 individual properties and more than 3,600,000 acres of land. Aiken, Charleston, and Beaufort, South Carolina, boasted their share of shooting preserves. Brunswick and Albany, Georgia, and Union Springs, Alabama, were other popular sites.

Entrance, Mistletoe Plantation

NUMBER AND ACRES OF NORTHERN-OWNED HUNTING PLANTATIONS IN FIVE SOUTHEASTERN STATES
Pre-World War II
(McGorty, 1992)

STATES	NUMBER OF PLANTATIONS	OWNED ACREAGES	TOTAL OWNED AND LEASED ACREAGES
South Carolina	220	1,500,000	2,000,000
Georgia	100	775,000	900,000
Florida	40	250,000	400,000
Alabama	20	100,000	200,000
Mississippi	10	50,000	100,000
TOTALS	390	2,675,000	3,600,000

Millpond Road, Thomas County, Georgia

The explosion of late nineteenth- and early twentieth-century shooting preserves resulted directly from several independent yet inter-related incidents. The development of new industry — oil, rail, shipping, and steel — produced great wealth and a new leisure class. It was during these same years that new technology yielded breech-loading, choke-bored shot guns, forever replacing their smoking, muzzle-loading predecessors. Improvements in the training and breeding of dogs ended the custom of trapping game birds, and institutionalized the use of dogs in hunting tradition.

The establishment of hunting plantations brought many benefits to Southeastern communities. In the Red Hills Region, the plantation economy's presence endowed Thomas and Grady Counties in Georgia with substantial employment opportunities, medical facilities, and educational experience.

Today, very real threats to the region's park-like landscape, abundant wildlife, and ecological systems are posed by a variety of non-traditional development proposals that in and of themselves pose little danger to local historic and land-based values. However, the fragile balance maintained throughout the region will be irrevocably altered by unrelated non-traditional, yet incremental development choices whose implementation over time will forever change the face and function of the Tallahassee Red Hills.

Southwestern Georgia's Red Hills Region is comprised of 375,000 acres of managed wild lands. The region's beauty, ecology, and architectural resources are fragile qualities, values easily lost through random growth and poor planning decisions. Without thorough knowledge of regional resources and sound planning documents, residents of the Tallahassee Red Hills are destined to make poor legislative and development choices.

EMPLOYMENT ON SELECTED PLANTATIONS
Circa 1980
(McGorty, 1992)

PLANTATIONS	APPROXIMATE ACREAGES	TOTAL NUMBER EMPLOYEES	ACRES PER EMPLOYEE
Welaunee	13,000	22	591
Millpond	10,000	23	435
Sinkola and Bickaway	9,700	30	323
Foshalee	7,500	20	375
Pebble Hill, Miami, Mayhaw and Honey Lake	10,000	45	222
Cherokee	6,700	12	558
Holly Hills, Dekle and Meander	10,000	21	476
TOTALS	66,900	173	387

Metcalf

Metcalf is representative of those late nineteenth-century South Georgia communities created by the presence of a railroad. Metcalf was a center for commerce and the trade of agricultural products during its productive years. The surviving structures are significant examples of commercial and residential Victorian architecture.

As soon as the Thomasville and Augusta Railroad Company announced in 1887 that it would build a railroad from Thomasville, Georgia, to Monticello, Florida, a settlement began to develop at the mid-point between the two towns. The tracks were laid and the yellow frame depot was built in 1888 (Rogers, 1973). By the time the first train with its fifteen cars arrived at the new station on August 24, 1888, the town already had an academy, several stores, a church, depot, and many residences. One year later, a citizen wrote to the *Daily Times Enterprise* of Thomasville: "I tell you, Metcalf is on a regular boom. Cotton is coming right along, and trade is picking up every day. We're bound to be a live town. No mistake about it." And for at least two decades, his prediction was true. Older citizens of Metcalf today remember when Metcalf was a center for commerce and agricultural trade, when bales of cotton were lined up along the railroad tracks as far as the eye could see on both ends of town.

Metcalf was named for Dr. John T. Metcalf, a New Yorker, who, like many other wealthy Northerners, spent his winters in Thomas County. He was a tireless promoter of the area's resources. The *Daily Times Enterprise* of January, 1890, referred to him as a "cultivated gentleman, famous surgeon and physician, the Nimrod of his profession and the firm friend of Thomasville."

By 1889, Metcalf was large enough to justify a section in the *Daily Times Enterprise* devoted to "Items from Metcalf" and later, in 1890, "Metcalf Musings." The opening of new stores and the construction of residences in Metcalf was chronicled in that journal. It noted the completion of the

Depot, Metcalf, Georgia

Commercial Area, Metcalf, Georgia

new Baptist church in 1889, which is still standing and is one of the best extant structures of early Metcalf. By December of 1889, the newspaper noted that "We need only a barber shop and bank, and Metcalf would be pretty well able to take care of herself." In 1889, the town was incorporated and, in 1890, the corporate limits were defined. Agriculture and timber were the mainstays of Metcalf's commercial business. Rail service there made Metcalf a center for shipping these products. The main agricultural products were cotton, watermelons, and pears; still standing is a large cotton gin in the center of town.

Church, Metcalf, Georgia

The town continued to grow until the early twentieth century. Some of the best extant buildings there today indicate from their construction dates that the town was still expanding as late as 1906, when the bank was built. Soon after this date, however, several factors came into play that led to Metcalf's decline. Nearby Thomasville, only ten miles away, was the county seat and center of population. Thomasville offered more attractions for winter residents, a larger railroad complex, and had a 60-year head start, having been incorporated in 1825. It soon outpaced Metcalf, and Metcalf residents moved there. For example, Truman Holland built his residence in Metcalf in 1900 and in 1916 began banking operations there. Within a few years, however, he moved his home and business to Thomasville, where the Commercial Bank of Thomasville, which began in Metcalf, still flourishes. The frequency of rail service to Metcalf declined, bringing decreased trade, merchandising, and population. What had once been a promising "boom" town was, by the 1920's, a mere shadow of its former self.

Today, a few commercial buildings, homes of early residents, the Baptist church, and the depot remain as reminders of Metcalf's heyday. Notable among these structures is the Rushin-Willet House, built in 1890 by J. M. Rushin. Rushin was said to be "one of the successful men of Metcalf" with a "fine farm a few miles south." The Crenshaw-Thomas House, circa 1890, was built by this family

Victorian Cottage, Metcalf, Georgia

when they moved to Metcalf in 1890 to open a shop opposite the depot. After a short stay, they sold their house to the Futch family, who, prior to 1895, sold it to the Copeland family. Isobel Copeland Thomas was born there in 1895 and has lived there since that date. The now dilapidated Horne Cotton Gin, built circa 1900, still stands.

The Metcalf historic district includes the residential and commercial areas of Metcalf, Georgia. The thirty-five significant structures in this district date from 1887 to 1920 and consist of representatives of the late Victorian era. They are simple versions of what one usually envisions as Victorian, but they do possess many features of the Queen Anne Style and some of the Eastlake Style. In addition, the district contains twelve structures considered intrusions because of their recent construction dates, but they do not destroy the integrity of the district.

The focal point of this railroad town is the Metcalf depot. Built in 1887-88, the depot, like most of Metcalf's buildings, is constructed of the longleaf yellow pine that is native to the area but is now a rare building material. It is a typical "railroad style" structure with its overhanging roof supported by brackets and was built according to specifications of Plan A of the Atlantic Coastline Railroad's *Type Book of Designs for Buildings*. The original four rooms included a passenger room, two offices, and, on the south side, a freight room with an uncovered loading platform that is no longer there. Freight floors are constructed of two-inch planks with one-inch tongue and groove in the passenger and freight offices. Walls and ceiling are made of one-inch tongue and groove beaded paneling although much of the wall paneling is gone. The roof is tin and the exterior is pine board and batten, originally painted yellow, with saw tooth molding along the barge board cornice and a Maltese cross design in the angle of the gable. The single chimney has four-foot brick walls and a brick corbeled cap three inches above the ridge. A semi-hexagon bay faces the tracks from the passenger area. The building was deteriorated, but restoration began in October of 1977 and has been completed.

The Baptist church, built in 1889-90, features a saw tooth molding similar to that on the depot and other structures in Metcalf. It is a two-story, frame building with a front gable. The gable is ornamented with pierced, elongated saw tooth molding along a barge board while the eave itself has a short, more delicate saw tooth molding. Windows are long-paned, two over two with plain pedimented windows on the first floor. Three windows with small four over four lights on front façade of the second floor receive no special treatment. The six-panel door has a plain pediment with pilasters and a four-pane transom. The steeple is situated on the ridge immediately behind the front gable. It has pedimented windows, a shingled roof, and saw tooth trim along the eave and barge board.

The Rushin-Willet House was built by J. M. Rushin in 1890, according to accounts in the Thomasville *Daily Times*. Containing seven rooms and a veranda, it is divided by a central hall with the four rooms on the right being one behind the other and projecting further toward the street than the three rooms and veranda on the left. It has many features attributed to the Queen Anne Style including a cottage bay window projecting boldly from the front right room; steep gables on the front and sides with ridge lines meeting at right angles; scroll design brackets ornamenting the porch posts; two-dimensional saw tooth gingerbread trim along the barge board and eave; and brick raised cellar with weatherboarded upper surfaces. The front door is carved with curved arch glass panels and a rectangular transom. The windows are two over two lights and the roof is tin. The floor plan and overall exterior effect is similar to Design XI, Cottage for a Country Clergyman by A. J. Downing. The rooms all have beaded wainscoting and ceilings and have carved mantels of longleaf yellow pine.

The Crenshaw-Thomas House is thought to have been built circa 1890. The house is one of only two 2-story houses in the town. It is weatherboarded with one gable on each side. The upper surfaces of the gables consist of round butt shingles, and scroll brackets support the eaves. The house has a veranda on the front façade and left side and rear. The front veranda has simple Tuscan columns. A semi-hexagon bay projects from the parlor on the east side. The interior is particularly notable for its beaded wainscoting and ceiling in the side hall and for the parlor ceiling, which is an inlaid beaded ceiling in a diamond pattern. The parlor mantel is an elaborate spindle designed in the Eastlake Style. The house has a three-room side hall floor plan. Walls are plaster and wood is native longleaf yellow pine. The straight stair is flanked by a carved newel post with a round medallion on each side.

A later but notable structure is the E. T. and E. H. Horne House. A marble stone in the walkway gives the owner and building date, 1915. It is a one-story bungalow with large Tuscan columns supporting a front portico and large front gable. The gable has scroll design brackets and the two windows are actually french doors with transoms. The living room features large attached beams on the ceiling.

The main street of Metcalf is Georgia Highway 122, called Reynolds Street. On the west side are four commercial buildings and a one room "courthouse" and the site of the former jail, which was behind the courthouse. The two extant frame buildings may date to 1888, but, more likely, they date to 1900, shortly after a fire destroyed many early stores. Two other stores are brick. The most southerly one was the first bank building and features a pressed tin ceiling and a vault room whose entrance is framed by ornate Corinthian pilasters. A large brick building on the corner of Reynolds and Broad Streets has fine brick detailing in a saw tooth design above the windows and a low gable with a frame surface. The door is six panel and windows and doors have segmental arches. On the east side of Reynolds, in addition to the depot, are two frame warehouses and the Horne Cotton Gin, a deteriorated two-story frame structure dating from circa 1900 (Thomasville Landmarks, Inc. Files).

Glasgow

The East Glasgow (14th) district in Thomas County was a farming community with Scottish settlers arriving here in 1826. Among them were Thomas W. Lewis and William Vaughn, settlers originating from North Carolina. Over several years these gentlemen jointly acquired 1,680 acres, property used primarily for cotton cultivation. These holdings were named Easterlin Plantation for Lewis's wife Susie L. Easterlin Lewis (Thomas County Deed Books, Grantor, 1826-1910).

Commercial Property, Metcalf, Georgia

The Glasgow district retained its rural identity, and by 1908, the community contained little more than the Sanctum Church and a crossroad store at the intersection of U.S. 19 and the Thomasville-Monticello Road (Twelve-Mile Post Road). By 1939, the district's large landholdings had been divided into black-owned or occupied farms, and many tenant dwellings dotted the roadway. While most of these buildings are gone today, the rural character remains (Map, Thomas County, Georgia).

GRADY COUNTY

Cairo, Georgia, was founded in the late 1860's when representatives of the Atlantic and Gulf Railroad began purchasing right-of-way from Thomasville to Bainbridge. This portion of Southwest Georgia, although inhabited, had been slow to develop. In the region west of the Ochlocknee River, yeoman farmers with few or no slaves populated the area. It contained a number of settlements, pockets of development known as Calvary, Tired Creek, Sofkee, Whigham, Beachton, Duncanville, and Pine Park. However, Cairo's future town site remained farm and woodland until the railroad arrived late in the 1860's (Grady, 1983).

By June 14, 1880, Cairo boasted fifty-five households within a half-mile radius of the rail bed. This community had only a handful of stores along Broad Street, but due to its location on the rail line and the intersection of several regional roads, Cairo became the trade center for this portion of Thomas County.

By 1904, Cairo and its neighboring community of Whigham each contained a population of several hundred people. Adjacent settlements, Pine Park to the east, Calvary and Duncanville to the south, and Akridge to the north, continued as community centers, although none of these developments had the good fortune to be located on the railroad (*Messenger Historical*, 1967).

As Cairo's importance to these communities developed, a movement to carve a new county from the western portion of Thomas and the eastern section of Decatur County began (Decatur County Deed Books). Demands for a new county were legitimate as it was often inconvenient, if not impossible, to transact business or legal affairs in either Thomasville or Bainbridge. Efforts in forming a new county originally began in 1875. For a considerable period these attempts were unsuccessful. The booster spirit was strong, however, and in 1903, the *Cairo Messenger* mounted an almost weekly campaign for the establishment of a new county with Cairo as the site of the county seat although at this particular time in its history, Cairo lacked a municipal water supply, electricity, and masonry school buildings. These efforts finally proved successful, and Grady County was formed on January 1, 1906. Cairo was selected as the seat of county government. The new county was named for Henry W. Grady, the Georgia journalist who advocated modern agricultural practices and the development of local resources in planning a prosperous future for the South (*Messenger Historical*, 1967).

While Grady County's history did not officially begin until 1906, events occurring before that date set the stage for development occurring later in the nineteenth century.

Southwest Georgia did not experience the physical destruction of the Civil War. However, this portion of Georgia was not exempt from economic hardship that prevailed during the years of Reconstruction.

Very little currency circulated during this time in South Georgia, and in the July 12, 1865, edition of the *Thomasville Enterprise*, the following advertisement appeared:

> Due to the scarcity of paper, the paper will now be $1.00 per annum. It may be paid in: money, flour, sweet potatoes, bacon, pork, Irish potatoes, corn, butter, tallow, etc.

With no currency and even less available credit, many Thomas County farmers were forced to borrow money to purchase seed and fertilizer. Other local farmers found themselves mortgaging future crops to purchase farm supplies. In either arrangement, the advent of bad weather or low prices brought financial ruin to many farm families. The end of this destructive cycle began a tradition of share-cropping and tenant farming (Banks, 1905).

Thomas County, along with those in other agrarian Southern states, found itself purchasing high priced supplies from Northern states and selling cotton to England for a low price established in the port city of Liverpool. From 1870 to 1900, land in the South averaged less than $15 annually per acre. In 1878, cotton sold for $.10 per pound, and in 1898, for $.05. These financial conditions encouraged the growth of the Agrarian Movement, which was strongly supported in the area later to become Grady County (Rogers, 1973).

The Patrons of Husbandry, or the Grange, was organized nationally in 1867 by Oliver H. Kelly, a clerk employed by the Agricultural Department in Washington, DC. Kelly's intent in creating the Grange was to provide social, economic, and educational opportunity for America's farming families. The concept spread rapidly across the South, and by 1875 membership in the Cairo Grange reached one hundred. Additional organizations in South Georgia were formed in Duncanville, the Glasgow district, and in Boston.

The Cairo Grange, though short-lived, did meet with some measure of success. Lead locally by Peter Vanlandingham, the Cairo Grange negotiated cooperative purchasing agreements. Cairo's grange remained a non-political body although a local patron believed it "morally impossible that such an association of the very best men of the land...should grow...without materially influencing the conduct of nation, state, and local matters." By 1881, Grady County lacked a central agricultural organization. Since the Grady County Grange did not represent the mass of farmers (it had few if any share croppers) and did not limit membership to those involved directly with agriculture, the organization closed its doors in late 1880.

Several years later, in 1908, the Farmers Union became active in local agricultural issues. Lead by T. M. Whigham and J. A. Wynn, this locally based organization strove to "aid farmers in a financial way, make them more fraternal, and stir up the farmers to a sense of duty in educating their children." A co-operative for tobacco growers was organized in 1908. It was also in this year that the Farmers Union initiated plans to build a warehouse in Cairo. The warehouse was constructed in 1909 and managed by S. P. Vanlandingham. W. B. Roddenbery, speaking at a Union meeting, advised, "Grow crops you can grow more profitably and leave off cotton..." (Brooks, 1914).

The cotton market continued to fluctuate with the commodity selling for 12¼ cents per pound in 1911. Farmers predicted the arrival of the boll weevil in 1912, although the insect did not appear until 1915. With the boll weevil's arrival, Grady County's cotton crop was cut by one-third. Grady County, along with adjoining counties, found itself quarantined from the remainder of the state. Citizen committees and agricultural groups met to begin attempts at fighting the insect. Recommendations for improving these circumstances ranged from "cutting cotton acreage by twenty per cent and planting other crops" to organizing a live stock association which advocated raising livestock and grain (Devine, 1979).

Problems with the boll weevil continued in 1916, with 75 percent of Grady County's farmland infested. Farmers attempted to diversify, producing sugar cane, sweet potatoes, rice, and shade tobacco.

Although Grady County was a major producer of cotton, the county was also known for its production of sugar cane syrup. By 1914, Cairo had become the nation's second largest producer of cane syrup. Due to this level of production, Congress authorized the establishment of a sugar cane experiment station with an initial appropriation of $10,000. In December, 1914, the *Cairo Messenger* reported, "on Saturday 1,200 barrels of syrup were sold in Cairo putting $12,000 in circulation and making it the busiest day of the year." A 1915 edition of the *Cairo Messenger* reported a listing of deposits for the following banks: Farmers and Merchants — $83,000, Cairo Banking — $146,000, and Citizen's Bank — $171,000. By 1917, the three banks totalled one million dollars in deposits (Rogers, 1973).

The packing of "patch cane" syrup was started on a large scale in Cairo by W. B. (Walter Blair) Roddenbery who in 1890 developed a family farm and mercantile into a major food production industry. By 1920, other food items were added and the W. B. Roddenbery Company was born. The family's syrup was so well received that in 1906, Roddenbery Cane Syrup was awarded a medal for excellence at the St. Louis World's Fair. Three years later, the product won a gold medal at the Jamestown Exhibition. Today, the W. B. Roddenbery Company employs five hundred workers and markets its products nationwide. However, the Roddenbery family's contribution to Cairo's development has involved much more than industry.

Seaborn Anderson Roddenbery was born in Thomas County on February 18, 1836, and died in Cairo on September 23, 1896. Although trained as a medical doctor, he opened a store in "the Village" (later Cairo) in 1867. In 1872, he became Cairo's third mayor and was appointed postmaster of the new Cairo post office by President U. S. Grant (Roddenbery, 1991).

Roddenbery's interests continued into education when, with his contemporary William Ayden Powell, Sr., the two gentlemen became Cairo's "pioneer board of education." Together, they persuaded Robert H. Harris, a former Confederate officer, to move to Cairo as master of the Cairo Academy.

W. B. Roddenbery, son of Seaborn Roddenbery, led the fight in the creation of Grady County. In 1906, he was elected to the newly organized Grady County Board of Commissioners and served as that body's first chairman. During his term of office, the commissioners organized the county and constructed the county's jail and courthouse. Roddenbery did not seek reelection (Thurston, 1979).

W. B. Roddenbery was among the first to advocate agricultural diversity. He was recognized for the following point of view: "What can be produced in this section can also be processed and the economic well being of Grady County and this area depends upon the operation of plants designed to utilize the raw products of the farm."

While the county's industrial and educational needs were met very early on, Grady County's roadways left something to be desired. Badly rutted and poorly cleared roads became a Grady County tradition. In 1910, during an automobile tour sponsored by the *Atlanta Constitution*, the *Augusta Chronicle*, and *Macon Telegraph* reported, "On reaching the Grady County line, no sign was needed. The line across Grady was the worst on the tour, the people of this County having had to erect a Court House and bear the other expenses incident to the joys of living in a new county..." (Rogers, 1973).

The legacy of poor roadways continued, and in 1911, the county commission set priorities for those roads requiring repair. The use of convicts in road repair and the requirement that all men sixteen to fifty contribute time to road repair helped in a small way to improve the situation. The September grand jury gave the road commissioners twelve months to correct poor road conditions. They specifically cited the Swamp Creek bridge on the Calvary-Bainbridge Road, the Sofkee Creek bridge on the Hawthorn Trail, the Lime Sink bridge, which had been condemned, and the Cairo-Whigham road. The Duncanville-Pine Park road was deemed "hardly passable" since stumps within the roadbed needed to be removed. Cairo's Broad Street fared no better when area farmers threatened to market their produce elsewhere as the deep sand on Broad Street entrapped heavily loaded wagons. Cairo's city council did respond and passed local legislation authorizing street paving with assessments made to adjoining property owners.

Road problems were finally settled in 1919 when Cairo voters passed a $14,000 bond issue to pave Broad from Mott Street south to Ochlocknee. One block of Bryan Street and Central Avenue were also included.

In that same year, the Grady County Commission passed a $250,000 bond issue and acquired a matching share from the federal government. E. D. Rivers (future Georgia governor) and C. E. Mauldin headed this successful campaign (*Messenger Historical*, 1967).

Grady County received its second train service in 1908 when the Pelham and Havana (P. & H.) Railroad established rail service. Known locally as the "Pore and Hungry," the P. & H. provided service from Cairo to Havana, Florida. The train lacked a turntable and consisted of an engine, one passenger car, and several freight cars. Rail service never extended north of Cairo to Pelham.

Early in 1924, the Georgia and Florida Public Service Commissions conducted a public hearing and recommended the P. & H. be junked. The receiver's sale was held in June, 1924 with Turner Supply Company of Mobile, Alabama, purchasing the system for $35,000. The rails, locomotives, and additional equipment were removed as "junk."

In April, 1917, the United States declared war on Germany. June 5, 1917 was declared draft registration day and designated a local holiday by Mayor A. W. Miller. Registration was held in the county's ten polling precincts with "every male between eighteen and thirty, single or married, sick or well, black or white" expected to register. A total of 1,499 Grady County men registered for the draft, including "three jailmen and seventeen convicts."

Grady County participated in all Liberty Bond drives, starting each effort with courthouse speeches, bell ringing and whistle blowing. Sunday school classes contributed "castaway clothing" to "suffering Belgians," and the Cairo Methodist Church held a "flag raising service" to honor young men fighting "for democracy in the World War." Negro citizens held a Fourth of July War Savings Stamps march from the courthouse to the A.M.E. Church; they heard a speech from Prof. H. H. Holder on "Why We Celebrate the Fourth," and a "glowing tribute to Negroes for loyalty" by Judge R. C. Bell. The Grady County Medical Society volunteered en masse, and an officer from Fort McPherson was sent to examine the doctors (Rogers, 1979).

With the war ending on November 11, 1918, the *Cairo Messenger's* November 15 headline read, "Great World War Is Won By The Allies." The story reveals, "United in a great spontaneous outburst of joy...expressed...with shouts and song, the parades of both young and old, the blowing of horns, firing of cannon crackers,...the blowing of the fire whistle and all other whistles, the fire truck making round after round of the city, liked to have never wore its ardor out in Cairo last Monday."

In late 1918, an influenza epidemic hit Grady County, as it did much of the nation. In October, schools and churches were closed. Superior and city court sessions were suspended and the Red Cross annual meeting postponed. After reopening for a week in November, schools and all public places were again closed by proclamation until January 1, 1919. The epidemic resulted in thirteen deaths in Grady County.

The 1920's were prosperous years for Grady County. Local newspapers made little mention of the Great Depression until 1931, when Rev. J. P. Swann wrote in the *Messenger*, "The world is on wheels on the installment plan." A Chamber of Commerce survey revealed "that local business was off 18.3 percent." It was also in 1931 that several local stores refused to extend credit and sold items on a cash only basis (*Messenger Historical*, 1967).

Local governments took steps to help mitigate the crisis. Both city and county commissions reduced taxes one mill and cut salaries by 10 to 20 percent. The city reduced the electrical rate by 10 percent while the county stopped all bridge construction.

On December 1, 1931, "after seven hours of deliberation, the Board of Directors" of the Citizen's Bank decided "to close the institution" and notified the public, "This bank has placed its assets under control of the State Superintendent of Banks." The bank's cashier, who was not responsible for the institution's failure, committed suicide. In January, 1933, Grady County lost a second financial institution when the Farmers and Merchants Bank was liquidated.

In April, 1933, one hundred and fifty Grady Countians eighteen to twenty-five applied for forty positions allotted the county for Civilian Conservation Corps (CCC) service. Four hundred and fifty-five citizens were employed at thirty hours per week on the Civil Works Administration's (CWA) streets and roads project. In December, 1933, the CWA pledged to expend $15,000 in Grady County to exterminate rats. Only thirteen local people declined to sign the National Recovery Act (NRA) consumer card, and by August, "The Blue Eagle of the NRA had spread literally over this entire community" (*Grady*, 1983).

By 1934, Cairo recognized the need for a new post office. Funding was allocated through the Public Works Administration (PWA). However, funds were stopped by "a little under-secretary of the PWA" who stated Cairo did "not need a post office building." In June, 1934, Congressman Cox and Senator George "defied PWA officials" by specifically earmarking construction funds in a "deficiency appropriation." The building was completed in 1935.

In August, 1935, the Cairo city council decided to replace all street names except Broad and Railroad with numbers. The *Cairo Messenger* reflected, "No more will Cairo streets signify pioneer families; no more will the names given certain streets by the city's earliest settlers, such as Decatur, Mitchell, Pearce, Ochlocknee, and Wight be used" (*Historical Messenger*, 1967).

ESTATES AND PLANTATIONS

The Birdwood Estate

Thomas College (the former estate of William Cameron Forbes) is located in Thomasville, Georgia, at the intersection of Millpond Road and Pinetree Boulevard. Designed in the Georgian Revival style, the property was originally known as Birdwood. The Birdwood estate was built in 1931-32 for Forbes (1870-1959) of Boston, Massachusetts. A grandson of Ralph Waldo Emerson, Forbes performed public diplomatic service for the United States in several capacities.

In 1902, President Theodore Roosevelt asked Forbes to work with the building of the Panama Canal, but, before arrangements were completed, a vacancy occurred on the Philippine Commission. In filling that vacancy in 1904, he became the secretary of commerce and police in the Philippines in addition to holding a seat on the commission. In 1908, he became vice-governor there, and President William H. Taft, also a Republican, appointed him governor general in 1909. Forbes opposed Filipino independence and worked hard to develop the islands' economy. He also concentrated on the Philippines' infra-structure by improving transportation, working with its problems in disease control, and promoting foreign investment in the islands. Politically, Forbes began to lose favor in the Philippines because of his opposition to independence. With the inauguration of Woodrow Wilson, a Democrat, as president in 1913, he was asked to resign. Returning to business, he served as a consultant and director of many companies, and was receiver of the Brazil Railway Company between 1914 and 1919. He never lost interest in the Philippines, and in 1921 President Warren G. Harding chose him to serve with General Leonard Wood in investigating the American administration of the

Administrative Building, Thomas College (Formerly Birdwood Estate)

islands during Wilson's presidency. In 1928, he published a book entitled *The Philippine Islands*, a political and developmental history of the American period.

In 1930, President Herbert Hoover appointed Forbes to head a commission for studying conditions in Haiti. Pleased with the results, Hoover appointed him ambassador to Japan, a position he held between June, 1930 and April, 1932. It was during this period that he planned his estate in Thomasville, Georgia. Forbes agreed to remain in Japan for only a year and a half, and at the end of that time, Secretary of State Stinson accepted his resignation due to differences in opinion regarding American policy in Japan.

During the 1930's, Forbes was chairman of the executive committee and the board of trustees of the Carnegie Institute of Washington. In 1935, he headed the American Economic Mission to the Far East, a study group sponsored by the National Foreign Trade Council.

During his years in the Philippines, Forbes became acquainted with Robb and Placidia White. Mr. White was a clergyman in the Protestant Episcopal church, and Mrs. White was an avid polo player. It was this shared enthusiasm for polo which apparently cultivated their friendship. In 1922, White became rector of Saint Thomas Episcopal Church in Thomasville. Forbes' visit there led to this choice of Thomasville for his seasonal residence. He subsequently introduced polo to Thomasville. He imported some players but also used some local ones. Some teams came from colleges and military bases. After he left Thomasville, polo died out as an activity.

Forbes was a polo player of international caliber. He wrote a manual in 1911 entitled *As to Polo* which by 1950 had sold 6,000 copies and was considered the authoritative guide to the game. Forbes' Thomasville estate included both regulation and practice fields. Stables housed his ponies,

Administration Building, Thomas College (Rear)

and a pony hospital was erected across Pinetree Boulevard off the nominated property. The main house had six guest rooms to accommodate a polo team or other visitors while in Thomasville. Forbes stayed at Birdwood, his permanent seasonal home, during late fall and winter, often from October through March. During the rest of the year he lived in Massachusetts.

Birdwood was designed by the architectural firm of Shepard and Stearns of Boston, Massachusetts. The plans were drawn in 1930 but were not implemented until 1932 when Forbes was planning to return from Japan. The architectural landscape firm of Stiles and Van Kleek of Boston and St. Petersburg, which had done the adjacent Glen Arven Country Club in 1930, planned the grounds which included woods, open space, and the polo area. In 1946, Forbes deeded 6.21 acres on the north end of his property to Placidia White. In 1950, he sold his remaining 45.8 acres at Birdwood, which included the main house and polo grounds, to Greene W. Alday. B. L. Brewton bought the property in the same year with intentions of developing the land into a subdivision.

The Primitive Baptist Church had been planning the establishment of a denominational college since 1947. By 1950, the plans had progressed to the point of securing a site. Macon, Columbus, and Waycross were all considered, but Thomasville was finally selected due to the availability of the Birdwood estate, deemed adaptable to the needs of the college. J. Harley Chapman, S. A. Chastain, and James F. Pettigrew, all of Thomas County, signed a security deed for the property in November, 1950, and the establishment of Birdwood College proceeded. Although they hoped to open for enrollment as early as 1951, the college did not begin classes until the fall of 1954.

Birdwood College struggled from the beginning. It had limited support from the Primitive Baptist church, and though initial community support from the citizens of Thomasville was strong, it started to wane by the 1970's. Lack of accreditation was one factor that contributed to its struggle through the years. In January, 1976, the State Board of Education certified "that Birdwood Junior College had met the standard requirements prescribed by regulation of the State Board of Education for Georgia colleges issuing diplomas and conferring degrees of Associate in Liberal Arts, General Education, Business Administration and Future Teachers in this State."

By the 1970's, sentiment in the community began leaning toward the establishment of a state-operated junior college in Thomasville. Late in 1973, a bond issue to support such an institution was presented to the voters of Thomas County, but failed 3,066 to 3,159. The state junior college subsequently was placed in Bainbridge.

Realizing that they needed community-wide support in order to survive, Birdwood officials decided to convert the institution into a community college. This decision meant gradually giving up ties with the Primitive Baptists. One of the first steps toward this end was changing the name in August, 1976, to Thomas County Community College, Inc.

Since 1976, the college has made the transition from a denominational school to a private four-year college. The physical campus is relatively intact from the days of Cameron Forbes, and the main house now serves as the administration building (Thomasville Landmarks, Inc. Files).

Melrose House and Sinkola Plantation

Melrose House and Sinkola Plantation are located 3.75 miles southwest of Thomasville, Georgia on either side of U.S. Highway 319, the Thomasville to Tallahassee Road. They comprise one historic estate, developed between the 1820's and the 1980's. A series of owners, all of whom played important roles in the history of Thomas County, contributed to the development of the complex.

The estate consists of two major groupings of structures on both sides of a major highway; it has over fifty buildings of varying styles, all of which were designed to be compatible with the original structure, the main house of Melrose. Uses fall into three main categories: residential, agricultural, and recreational.

Architecturally, the buildings fall into several categories. The Greek Revival style can be identified in the original part of the Coalson-Wyche House. Elements of this style reflected in this house are the central hall plan, entrance door with sidelights and transom, and the symmetrical massing. The Georgian Revival style is found in the additions to the main house and the large number of twentieth-century outbuildings. Elements of this style include the use of brick, porticos, and a symmetry of form. Many of the buildings on the plantations show a mixture of these styles. Residential buildings are made predominantly of wood while agricultural structures are brick, although exceptions exist. Both of the two main groupings of buildings are arranged around large main dwelling houses with complementary service buildings. Informal roads were planned with the service buildings lining them on both sides.

The first grouping centers on the main historic house of Melrose House and is located on the northwest side of the Tallahassee Road. An antebellum structure that was greatly expanded around the turn of the twentieth century, this house is the nucleus of the plantation complex. Beside it to the southeast is a second large dwelling, Owl's Nest, which is the main house for Sinkola Plantation, dating from the 1920's. A third dwelling, Squirrel's Cottage, lies beyond it and is used as a guest house. Close to these dwellings are a pool house, wood house, and laundry. Northwest of the three main dwellings is a grouping of three cottages, a large walled garden with a greenhouse, a dairy

Main House, Sinkola Plantation

Entrance to Melrose House

house, two large garages, an office, a stable complex for horses, two small barns with a barnyard, a shop, milking barn, lunch room, pump room, theater, chicken shed, and assorted implement sheds.

The second grouping of buildings is located on the southeast side of Tallahassee Road approximately one-half mile southwest of the first complex. Its central focus is a two-story frame manager's dwelling that dates from the 1920's and faces the highway. Behind it is a complex of buildings consisting of a shop (formerly a commissary), an office, a garage, a barn, a lunch room (formerly a fuel house), cooling house, processing shed, machine shed, paint house, office (formerly a lunch room), green houses, granary, horse barn, wood house, water tank, mule barn, kennel house, kennel cook house, and various tenant dwellings. All of this complex was developed in the 1920's and 1930's.

Plantation Office, Sinkola Plantation

The natural terrain of Melrose and Sinkola Plantations consists of gently rolling and heavily wooded with virgin pine and oak. Some low swampy areas are found on the south side of Tallahassee Road, including several sink holes, from which the name "Sinkola" was derived. The elevation above sea level ranges from about 240 to 290 feet.

The property is divided into four areas:
1. the main house at Melrose, Owl's Nest, and service buildings;
2. the manager's house at Sinkola and farm buildings behind it;
3. wooded land north of Tallahassee Road;
4. wooded land south of Tallahassee Road.

The land is divided into land lots of 250 acres each. Plantation roads have no pattern of layout, but simply give access to various points around the plantation. Most roads generally lead into the two main complexes and service the various houses and service buildings. Tallahassee Road bisects the planation at an angle from Thomasville to the east, following a southwesterly path toward Beachton and Tallahassee, Florida.

Open fields for grazing of livestock can be found surrounding both main building complexes. Other fields are scattered throughout the mostly wooded land, with the primary function of serving as shooting areas for quail and other game.

Buildings in both main complexes are grouped according to function. For instance, on the north side the three main houses used as the owner's residences and their guests' quarters are relatively close together along with the pool house, laundry and wood house. The three cottages for professional plantation staff members and their families are grouped together beside the garden and green house, and near the garages, office, stables, and barns for which they were responsible.

Horse Barn, Sinkola Plantation

The building complex south of Tallahassee Road is also laid out according to function. Behind the manager's house is the office and plantation commissary (now a shop) along with various buildings for various farm machinery and equipment. Also grouped together are the horse and mule barns with their grain bin, and the dog kennels with both the cook and trainer's dwellings.

Three tenant dwellings for farm workers and their families are also grouped together near this last complex. Other similar dwellings are scattered throughout both plantations, some serving as gate houses.

The main house of Melrose was originally built of logs with four rooms and a wide hall or breezeway. The house was weatherboarded by the mid-nineteenth-century with the long veranda across the front.

Around the turn of the twentieth century, the east wing was constructed with compatible design, scale, and proportion. The west wing followed shortly thereafter, and a two-story guest house with bowling alley was connected to the rear by a covered walkway. This last addition was removed by the mid-twentieth-century. The central, original section of the house can be described as a vernacular plantation farm house with gabled roof and exterior brick chimneys.

Main House, Melrose House

Beginning in the 1930's, many other buildings were constructed for varying purposes on the plantation before it was divided by the heirs. The complex of brick structures that includes the walled vegetable garden and greenhouse, garages, office, stables, groom's cottage, mule barn, carpenter's shop, milking barn, and bull and calf barns was designed in the Georgian Revival by the Cleveland architectural firm of Walker and Weeks.

The same firm designed at least one of the four frame Colonial Revival cottages located beside this complex. The Parrish Cottage, Waldorf, Banksia Cottage, and the Squirrel's Cottage all can be described as one or one and one-half story frame dwellings built in the 1930's. The two-story manager's house at Sinkola on the south side of Tallahassee Road is very similar, but on a larger scale. It was completed earlier, in 1923, probably the first of these five houses to be built.

The Owl's Nest, which was begun in 1927 as a guest house, has been expanded several times, and now serves as the main residence of an owner. The original was designed by Walker and Weeks in the Colonial Revival style. The kitchen wing was added by the same firm in 1948, along with the first two rear bedrooms. The sunken living room to the left of the front door was designed by another Cleveland architectural firm, Schafer, Flynn, and Williams, and added in 1960. Other small additions and remodelings have been made frequently at Owl's Nest including the rear bedroom/office suite, the patios, and a kitchen expansion and remodelling as recently as 1984.

Cattle Barn, Office Complex, Melrose House

The plantation farm buildings and tenant dwellings are all similar simple frame structures with either weatherboard or board and batten siding. Most are relatively small, and their design reflects the use for which they were intended.

Two additional recreational buildings on the plantations are Showboat and the Pool House. Showboat is a large frame building with wide weatherboard siding and a highly decorated porch in-antis. Designed to resemble a showboat on a river, this building was used as a theater for both motion pictures and live productions. The interior includes a stage with dressing rooms on either side. In the balcony is a projection booth. The interior walls are made of pecky cypress. A small bridge spanning a goldfish pond gives access to the front porch.

The pool house is a large brick and steel structure housing a heated swimming pool. The structure contains both men's and women's dressing rooms, a bar, sitting area with fireplace, and a full sized pool. All floors are tiled, and the structure has a translucent fiberglass roof and a series of sliding glass doors overlooking a large courtyard. The courtyard is surrounded by a high brick wall and is sown in grass with large bushes planted on the front nearest to the highway.

The nature of a Southwest Georgia shooting plantation requires that it have a well managed, mature pine and oak forest, although many other varieties of trees may grow there. This is the case with Melrose and Sinkola, where annual burnings and selective cutting for timber keep the underbrush low, creating an ideal habitat for propagating bobwhite quail.

In contrast, the areas around the main houses are highly landscaped with formal boxwood gardens and well manicured grass lawns. The grounds off the main house at Melrose feature a sunken rose garden dating from the early twentieth century, a large reflection pool with goldfish, and the old

The Show Boat, Melrose House

Pool House, Melrose House

Wyche family cemetery, overgrown with English ivy. Adjacent fields for horse grazing are enclosed with a wooden plank fence, and large live oaks form a canopy over the drive leading to the main house. Similar trees line the drive through the vegetable garden, stables, cottages, and Showboat. A magnolia-lined drive giving direct access to the Owl's Nest from Tallahassee Road is a relatively recent landscape feature.

The manager's house at Sinkola, on the south side of Tallahassee Road, is less elaborately landscaped, although a formal boxwood hedge is planted between the front gate on the highway and the house. Its accompanying farm buildings to the rear are not landscaped other than being surrounded by well-kept grass lawns. Drives giving access to this complex from the main highway are sunken sand roads cut through the natural forest.

Manager's House, Sinkola Plantation

The archaeological potential is unknown. At least ten slave dwellings were located on the antebellum plantation, but their locations are not known. An earlier stable existed where Showboat was later built. The guest house with a bowling alley formerly attached to the main house was located a few yards from the north beyond the present porte cochere.

Melrose and Sinkola represent an important aspect of the history of Thomas County from its earliest settlement to the present. Beginning as one large cotton plantation, the house and land have also sheltered refugees during the Civil War, displaced Southerners following that war, and Northern industrialists and their descendants who have used it as a seasonal residence, farm, and hunting preserve since the 1890's. Most recently, a portion, including the old main house and its service buildings, has served as a residence and convalescent retreat for a local plastic surgeon and his patients.

The plantation originally consisted of 1,500 acres, or six land lots of 250 acres each, purchased and assembled by Henry Wyche by 1839. This acreage was kept essentially intact until the twentieth century when a new owner, H. M. Hanna and his descendants, began to expand their holdings to increase the area available for wildlife propagation.

The antebellum house, which is presently absorbed in the expanded twentieth-century house, dates back to the earliest ownership. Paul Coalson (1797-1830), a lawyer, came to Thomas County when it was established in 1825. He was from Pulaski County, and, after graduating from college, returned there to marry Elizabeth Blackshear (1805-1853) in 1823. Her parents, Edward and Emily Mitchell Blackshear, were also among the earliest and most prominent settlers of Thomas County, her father establishing himself at Cedar Grove (now Susina Plantation) in Thomas (now Grady) County. Her brother married a sister of the man who built Greenwood Plantation, also in Thomas County, and her uncle, Richard Mitchell, established Fair Oaks Plantation.

Coalson's assemblage of land from 1825-1830 consisted of half the historic acreage, making a total of 750 acres, for which he $730, less than $1 per acre. At his death, he owned fourteen slaves, various livestock, and many bales of cotton. Family tradition holds that Coalson built the original antebellum plantation house during his brief ownership of land lot 237, very close to land lot 236, which he actually purchased in 1825. Since he did not actually own lot 237 at the time of his death, the house apparently was built across the lot line by error.

Mrs. Elizabeth Coalson, after being widowed for five years, remarried in 1835 to her first cousin, Henry Wyche (1812-after 1862), also from Pulaski County. She had four more children by him. Wyche's brother owned the original plantation where Mill Pond is located today and two of his sisters were each married (at different times) to Hardy Bryan, one of the wealthiest men in the area and whose historic home survives in Thomasville and is also in the national register.

Under the Wyche ownership, the plantation was expanded to include 750 more acres, so that by 1839 he had assembled the original 1,500 acre tract. If the extant antebellum house had not been built by 1830 when Coalson died, then it very likely was by 1840. In that year, Wyche reported having 32 slaves. By 1850, he had 48 slaves and by 1860, 54, with ten slave dwellings. The 1860 agricultural census indicates that half the land was improved. The farm had various livestock and produced Indian corn, oats, rice, and 65 bales of ginned cotton at 400 pounds per bale, plus peas, beans, Irish potatoes, and butter.

Mrs. Elizabeth Blackshear Coalson Wyche died in 1853. Wyche then married Artemisia Lester and had three more children. When he offered the plantation for sale in 1857, the advertisement shed some light on the extant structures, for in the ad he mentioned a ginhouse and screw, outbuildings (not specified), and a "good comfortable dwelling house," and lots of fruit trees.

As the Civil War began, the Wyches decided to sell their plantation and did so on August 26, 1862 to William R. G. Gignilliat, a coastal planter from McIntosh County. He moved to Thomas County to escape the raids and ravages of the war as it came to the Georgia coast and continued to practice rice cultivation, something he also practiced on the coast. He quickly became a prominent member of local society.

While he may have escaped the direct attacks of the war, Gignilliat did not escape its effects. At the end of the war, in 1864, the Confederate government impressed 10,000 bushels of corn from his Thomas County plantation, and after the surrender at Appomattox, he was also relieved of 191 pounds of bacon.

After the war, Gignilliat resorted to sharecropping, hiring back the former slaves and paying them to work by sharing the products of the harvest with them. If he provided rations, he gave them only one third of the crop; if they fed themselves, then they got half the crop. This new system of contract farming was conducted under the auspices of the Federal Bureau of Refugees, Freedmen and Abandoned Lands.

On January 1, 1869, Gignilliat sold the 1,500 acre plantation to another coastal Georgia refugee, Dr. Samuel John Jones (1838-1889) of Liberty County, who fled the military aggression after the war. After his marriage and medical training, Jones had returned to Liberty County to practice until 1863, when he entered Confederate military service. While on sick leave during the war, he journeyed to Thomasville with his family and Professor Joseph LeConte, a famous Liberty Countian. At that point, he purchased the Coalson-Wyche Plantation.

The 1870 census agricultural schedule indicates Jones had 750 acres of cleared land and 750 acres of woodland, still keeping the plantation at its 1,500 acre antebellum size. The number of workers and the produce was down from pre-war levels. He raised 1,000 bushels of Indian corn, 50 bushels of oats, and no rice. Only eight bales of cotton were ginned, down considerably from the days of pre-war, slave-based cotton farming.

Conditions no doubt improved gradually as Reconstruction was lifted and Jones, along with other Southerners, learned to cope with the new society. His first wife, Mary Hayes, died in 1877, and he remarried in 1878 to Mar Elizabeth "Lizzie" Mueller. He died in 1889.

On January 15, 1891, Mrs. Lizzie Jones, the widow, sold the plantation, now 1,328 acres to Charles M. Chapin of Bergen County, New Jersey. Chapin was a son of Salome M. Hanna (1844-1907) and her first husband, George W. Chapin (1837-1884). She had remarried in 1886 to J. Wyman Jones (1822-1906), founder of Englewood, New Jersey, and a wealthy businessman. Shortly after their marriage, they began coming to Thomasville to spend the winters in the milder climate of Southwest Georgia. Jones purchased the old McIntyre place on Lower Cairo Road in 1888 and assembled the wooded park on Old Monticello Road that in 1895 became Glen Arven Country Club.

Charles Merrill Chapin (1871-1932) suffered poor health as a teenager and had come to Bainbridge, Georgia, near Thomasville, with a tutor, in the 1880's. Not satisfied, he followed advice that he try Thomasville, forty miles to the east, and was much happier. After his mother and step-father acquired land there, he offered to buy Elsoma from his parents as his own winter residence. When his parents declined, he then purchased the Coalson-Wyche-Jones place in 1891.

The Chapin era at this property lasted only from 1891 to 1896. Chapin came primarily for his health, but he also enjoyed hunting; like many other Northerners, he purchased the plantation for both reasons. In May, 1894, he married Lili Lewis; two years later they sold this plantation and eventually purchased Elsoma, which is owned by their descendants today.

After its purchase by Howard Melville Hanna (1840-1921), the plantation was renamed "Melrose" after the new owner. Hanna was Chapin's uncle and his purchase signaled the full beginning of the new era. Hanna, a native of Columbus, Ohio, was one of four siblings who eventually owned property in Thomas County. The other three included, besides his sister Salome (discussed above), their brother, Mark Hanna (1837-1921) who entertained presidential candidate and future president William McKinley in 1895 and 1899, and another sister, Seville, and her husband, Jay C. Morse, who owned Inwood Plantation.

Mel Hanna was inclined toward business, finance, and industry instead of politics. He had been very successful in the family's business and was also connected to the original Standard Oil Company and American Tobacco Company.

In 1863, Hanna married Kate Smith from Connecticut, and they had six children, three of whom lived to maturity and continued the family's association with Thomasville. Later in 1896, Hanna purchased the nucleus of present-day Pebble Hill Plantation, which adjoins Melrose on the west. In 1901, he deeded Pebble Hill to his daughter, Kate Hanna Ireland, and gave Melrose to his son, Howard M. Hanna, Jr., reserving for himself a life estate. In 1902, he purchased Winnstead to the north of Melrose and later gave it to another daughter, Gertrude Hanna Haskell. He eventually amassed 14,000 contiguous acres, all of which is still owned today by his descendants.

Expansion began on the main house at Melrose with the help of a local contractor/builder, William Miller (1860-1936). The original core of the antebellum plantation house, essentially four large rooms with a central hall, was expanded to the northwest, creating a larger dining room and stairhall. The two rooms on the right were opened up as one large living room with two fireplaces. A porte cochere was added at the back of the hall and became the principal entrance to the house, thus changing its orientation.

By 1905, the first phase of the east wing was being added and was later expanded by 1924 to include three bedrooms and a sitting room. The west wing initially had two extra bedrooms and later two more were added. A two-story guest house, which included a bowling alley was connected to the back of the house by a covered walkway in the early twentieth century, but the walkway had been removed in the 1920's.

Landscaping around the house was not impressive when the Hannas came into possession, but extensive plantings were made in the early years, including a sunken garden at the northwest corner of the house next to the east wing (Thomasville Landmarks, Inc. Files).

Millpond Plantation

Millpond Plantation has been significant nationally and locally in several respects. It was the home of two of Thomas County's pioneer families and of some of the nation's leading financiers, industrialists and philanthropists. Its architecture represents a style unique to the area. A leading landscape architect of the period landscaped the grounds, and a noted architectural firm designed the buildings. Its twentieth-century owners were leaders in the arts, industry, economics and social service enterprises in the United States. The plantation itself has been a center for agriculture, conservation of natural resources, and wild life preservation.

Millpond Plantation, near Thomasville, originated circa 1825, just as Thomas County was being settled following the land lottery of 1820. On February 21, 1825, Thomas Clark Wyche (1801-1870) purchased from Bryan Hardy for $250 the first Millpond lot, number 51, consisting of 490 acres in the 13th District. On this land, he settled his family, including his wife, Catherine McIntyre Wyche (1809-1861), his parents, Littleton and Susannah Wyche, and ten younger brothers and sisters plus six slaves. He bought additional land in the next years, but his first lot proved of greatest value. Lot 51 was the site of his home and the "millpond" where he, and later his son-in-law, John Lanier Linton, operated their grist mill. By 1860, Wyche owned about 1,600 acres — 400 improved and 1,200 unimproved — valued at $5,000. He raised cotton, corn, livestock, sheep, and swine. The youngest child of Thomas and Catherine Wyche, Alice M. (1840-1893), married John Lanier Linton

Main House, Millpond Plantation

(1836-1908). Linton served in the Civil War and returned to Thomas County and began buying property there. Alice Wyche Linton had inherited Millpond upon her father's death in 1870 so Alice and John Linton purchased several adjoining land lots and by 1885, Millpond consisted of over 3,000 acres. It was then farmed by tenant farmers or sharecroppers. The Lintons owned extensive property in other parts of the county and in the city of Thomasville. In 1888, John Linton built a large, two-story residence on Broad Street near the courthouse. Linton also owned part of the Young Hotel and the livery stable. In 1890, Alice Linton died. Her portion of Millpond passed to her children and was divided equally among these heirs in 1891 with mill and pond privileges to be shared.

The turn of the century brought a new era to Millpond. In the years since 1875, Thomas County had gained a reputation as a winter resort. The mild climate was said to be good for one's health, and an abundance of wildlife, especially quail, provided sport for hunters. These attractions drew winter residents from New York, Cleveland, Philadelphia and other cold Northern cities — men such as Oliver H. Payne of Standard Oil, Justus Strawbridge of Philadelphia's Strawbridge and Clothier, Mark Hanna, Cleveland financier and politician, New Yorker John W. Masury of the Masury Paint Co. — the list goes on. Then, in 1903, came Jeptha Homer Wade.

Wade was a Cleveland financier and philanthropist. He was the grandson of another Jeptha H. Wade (1811-1890), the first president of Western Union Telegraph Company. Wade was born in Cleveland on October 15, 1857, the son of Randall P. and Anna McGaw Wade. In 1880, he married Ellen Garrettson of Cleveland, and they subsequently had three children, Jeptha H., Jr., George Garrettson and Helen. Wade's many business ventures included serving as owner and president of Wade Realty Company, president of Montreal Mining Company, and director of the Union Trust Company, Guardian Trust Company, Grasselli Chemical Company, Sandusky Cement Company, Cleveland Cliffs Iron

Entry Way, Millpond Plantation

Company, National Refining Company, Baker R and L Company and the Cleveland Stone Company.

His philanthropic endeavors were directed toward the Wade Benevolent Fund, the Community Fund, Lakeside Hospital, the Cleveland Protestant Orphanage, the Western Reserve Historical Society, the Museum of Natural History, local schools, the Cleveland Museum of Art (of which he was president), and countless other organizations. He donated a large and valuable collection of paintings, sculpture and other art objects to the Cleveland Museum of Art. Jeptha H. Wade was said to be Cleveland's greatest benefactor. He also made contributions to the Thomas County area during his residency there.

Wade increased his Thomas County land holdings to upwards of 10,000 acres and built his massive Spanish Revival style home on Millpond. Since landscaping was a hobby, Wade took an active part in developing the grounds. He increased the size of the millpond and leveled a hill beside the house in order to view the pond from the main house. He ordered the planting of separate gardens for roses, palms, poppies, dogwoods, crabapples, lilies and tropical ferns and shrubs. The gardens were kept and nurtured from 1915 to 1955 by the superintendent, Alfred F. Wilkinson, who had been trained in the gardens of England. Upon its completion, Millpond was declared by editors and plantation owners to be a superior showplace of the South. After 23 winters at Millpond, Jeptha Homer Wade died at Millpond on March 6, 1926. His passing was much lamented in Cleveland and Thomasville, and newspapers of the day carried lavish accounts of his many accomplishments and contributions.

In 1926, Millpond was placed in trust and its use was given to Jeptha Wade's children, Jeptha Jr., Helen (Mrs. Edward B. Greene) and George Garrettson (1882-1957), all of Cleveland, for their lifetimes. In 1959, with George, Jeptha and Helen Wade deceased, Millpond had to be sold,

Garden, Millpond Plantation

Rose Garden, Millpond Plantation

according to the terms of the trust that had been set up by the first Wade of Millpond. The children of George Wade and Helen Wade Greene then purchased Millpond from the trust in 1961. The new owners were Jeptha H. Wade, III, Irene Wade (Mrs. Ellery Sedgwick, Jr.), both children of George Wade, and Helen Greene (Mrs. A. Dean Perry), daughter of Helen Wade Greene. The plantation is still in their possession today. Millpond was at that time divided into three tracts. The center portion with the main house and outbuildings is owned by Mrs. Perry. The land east of Millpond Road belongs to Mrs. Sedgwick, and the land west of the new Metcalf Road belongs to Wade. However, the three owners share in the use of the main house as they are all frequent winter visitors to Thomas County just as their grandfather had been 70 years ago.

Water Tower, Millpond Plantation

In its 151 year history, Millpond has grown from a 490 acre land lot, to a 1,600 then 3,000 acre planation, to a 10,000 acre estate. While the twentieth century has brought architectural changes and modernization to Millpond, many of its original natural features remain as vestiges of the past. The old red clay Linton Mill Road, now known as Millpond Road, still winds through the eastern portion. The mill is gone, but the pond remains. Pine trees and wildlife are still abundant, and the southern area boasts a stand of virgin longleaf pine, one of few in the United States. Agriculture was the basis of Millpond's existence in the first 75 years and has continued to be important in the last 75. Millpond agriculture operated successfully first under the slave system and then under the sharecropping system. Other enterprises including forestry, milling and hunting have also been significant, and most of these enterprises have made Millpond a self-supporting venture from its beginning. It is one of the rare examples in Georgia of an antebellum plantation that not only survived the dissolution of the slavery system and the ravages of war, but continued to grow and prosper to the present time while maintaining its natural and historical integrity (Thomasville Landmarks, Inc. Files).

Horse Barn, Millpond Plantation

Pebble Hill Plantation

Pebble Hill Plantation has both influenced and reflected the history of Thomas County and Southwestern Georgia. Established in the mid-1820's, the property's early development is similar to that of many other Southern plantations. In the 1890's, however, Northern interest and investment signaled a change in fortune, and Pebble Hill assumed a new direction and significance.

In 1818, the State of Georgia formed three counties along the state's south and southwestern borders from recently ceded Indian territory. These counties were Early, Irwin, and Appling. These counties were quite large and would be subdivided as growth made necessary. The land was distributed in the land lottery of 1820.

By 1823, growth made the formation of Decatur County necessary, and it was carved out of portions of Early County. The formation of yet another county became an issue in the state elections of 1825. Thomas Jefferson Johnson, who would later build Pebble Hill, campaigned in favor of a new county and was elected to the legislature. Johnson was the son of a successful Pulaski County planter and came to Southwest Georgia to establish a plantation like his father's. After winning the election, Johnson presented a bill to the legislature calling for the formation of Thomas County. The bill became law in December, 1825, and elections for county officials soon followed. County commissioners chose a site for the county seat. Johnson owned the land lot chosen and sold it to the commissioners for a ten-dollar profit. On December 22, 1826, the state legislature officially recognized the county seat to be Thomasville. Although Thomasville was not named for Johnson, he most likely influenced its designation. Johnson's relative, General Jett Thomas, was a distinguished architect and also served as a military commander in the War of 1812. Johnson evidently submitted his name for both the county and the town.

Johnson acquired several land lots during the 1820's and in 1825 purchased lot 246, on which he built his house. Johnson married Jane Wilkinson Hadley in March, 1827, and brought her to his new home. While the exact date of construction of this first house is unknown, Johnson had been living on the property since 1825. The structure was a simple two-story dwelling with farm outbuildings and slave cabins nearby. The Johnsons had three children in three years, and Jane died shortly after the birth of the third child. She was buried on the plantation in what would become the family cemetery. Johnson married again in 1839, to Martha Evans Everett, but they had no children. One of Johnson's children, Julia Ann, survived to adulthood.

Before his death in 1847, Johnson amassed at least 3,000 acres of land. He and his twenty slaves created an almost completely self-sufficient plantation. Johnson produced both sea island and short staple cotton in large quantities, but he also harvested corn, tobacco, and sugar cane. He had 104 head of hogs, 24 head of cattle, and 90 head of sheep, and held several work animals including oxen, horses, and a mule. Because he did not rely completely on cotton for income, his plantation was quite profitable. He became one of the county's wealthiest citizens and extended loans to many local farmers and businessmen. Usually taking land as collateral, Johnson was known as a fair and understanding banker, sometimes extending terms during agricultural crises.

Upon his death, Johnson left the plantation to his widow, Martha, and his daughter, Julia Ann. They were assisted in managing the operation by Ewen McLean, the husband of Johnson's niece, Cynthia Thomas. Julia Ann was married to John William Henry Mitchell, Sr. sixteen months after her father's death. When Mrs. Martha Evans Johnson died in 1850, the Mitchells became the sole owners of the plantation. They soon began work on a new main house to replace the existing one. The Mitchells hired John Wind, an English-born architect, to build a one-story frame structure. Wind was well known in Thomas County, having already designed the Thomas County Courthouse, Thomas Jones' Greenwood Plantation, and several other residences and public buildings. Later, Wind would advertise that the Mitchells were satisfied customers. The house Wind built was H-shaped and contained a kitchen and eight rooms.

The Mitchells soon filled the house with five children, four of whom survived childhood. Their eldest, Jane Temperance, gave the plantation its name. Although Julia Ann tried diligently to keep the walks well swept, pebbles constantly fell back onto them. Jane complained to her mother that they lived on a "pebble hill," and the name has remained to this day.

Mitchell increased the efficiency and profitability of the plantation through hard work and innovative planting methods. He added peas, beans and potatoes to the already diversified crop production, and by applying irrigation methods, became one of the county's largest rice planters. Mitchell was more conservative than his father-in-law and did not loan money to any degree. He did, however, acquire additional land for Pebble Hill.

During the Civil War, the crops produced in the county became crucial to the Confederacy. Mitchell sent a substitute to fight in his stead during the first years of the war so that he could remain to oversee operations at Pebble Hill. In 1864, Mitchell was appointed adjutant of the county's militia battalion. The battalion was called to action by Governor Joe Brown to defend Atlanta. The troops moved south through Macon and Savannah as Sherman marched to the sea, but were withdrawn in February, 1865, as the Confederacy collapsed. Mitchell returned to a Pebble Hill short of supplies and labor. With determination, he began the spring planting, but died of pneumonia on March 5, 1865.

Mitchell died intestate, and Julia Ann was appointed administrator of his estate. The abolition of slavery posed a serious threat to the planting season as well as to the value of the estate. Despite these setbacks, Julia Ann and her children managed to hold on to the plantation through the 1870's. Julia Ann budgeted strictly and sent both son, John W. H., Jr., and daughter, Mary Elizabeth, to school. She also found money to pay for harvesting crops, maintaining structures and obtaining equipment. By 1875, she had $800 deposited in the town's first bank.

For unknown reasons, in 1876, Robert Hardaway brought suit against Julia Ann as a trustee. The court ruled that the land was to be divided between Julia Ann and her children: Jane Temperance Stevens, Martha Josephine Stubbs, Mary Elizabeth (Bettie) Davenport, and John W. H. Mitchell, Jr. By this time, Julia Ann had developed heart disease and in January, 1881, she died.

Much of the central core of Pebble Hill devolved to Martha Josephine as a result of litigation and inheritance. Jane Temperance sold her portion of Pebble Hill in 1885 to Charles Thorne of Illinois. John W. H., Jr. held his portion and continued to live in the main house along with Martha and her daughter. Bettie's holdings did not include Pebble Hill proper. Martha married again in 1889, and moved to New York with her new husband, James Munro. Her brother served as her agent in managing her property. In 1895, her holdings were sold to Horace J. McFarlan of New Jersey. Since Mitchell sold most of his holdings, Pebble Hill, as it had been developed by Thomas Jefferson Johnson and expanded by Julia Ann and John W. H. Mitchell, Sr., no longer existed as a productive entity.

While all these land transactions involving Pebble Hill were taking place, the economy of Thomasville was changing. By war's end, soaring prices and lack of capital had slowed the Southern economy almost to a halt, but conditions in Thomasville improved rapidly after the war. The Atlantic and Gulf Railroad ended in the town, and fear of malaria and yellow fever prevented extensive travel further south. During the 1870's, Northern industrialists began visiting the Thomasville area seeking relief from bronchial and pulmonary ailments. They believed that the pine scented air and warm climate were beneficial. Locals did not discourage this belief. Hotels and boarding establishments opened to accommodate the visitors, who soon discovered the abundant opportunities for hunting and fishing. By the 1880's, most of the town's winter guests were physically well, although those with physical infirmities continued to come also. Thomasville became such a popular winter resort that the population soared to three times its summer count of 5,000.

Between 1888 and 1891, J. Wyman Jones, a wealthy New Jersey businessman, established a wooded park stocked with game birds and wild animals, thus creating the first local hunting preserve. In 1895, he renamed it the Glen Arven Country Club and opened one of the first golf courses in the country. Jones acquired other land from local farmers who were unable to raise enough crops to pay their taxes. He and his wife, Salome Hanna of Cleveland, Ohio, purchased the old McIntyre place on the Tallahassee Road and renovated it into a handsome residence, renaming it "Elsoma." By this time, several other wealthy Northern visitors had purchased lands and established permanent homes in the Thomasville area. Most of these residences were converted into hunting preserves. Even after railroad was constructed south into Florida and the fear of malaria and yellow fever were overcome, many Northerners remained in Thomasville specifically for the pleasure of hunting.

Salome Hanna Jones' brother, Howard Melville "Mel" Hanna, accepted his sister's advice and came to Thomasville in 1895. During his trip, his brother, Mark, hosted William McKinley and his wife. The McKinleys came ostensibly for Mrs. McKinley's health, but William used the time to confer with leading members of the Republican party in the South. After securing their support, he went on to win the party's nomination and the presidential election in 1896. President McKinley and his wife returned in 1899 to visit the Hannas in Thomasville again.

In November, 1896, Mel Hanna purchased Melrose Plantation from his nephew, Charles Chapin. Chapin, Salome's son by her first marriage, had purchased the property soon after the Joneses came to Elsoma. Melrose bordered Pebble Hill on the north side. Within a few months, Hanna cast his eyes on Pebble Hill. Owner Horace McFarlan had recently sold the property to Judge Henry W. Hopkins, a local Thomasville civic leader, who in turn, sold it to Hanna. By the turn of the century, Hanna had acquired Melrose, Pebble Hill and numerous other tracts in the area, converting the farmland into wildlife preserves and shooting plantations.

In 1901, Mel Hanna gave to his daughter, Kate Hanna Ireland, the house at Pebble Hill and the land around it. She later acquired more land from her father and brother, Howard. Through the years, she acquired land surrounding Pebble Hill by purchase and increased her holdings to more than 4,000 acres. Each winter, she brought her children, Robert Livingston, Jr., ("Liv") and Elizabeth ("Pansy"), south from Cleveland to stay at Pebble Hill. Mother and children became very attached to the plantation, and Kate devoted much of her energy to the expansion and development of Pebble Hill.

Pebble Hill Oak-Lined Drive

Kate set about the renovation of Pebble Hill with vision and determination. She added gardens near the main house and in 1914, added the east wing. Italianate in style, the addition included a loggia and several large rooms. She also had constructed for her children a log cabin that they used first as their winter school and then as a playhouse. Stables and a carriage house were built, and existing outbuildings were repaired and reopened for use.

Pebble Hill School Building

Maintaining a shooting plantation was a complex operation. Large expanses of land were burned off each season to allow freedom of movement for both wildlife and hunters, and fields of corn and other grains were planted and left, unharvested, to attract game birds, particularly quail. Local residents were hired and trained to assist in running the plantation and in organizing the hunts. Since hunting season meant many guests remained for extended periods, a large house staff was required to meet the needs of the family. To house all these workers, cottages were constructed on the grounds. More than sixty such families lived on the property. Support structures were also added, including a staff kitchen and laundry building called the Waldorf, and schools to educate the children of workers. A large vegetable garden supplied the staff with food, and the plantation's corporate arm, Pebble Hill Products, supplied dairy products and meats through the plantation store.

Pebble Hill Products came into existence during the 1920's when Kate Ireland established her champion Jersey herd. In 1920, she purchased her first thoroughbreds and in 1922, with the aid of Paul Sparrow, her new herdsman, she purchased a herd of Jersey cattle, adding to them some stock from Canada. By 1930, the herd was producing championship stock. Well-known Pebble Hill cattle included Brampton Standard Sire, who won 14 Grand Championships, and Xenia's Sparkling Ivy, who won numerous honors of her own and gave birth to five Superior Sires.

Divorced in 1919, Kate Hanna Ireland was remarried in 1923 to Perry Williams Harvey, an executive with the Hanna Company in Cleveland. Harvey shared his wife's love for Pebble Hill and assisted her in developing the Jersey herd. He was himself an authority on game birds and extremely interested in trotting horses. He was part owner of Pastime Stables in Thomasville.

In 1927, the Harveys commissioned Cleveland architect Abram Garfield (1872-1958), son of the late President James A. Garfield, to design a complex of service buildings, including a dairy, cow barn,

Employees' Church, Pebble Hill Plantation

stables and carriage house. Included in the complex were apartments and offices for workers. The dairy complex reflected the European heritage of its occupants, featuring Norman towers and Georgian serpentine walls. Garfield also oversaw the construction of matching gate houses at the front entrance to the Pebble Hill property and added brick walls to the family cemetery, the black cemetery and the tennis courts. At the same time, the cemeteries were cleaned up and repaired, and Mrs. Harvey had concrete markers erected.

Cow Barn, Pebble Hill Plantation

Mrs. Harvey's concern for Pebble Hill and her interest in championship cattle were matched by her sense of civic responsibility. Besides offering employment to local families during the Depression in the 1930's, she supported several local charities and established the Pebble Hill School and Visiting Nurse Association. Medical care in Southwest Georgia was limited, and workers at most of the plantations did not have adequate funds for even emergency care. The association provided registered nurses to travel throughout the county, primarily to the plantations, to provide medical care for the poor. Many plantation owners gave money to support the program since it aided their employees. A nurse's office was built at Pebble Hill, which served as the headquarters for the association. Miss Ireland assisted her mother in administering this program.

Serpentine Wall, Pebble Hill Cattle Barn Courtyard

To provide an opportunity for the children of her employees to complete at least a seventh grade education, Mrs. Harvey built two schools on the property (one on the west side of the property and one on the east) and hired black teachers to lead the classes. Students received hot meals for lunch, and the teachers boarded on the plantation.

During Mrs. Harvey's ownership of Pebble Hill, three important celebrations were observed: Easter, Emancipation Day, and Christmas. Easter was a family event that featured an egg hunt for the children, dinner for all, and dances and plays by the employees. Employees from several local plantations were invited, and many families traveled eight miles by wagon from town. Upon arrival, each family was marked off the invitation list and proceeded to the tennis courts and carriage green. Each child came to Mrs. Harvey and Miss Ireland to receive a basket for the egg hunt. Two of the hidden eggs were gold. The first gold egg found brought a five-dollar prize; the second, a two-dollar prize. Families ate together at long tables and feasted on sandwiches, fruit, cakes, punch and milk. After lunch, the children sang songs and gave speeches. They were rewarded with toys or hair ribbons. The adults presented mimes, dances, and plays, and they sang songs as well.

Pebble Hill Cemetery

The celebration of Emancipation Day reflected the Northern roots of many employers. Each year at Pebble Hill, and other local plantations, the employees received a holiday and a special meal on May 20. Employees assisted in clearing the black cemetery and joined in a picnic afterwards. This tradition continues.

Christmas was awaited with great anticipation because the Harvey family chose special gifts for everyone associated with Pebble Hill. The gifts were wrapped and presented at a Christmas party. Men commonly received shirts or pants. Women were given bolts of material. The children received ties, hair ribbons, or toys. Each family received linens, and large families received extra blankets. Mrs. Harvey and her children presided over the celebration and distributed the gifts personally.

In 1932, Perry Harvey died of heart disease, following a bout with influenza. He was buried in the Hanna-Harvey extension to the Pebble Hill cemetery.

Another tragedy struck Pebble Hill in the winter of 1934 when fire destroyed most of the main house. Several house guests were visiting, and the fireplaces were all in operation. The plantation fire engine, as well as engines from Thomasville, rushed to the scene, and most of the furnishings were saved. No lives were lost, but only the 1914 addition to the house was saved.

Reconstruction began almost immediately. Mrs. Harvey called upon Abram Garfield once again, and he designed a three-story residence in the Georgian style. The new residence was of modern steel-concrete construction and had a brick veneer. The surviving 1914 wing was raised, and a concrete floor was laid beneath for safety. Most of the construction work was accomplished by local residents eager for work during the Depression years. Mrs. Harvey commissioned landscape architect V. Ethylwyn Harrison from Cleveland, Ohio, one of the few female landscape architects in the nation, to add additional gardens to complement the new house. Mrs. Harvey died of pneumonia in May, 1936, just four months after the completion of the new house. She was mourned by rich and poor alike. Her legacy was a Pebble Hill steeped in history, carefully preserved, and rebuilt with a patient but determined vision.

Miss Ireland inherited the plantation and continued to take an active role in the operation of the property. Her time as owner was not marked by major building programs. Rather, she became the preserver of an outstanding estate. Inheriting her mother's passion for the outdoors, Miss Ireland loved wildlife and sports. She was a champion rider and one of the few female polo players of her era.

Wagon and Workmen, Pebble Hill Plantation

Dogs were Miss Ireland's principal interest at Pebble Hill. She increased the number of hunting dogs at the kennels and at one time owned a hundred. Her dog trainers and kennelmen worked year-round to train and maintain her dogs for the hunting season. During the season, she often set out at four or five in the morning and did not return home until dinner. The dogs flushed out wild turkey, quail, and doves, as well as an occasional bobcat.

In 1946, Miss Ireland married Parker Barrington Poe of Texas. The Poes traveled extensively and stayed at various times of the year in Georgia, Maine, and Kentucky. As Mrs. Poe grew older, she spent more and more time at Pebble Hill. She supported historical and environmental groups, and her lasting gift to Pebble Hill was the establishment of the non-profit Pebble Hill Foundation to manage the estate and oversee public visitation to the property (Thomasville Landmarks, Inc. Files).

Birdsong Plantation

The Birdsong Plantation consists of 565 acres of diverse topography near the Florida-Georgia border. Originally part of a vast longleaf pine forest, the property was extensively cleared for agriculture in

Main House, Pebble Hill Plantation

the nineteenth century. The lots making up the plantation were acquired by Shadrach and William J. Dickey between 1836 and 1872 and remained in the Dickey family until 1938.

Since 1938, it has been owned and managed by E. V. and Betty Komarek, active conservationists. The property has been managed for wildlife diversity through the creation and maintenance of a variety of habitats. Former fields are maintained as open areas through prescribed burning; farm ponds, streams, and a bay/swamp add wetlands; upland pine and hardwood forests and orchards provide food and shelter for wildlife. Beginning informally in 1980 and followed by incorporation as a non-profit organization in 1986, Birdsong has been operated as an educational nature center.

The rural historic landscape includes a 1912 dwelling, an 1858 barn, and twentieth-century outbuildings. The dwelling at Birdsong, the Dickey-Komarek house, is a frame, 1-½ story vernacular home with neoclassical revival elements, painted white. It was built in 1912 by adding to a mid-nineteenth-century dogtrot house, using heart pine cut on the property. The basic plan is rectangular, a central passage double pile house, with a one-story kitchen off the southwest corner. A side-gable roof over the house forms an intersecting gable roof with the kitchen.

The eastern half of the dwelling's front façade is faced with hand-planed boards and dates from the mid-nineteenth-century (photos 1, 2). There are three exterior red brick chimneys, one centered on each gable end plus a third, to the rear of the east gable. Both east chimneys were rebuilt in 1939, replacing 1912 chimneys that had fallen.

The outbuildings on the property, including the 1858 barn and non-contributing buildings supporting the nature center operation, are also of frame construction.

Main House, Birdsong Nature Center

Nature Center Office, Birdsong Nature Center

The prehistoric archaeological potential of the property has not been surveyed. The longleaf pine forest that once dominated the region was a hunting area for the Native Americans; the Tallahassee area to the south had continuous occupation from Paleo-Indians into the nineteenth century. Flint points have been collected from the fields at Birdsong.

1858 Barn, Birdsong Nature Center

The Komareks removed the walls and chimneys of abandoned buildings in the 1940's as part of their preparation for prescribed burning. The following sites of previous structures and features have archaeological potential:

a. The Ginhouse field derives its name from an 1850's structure for cotton ginning that was located near the center. A large roof, mounted on beams and posts, protected the cotton press and balling machinery. W. J. Dickey noted in his diary on August 11, 1858, "Finished weatherboarding shed around ginhouse." The ginhouse, likely the large building on the 1871 map (lot number 25) blew down in high winds circa 1900. The screw and other parts remained in the field until contributed to the scrap metal drives of World War I.

b. To the east of the Dickey barn is a depression planted with yuccas marking a nineteenth-century well site. It was open as late as the 1930's, although unused.

c. A road that appears on the 1871 map and the 1933 plat map of the property (identified as "plantation road" on the 1933 plat map) is still present south of the Holly Woods.

d. The nineteenth-century kitchen behind the house was five feet north of a well, still present and now capped.

e. The 1897-98 Bethpage School, described by Chandler Dickey in 1989 as located ½ mile west of the Dickey-Komarek house along Meridian Road, then south 100 yards, on the west side of a wagon road. There was a well nearby that the school used. Built by Arthur and Eddie Dickey, the school was a one-room building of longleaf pine; it was used until 1916, when a two-room school was built on neighboring Sherwood Plantation. An earlier one-room school sat near the Bethpage site on the east side of the wagon road.

f. A syrup shed in use for syrup making and hog killing until 1939 was located according to Chandler Dickey 150 feet due south of barn well (b). After 1939, the shed sheltered a hammer mill; the Komareks took it down and remember its location as Letts Mill woods southwest of the barn. The final syrup making at the shed took place in 1939.

g. The pre-1912 kitchen and dining room building was moved east of the nineteenth-century well (item b above) around 1916, continuing in use as a corn crib. It was torn down in the 1940's by the Komareks.

h. Directly north of the current pump house was a gum log "smokehouse" with a clay floor, torn down after 1943. This building was possibly item i below.

i. The ironing house, in the area of barn, 75 feet a little south of east from the well (item d.), "just out of the yard," according to Chandler Dickey, was "where the ironing was done" early in the twentieth century. It possibly was a former slave house; four small buildings with chimneys are located behind the Dickey house on the 1871 map, and may include items i, j, and k (Figure 4.1).

j. The cotton house, the 60 feet due south of the ironing house (item i) is where tenants brought cotton to be weighed early in the twentieth century. It is possibly a former slave house.

k. The guano house is 200-300 feet east of the cotton house (item j). Purchased acid and cotton seed meal were mixed on the floor of this building to use as fertilizer early in the twentieth century. This too was possibly a former slave house.

l. The Franklin tenant house is a three-room house described as ¾ mile west of Dickey-Komarek house on Meridian and 200 yards southeast of old Bethpage School (item e). West of Warren and Sarah Franklin's home, 100-200 yards, was a second Franklin tenant house occupied by their son, Warren, and his family.

m. The Dickey buggy house, converted to a garage in 1914, was located south of the house in the area of the Komarek garage/office. The pathway to the east of the house, leading to the back, was a driveway to this garage.

n. The family privies in 1939 were located behind the cow shed, on the edge of what was a chicken yard. In the early twentieth century, a one-acre garden occupied this area and the privy was located at the northwest corner of the garden.

o. The cow shed was built on the site of former enclosed stables.

p. The Wyche tenant house is located west of the Frog Pond in a field next to a woodlands.

q. Abandoned tenant houses, possibly former slave houses, were still evident at four or five locations in 1939 when the Komareks acquired the property, marked by chimneys and logs. It might be possible to locate these and determine which sites are Franklin and Wyche with a survey. One was known as the Harper house when it was torn down in 1941.

r. The 1916 Dickey tenant house had a small barn, located south of the house, used for storage and a well.

Notes to 1871 Map (Figure 4.1 on following page))

East to west, clockwise, within the current boundaries:

1. Near the location of Roy's house, on Lot 24, is a tenant house. Roy's was built in 1916 (according to Chandler Dickey). This house must be an earlier one on the same site.

2. On the property line between lot 25 and lot 24 is a tenant house with its associated field nearby.

3. Just south of the Big Bay is a tenant house that may be the one identified by David Dickey as the Wyche house, later the Kinchen house or it may be an earlier one on the site.

4. The building on lot 22 is likely the earlier one room (Bethpage) school remembered by David Dickey.

5. The large building east of the school, in the Ginhouse Field, is the ginhouse. The smaller building southeast of it is unidentified.

6. The main house group is anchored by the enlarged house, no longer the one-room 1851 log house, but with the frame room across the open dogtrot. Close enough to appear attached to the rear is the kitchen. Unidentified is the protrusion west from the house.

7. South of the main house, arranged around a square, are five buildings. Four of these appear to have chimneys and may be former slave quarters.

   a. David Dickey mentions a "cook house" and a "small sleeping cabin" in the area of the barn in his memory. His cook house is likely the former kitchen, which was moved near the barn in 1916; it would not be one of the buildings on the 1871 map. The sleeping cabin may be one of these four buildings.

   b. Chandler remembers three buildings in the barn area which were identified by their use — an ironing house, a cotton house, and a guano house. These may be the buildings on the map, possibly later uses of former slave houses. Chandler does not remember the sleeping cabin.

   c. The Komareks removed a smokehouse near the current pump house; it may have been the ironing house or one of these other outbuildings. They also removed a building they called the commissary, near the barn, which was used as a crib. It was likely the kitchen/cook house; Chandler recalls it was used as a crib.

8. The fifth building south of the main house is the large barn.

(Thomasville Landmarks, Inc. Files)

Figure 4.1 1871 Surveyor's Map

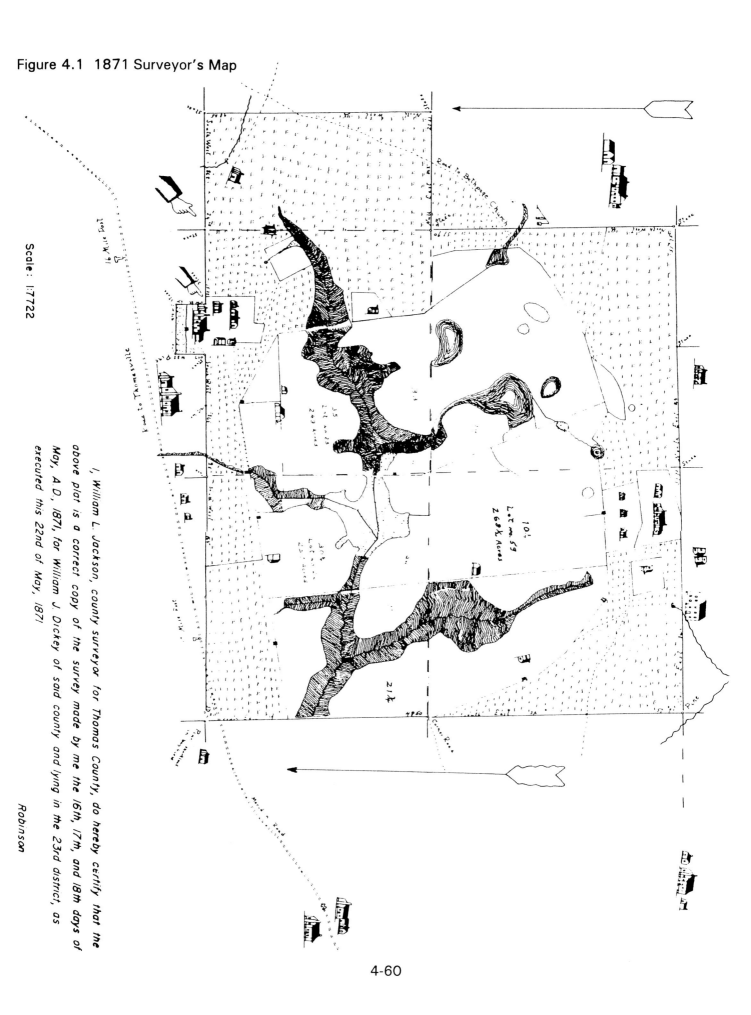

Scale: 1:7722

I, William L. Jackson, county surveyor for Thomas County, do hereby certify that the above plat is a correct copy of the survey made by me the 16th, 17th, and 18th days of May, A.D., 1871, for William J. Dickey of said county and lying in the 23rd district, as executed this 22nd of May, 1871

Robinson

Greenwood Plantation

The main house at Greenwood Plantation was built between 1835 and 1844 and was designed by English architect John Wind. Twentieth-century additions were designed by Stanford White, an architect with a leading New York firm, McKim, Mead and White. Mr. White described Greenwood as "the most perfect example of Greek Revival architecture in America."

The Greenwood main house is a two-story brick and frame Greek Revival dwelling. The bricks were burned in kilns on the plantation, and the timbers used were cut from the plantation and hewn by hand. The house was built over a nine-year period, 1835-1844, to replace an earlier frame house.

A large, wooden, pedimented gable roof is supported by four two-story Ionic columns set on square brick bases that rest directly on the ground, in front of the portico rather than resting on top of it. There is a two-story portico, the second story being supported by four simple columns rising from the deep first story. The front end gable, built of native red cedar, is ornamented by a magnolia blossom and flanking garlands. Four laurel wreaths adorn the simple frieze, one over each of the Ionic columns. The blossoms, garlands and wreaths were hand carved by the original architect, although parts of these have had to be replaced due to deterioration.

The interior has a fine symmetrical winding staircase at the rear of the front or main center hall. Wainscoting and interior doors are of panel design. Mantels are simple and straightforward, and door and window trim is extremely plain. There are dentil cornices throughout. The living room has Doric engaged pilasters, and the main hall is divided by a wide flattened arch supported by simple columns. The center front doorway consists of a double glass panelled door flanked by sidelights and capped with a leaded glass, rectangular fixed transom.

The floor plan of the original portion is a four-room, central hall plan with four rooms on each floor. Greenwood was enlarged and improved in the early twentieth century by the owner, Colonel O. H. Payne, including rear additions that attach the original kitchen to the main house, two one-story wings, sunken gardens, and iron gates. These additions were designed by Stanford White. The wings are rectangular and the front portico balusters of the second floor are repeated above each wing. These wings contain extensions to the living room and the two downstairs bedrooms. Both the wings and the rear additions are perfectly compatible with the original design. The gardens added by Colonel Payne included marble statuary, benches and fountains, but have since been removed. Further landscaping has been done by the Whitneys. The ornate bronze gates designed by White still remain in place.

Greenwood Plantation was first owned and the main house built by Thomas P. Jones. The Jones were among Thomas County's early settlers, acquiring four 250 acre land lots in District 18 from men who had drawn these lots in the 1820 land lottery. Jones acquired his first lot in 1827. Jones and his wife, Lavinia Young, had moved to Thomas County from the Savannah area. Six children were born to them after coming to Thomas County. By 1860, Thomas County ranked seventh in rice production in Georgia, and Jones was the county's leading rice producer with 8,000 pounds in 1860. In addition, he was one of the original trustees of the First Methodist Church of Thomasville and was one of the owners of the first bank to be chartered there. Jones owned more than 2,000 acres for several years, but after he sold some acreage, Greenwood in the last years of his ownership consisted of around 1,300 acres. Jones died in 1869, but his widow continued to live there until 1889 when she sold 1,300 acres to S. R. Van Duzer of New York. Lavinia Jones requested burial at the Jones' cemetery at Greenwood in her will. This cemetery is maintained at Greenwood today.

The new owners, the Van Duzers, began Greenwood's tradition of being a winter residence and hunting preserve. The Van Duzers had a town house in Thomasville and used Greenwood as a hunting lodge. They renamed the plantation "Vaalnysten." Van Duzer was a well-known merchant and manufacturer. When Van Duzer's health began to fail, he offered the plantation for sale.

In 1899, the Van Duzers sold Greenwood to Colonel Oliver Hazard Payne of New York. Colonel Payne commissioned architect Stanford White to design wings, rear additions, an iron gate, and sunken gardens, all of which were added to the estate, as was additional acreage. White had designed other notable buildings including Madison Square Garden, the Gorham and Tiffany buildings in New York City, the New York state capital in Albany, and others. Colonel Payne, born 1842, was a director of the Standard Oil Company and the American Tobacco Company and president of the Tennessee Coal, Iron and Railway Company. He helped finance the first Cornell Medical School and endowed it with $4,500,000. He also gave large sums to the University of Virginia and Western Reserve University.

Upon Colonel Payne's death in 1916, Greenwood passed to his nephew, Payne Whitney, according to the stipulations of Colonel Payne's will. Payne Whitney was the son of William Collins Whitney, former Secretary of the Navy, political figure and financier. Payne Whitney married Helen Hay, daughter of John Milton Hay, Secretary of State under William McKinley and Theodore Roosevelt and author of the Hay-Pauncefort Treaty. On Whitney's death in the late 1930's, Greenwood became the property of his widow, Helen Hay Whitney, who managed the place until her death around 1943-44.

In 1944, Greenwood was inherited by John Hay Whitney, (1904-), the son of Payne and Helen Hay Whitney. Until this time, Greenwood was still farmed by sharecroppers and used for quail hunting by the owners. There, as elsewhere in Georgia, sharecropping ended around 1945. Greenwood's purpose has been three-fold since then, according to John Hay Whitney's plans. It is a center for the development of Southern agriculture, and its facilities have developed hybrid corn seed that has increased the productivity of corn farmers in the Southeast. It is an example of natural resource conservation and land use planning. The forests are continually replenished. The home place contains a tract of virgin longleaf pine, one of few in the United States. The wild life management program makes Greenwood the home of quail, deer and other varieties of wild life. Finally, it serves as a winter residence for Mrs. Whitney, assuring quality maintenance for the historic main house.

Greenwood Plantation today consists of three non-contiguous tracts of land. The smallest tract, known as the "home place," was listed in the national register in 1970. This tract is the site of the main house, outbuildings, Jones cemetery, gardens, virgin longleaf pine stand, Pinetree Boulevard and the hybrid seed company, all of which contribute to the historical significance of this site and protect the environmental and historical integrity of the plantation. The Greenwood Plantation of the twentieth century combines nineteenth-century design and purpose with twentieth-century technology to continue its tradition as a successful, functioning plantation of South Georgia (Thomasville Landmarks, Inc. Files).

Fair Oaks Plantation

One of the original settlers to the Thomas County area, when it was still part of Irwin and Decatur counties, was a Virginian named Thomas Mitchell, a Revolutionary War veteran who had fought under Colonel Daniel Morgan. After the War, Mitchell and his wife moved to Georgia, and Governor John Milledge granted them land in Montgomery County. In March of 1824, Mitchell bought from Juniper

Hall, Jr. of Emanuel County some land in the frontier wilderness of Irwin and Decatur counties in the area that was soon to become Thomas County. He and his wife moved to Thomas County shortly after. Mitchell died in 1826 in Thomas County, and his will was the first to be recorded in the new county. He left to his heirs, his sons, John, Taylor, and Richard, three lots of 250 acres each in Thomas County. Prior to his death, Thomas built the first house at Fair Oaks for his family.

Colonel Richard Mitchell, the son of Thomas Mitchell, was a hero of the War of 1812. He married Sophronia Dickey of Thomas County and fathered nine children. Richard had inherited Fair Oaks with his brothers when their father died in 1826. Richard Mitchell became one of the leading planters in the area and was a popular man. He was

> one of the finest specimens of (physical) manhood and a genial gentleman of enlarged philanthropy, venturing to build a treadmill (a regular horse-killer) to grind meal from which went bushels to the poor, without money, and without price. The mill was too heavy; the horse died; the mill decayed and ceased grinding. He was a man of strong convictions and the courage to express them, who said to the writer that he never saw an honest Democrat. He was a Whig.

One historian considers Mitchell, with his broadcloth aristocratic bearing that was based on agricultural wealth, typical of Southern Whigs.

Colonel Mitchell built the second house at Fair Oaks for his family. It is not known whether the structure his father built was still standing at this time or not. This second house is no longer extant, although the third house, the Wind design, may have been created by adding to the second. Colonel Mitchell died in 1856 and was buried at Fair Oaks in the family burial area where

> his body was placed at his request, facing the west, because he hated the British so that he wished even in death to turn away from the direction that led 3,000 miles across the ocean to the land of our ancient enemy.

After his death, a third house was constructed on Fair Oaks by one of his sons for the widow and her children still living at home. Two and possibly three sons have been given credit for the construction of the house for their mother, but no records are known which would give one son validity over the others. A story is told of one son who was bringing a friend home from college and requested that the second story and portico be added to their home so that his friend would be impressed.

Sophronia Dickey Mitchell, Richard's widow, lived at Fair Oaks until her death in 1893. After she died, the unmarried children, Richard, Sarah Ann, and Emily (or Amy) Susan remained there. Emily married Kenneth T. McClean who inherited the property when she died. In 1924, McClean died, and Fair Oaks was sold to Mrs. Sam Jones Mitchell. She sold it to Mrs. P. W. Harvey, who restored the house, not changing the architectural style at all. Mrs. Harvey passed away in 1936 and her son, Livingston Ireland, inherited it. Mr. and Mrs. Brigham Britton acquired the property and later passed the house and grounds to the Brittons' son Charles and his wife Linda.

The original John Wind structure, the third house at Fair Oaks, built in 1856-1863, burned to the ground in September, 1962. The house had been restored several times before this disaster, but nothing major had been altered. The structure now standing is the fourth known house at Fair Oaks. It is an almost exact reproduction of the Wind house with a few changes, such as bathrooms and closets.

Main House, Fair Oaks Plantation

The house Wind designed was built between Colonel Richard Mitchell's death in 1856 and Wind's death in 1863. By this time, Wind had built many homes in the Thomas County area — Greenwood, Susina, Eudora, and others in the town of Thomasville and neighboring counties. Fair Oaks was his last major work.

In his design of Fair Oaks, Wind deviated from his usual traditional use of the Greek Revival vogue. In Eudora, he had combined elements of newer styles of architecture into a rather eclectic example of a Greek Revival-Romantic house. In Fair Oaks, he continued to experiment with various architectural concepts. The portico, with its square pillars and full-size balcony with a projecting central section, was typical of his oeuvre, excluding the flush frontal siding that may have been used by Wind as a signature.

Perhaps, with Fair Oaks, Wind was moving into a new period in his architecture. The Greek Revival had died elsewhere in the nation by the 1850's, and other styles much removed from it were beginning to take hold. The Oriental influences that were beginning to be seen in some of these styles affected Wind's design of Fair Oaks. He was progressing toward a more Oriental style and following in the trends of architecture elsewhere. Unfortunately, Wind died in 1863 before he could continue this progression, if indeed there was one. Fair Oaks, therefore, stands as a turning point, and a final monument, in his career as an architect (Thomasville Landmarks, Inc. Files).

Cedar Grove (Susina) Plantation

Between Thomasville and the Florida line lies the small community of Beachton. It is only a crossroads now, but in John Wind's time the community, then known as Duncanville, was the home of many of Thomas County's major planters. One such figure was James Joseph Blackshear, who established the Cedar Grove Plantation.

Blackshear came to Thomas County soon after it was established and in the first land lottery of Thomas County proper, in 1827, acquired his first lot in the area. He quickly became a prominent farmer and citizen, and in 1833, was selected by Governor Wilson Lumpkin to be a justice of the Inferior Court. On February 19, 1836, he was commissioned by Governor William Schley as an "Ensign" of the Georgia Guards in the 69th Regiment of the Georgia Militia.

He married Harriet Jones and in the 1840 census is recorded as having a household with numerous adults, including forty-three male slaves and fifty-nine female slaves. Blackshear was killed in 1843 and his widow continued operating the plantation. The 1860 census lists the value of her property at $250,000. Harriet Blackshear died in 1863 at Cedar Grove and was buried beside her husband. In 1887, Dr. John T. Metcalf bought the house and property from Thomas E. Blackshear and changed the plantation's name from Cedar Grove to Susina.

Around 1841, Blackshear hired John Wind to design a house at Cedar Grove. The house Wind designed and supervised was a two-story Greek Revival dwelling. Timber for the house was cut on the property, and the building was constructed with slave labor. It was covered in clapboard, and hand-forged square iron nails were used in construction.

Main House, Susina Plantation

A. Heywood Mason arrived in Thomasville from Philadelphia around 1880. Suffering with a respiratory ailment, Mason came seeking a healthy climate. He arrived with his wife, Anna, and their six-week old son, James S. Mason, II. The Masons enjoyed Thomasville and became regular winter visitors. When Susina became available in 1891, Mason acquired the property and remodeled the building to meet his family's needs. He retired from his Philadelphia based business and became a full-time resident of Grady County. His death followed in 1911. The property was subsequently inherited by Mr. and Mrs. James S. Mason, II. Upon Mrs. Mason's death in 1951, the property passed to A. Heywood Mason, II. Susina is currently owned by Ann Marie Walker who operates the property as a bed and breakfast (Thomasville Landmarks, Inc. Files).

SUMMARY AND RECOMMENDATIONS

This chapter has concentrated on three objectives. It has first sought to relay the regional's developmental history to local governing bodies and area residents by examining the functional and aesthetic relationship between historic resources and the rural environment. As a second aim, the chapter has recorded a range of plantation-related structures. As its last goal, this study has listed all Red Hills plantations eligible for the National Register of Historic places.

In the fall of 1988, a conservation association was formed by six non-profit organizations anxious to conserve wildlands in North Florida and South Georgia. These agencies, the Historic Tallahassee Preservation Board, the Tall Timbers Research Station, the Florida and Georgia Nature Conservancies, the Trust for Public Land, and Thomasville Landmarks, Inc., share a common concern about the unbridled destruction of 375,000 acres of managed wilderness.

These wildlands consist of seventy-one plantations that lie in a concentrated geographic region between Tallahassee, Florida and Thomasville, Georgia. This dendritic clay-soil region, termed the Tallahassee Red Hills, is characterized by densely wooded forests, grassy plains, and natural lakes.

The original plantation owners possessed a strong love of the land, and because of their ecologically sound management practices, the area today is a diverse habitat complex supporting a unique variety of historic structures, wildlife and plant life. In creating a conservation association, consortium members strove to develop a wildland network that preserved and reinforced regional ecologic, historic, and open space/scenic values.

Consortium members and area residents acknowledge change will occur throughout the region. According to 1988 Leon County Planning Department statistics, 67% of all new residential construction in Leon County occurs in the northeastern quadrant. Seventy-three percent of all new single-family subdivisions are erected in this portion of the County. The four-laning of U.S. Highway 319, which connects Thomasville and Tallahassee, will increase development pressure in the heart of Georgia's Red Hills Region. How then can Red Hills residents hope to anticipate, much less guide, inevitable growth and development pressure?

To provide an understanding of the hunting plantation movement in Georgia, future researchers need to undertake a building-by-building inventory of historic properties and landscape features found in Georgia's Red Hills Region. They must also research the history of individual plantations, paying particular attention to historic newspaper accounts, plantation log books, and diaries.

Researchers should interview former and current land owners, managers, house/groundskeepers, and tenants. Since succeeding generations have worked on these estates, an oral history project should complement the survey in identifying and documenting those folkways and traditions associated with plantation life.

In 1988, the Historic Tallahassee Preservation Board completed a survey and contextual study that recorded over 300 historic buildings and landscape features on twenty-two Florida estates totaling 88,000 acres of land. That survey led to the National Register nomination of Tall Timbers Plantation as the first and largest Florida estate to gain this designation due its significance and integrity as a cultural landscape. Additional nominations are now being prepared. Most importantly, the survey has been an important educational and planning tool. The architectural survey and research recommended for the Georgia Red Hills should parallel work completed in Florida.

REFERENCES

Banks, Enoch Marvin. 1905. *The economics of land tenure in Georgia.* Colonial University Press. New York.

Brooks, Carolyn. 1984. Thomasville commercial historic district. *National Register Nomination Form,* May 7. On file at the Office of Historic Preservation, Department of Natural Resources, Atlanta, Georgia.

_____. 1985. Bethany Congregational Church. *National Register Nomination Form*, January 21. On file at the Office of Historic Preservation, Department of Natural Resources, Atlanta, Georgia.

Brooks, Robert Preston. 1914. The agrarian revolution in Georgia, 1865-1912. Bulletin of the University of Wisconsin. Madison.

Decatur County. General Index to Deeds, Grantee, 1826-1910. Courthouse, Bainbridge, Georgia.

_____. Deed Books. Office of Clerk of Circuit Court, Courthouse, Bainbridge, Georgia.

Devine, Jerry W. 1979. *Development in Wiregrass Georgia, 1870 to 1900; a Study of Material Aspects.* Unpublished report commissioned by the Georgia Agrirama Development Authority.

Elizabeth F. Hopkins Collection. Genealogical Library. Thomasville Cultural Center. Thomasville, Georgia.

Grady, 1904-1953. 1983. Published by the Messenger Publishing Company. Cairo, Georgia, December 16. Roddenbery Memorial Library. Cairo, Georgia.

Kelley, Adriane L. 1977. *The plantation homes of John Wind.* M.A. thesis, University of Georgia, Athens.

Latrobe, Charles Joseph. 1835. *The rambler in North America, II.* New York.

Messenger Historical. 1967. May 31 1(1). Messenger Publishing. Cairo, Georgia. Roddenbery Memorial Library, Cairo, Georgia.

McGorty, Kevin. 1992. *Views from the road: a community guide for assessing rural historic landscapes.* Sponsored by the Trust for Public Land, the National Trust for Historic Preservation, and the Red Hills Conservation Association.

Niles, Andrea. 1985. Fletcherville historic district. *National Register Nomination Form*, February 28. On file at the Office of Historic Preservation, Department of Natural Resources, Atlanta, Georgia.

Paisley, Clifton. 1990. *The Red Hills of Florida, 1528-1865.* University of Alabama Press. Tuscaloosa.

Range, Willard. 1954. *A Century of Georgia Agriculture, 1850-1950.* University of Georgia Press. Athens.

Report of the Commission of Agriculture for the Year 1866. 1867. Washington, DC.

Roddenbery, Ms. Robin, Cairo Citizen, Cairo, Georgia. 1991. Interviewed by Nancy Tinker, 1 June.

Rogers, William Warren. 1963. *Antebellum Thomas County 1825-1861.* Florida State University Press. Tallahassee.

_____. 1964. *Thomas County during the Civil War.* Florida State University Press. Tallahassee.

_____. 1973. *Thomas County 1865-1900.* Florida State University Press. Tallahassee.

Spangle, Harold Henry, Jr. 1977. *The history of the black community of Thomas County, Georgia, from 1827 to 1909.* Thesis submitted to the Graduate Council of Valdosta State College, July 4.

Thomas County, Georgia. Undated map in the possession of Mr. John S. Hand, Thomasville, Georgia.

Thomas County. Deed Books. Office of Clerk of Circuit Court, Courthouse, Thomasville, Georgia.

_____. General Index to Deeds, 1826-1910., Grantor. Courthouse, Thomasville, Georgia.

_____. General Index to Deeds, 1826-1910, Grantee. Courthouse, Thomasville, Georgia.

_____. Register of Freed Persons. Office of Clerk of Circuit Court, Courthouse, Thomasville, Georgia.

_____. Tax Digest. Microfilm, Georgia Department of Archives, Atlanta, Georgia.

Thomasville, Georgia. County-Seat of Thomas County. 1885. Famous Resort for Northern Invalids and Pleasure Seekers. Bird's eye View Map. Milwaukee: Norris, Wellge and Co., 1885. Reprinted by Thomas County Historical Society.

Thomasville Landmarks, Inc., Files. Unpublished manuscripts containing notes and photographs of historic sites in Thomasville and Thomas County.

Thomasville *Southern Enterprise.* 1865-1867.

Thomasville *Times.* 1873-1889.

Thurston, George Lee, Editor. 1979. *The Roddenbery/Roddenbery Family Book.* Published by Julien B. Roddenbery.

United States Census, 1830-1860 and 1860-1890.

CHAPTER 5: GEOLOGY

INTRODUCTION

Richebourg G.
McWilliams

and

Candace Trimble
(associate)

This chapter presents
an assessment of
geological and related
factors affecting a
portion of the Red Hills
Region.

Purpose and Scope

The assessment of geological and related factors affecting the
area of this chapter is a significant step toward developing the
capability to understand, value, and make reasonable judgements
related to use and protection of an important resource. This
study evaluates the existing state of knowledge regarding the
environmental sensitivity of the groundwater system in the area
and provides other insights that could be developed locally. This
information can be used profitably in consideration of
growth/land use decisions and related matters.

Consequently, this assessment examines the current state of
knowledge related to the geologic history, stratigraphy, structure,
soils, aquifer systems, and water usage in the project area. The
study addresses surface geologic exposures, at a reconnaissance
level, and describes very pertinent surface features — sink holes
and drainage patterns — as they may relate to the groundwater
system. This section describes, insofar as existing information
will allow, the relative sensitivity of the groundwater system in
various parts of the area. Finally, the report provides a general
outline of additional local study needs, based on rather pointed
information gaps detected in the course of this work.

The following study is not a detailed, original scientific treatise.
It compiles and summarizes a great deal of work done by others.
Project work related to surface features provided new insight but
was limited by time and budget constraints.

General Setting

The area encompassed by this project lies within the Tifton
Uplands Physiographic District of the Coastal Plain Province in
Southern Georgia. Physiographically, it merges with the
Tallahassee Hills to the south.

The project covers the southwest portion of Thomas County and
a somewhat larger portion of southeastern Grady County. The
area is bounded on the west by the Ochlockonee River, on the
south by the Georgia-Florida state line, on the north by the
approximate latitude of the City of Thomasville, and extends
about one mile to the east of the town of Metcalf. The project
area is approximately the western half of the Georgia portion of
an area known as the Red Hills. Geologically, the project area

can be divided into two sub-areas: the Southwest Georgia Coastal Plain (south Thomas County and a part of southeast Grady County) and the Apalachicola Embayment-Gulf Trough, which covers a majority of the Grady County area (Figure 5.1). The geologic histories of the two areas have been quite different, resulting in differences in sediments and surface features that reflect them. Part of the discussions that follow conform to the two subdivisions (by name). In other cases, where more specifics were required, it was more convenient to use local landmarks.

GEOLOGIC SETTING

The Paleogeography of Southern Georgia: Upper Eocene to Present

For about 140 million years, from Late Jurassic (160 million years ago [m.a.]) until the Early Miocene (about 20 m.a.) South Georgia was often separated from Florida by a marine environment. Florida existed as a peninsula, an island or an archipelago (of islands). The topography was low and it was surrounded by a shallow shelf. To the north, silicious, clastic sediments were being deposited. To the south, carbonates and evaporites were laid down in lagoons and bays of the shallow continental shelf (Figure 5.2).

During Cretaceous time (>66.5 m.a.) the Gulf of Mexico and the Atlantic Ocean were connected by a channel known variously as the Suwannee Strait or Suwannee Channel (Applin and Applin, 1965; Huddleston, 1993). This channel separated present-day South Georgia from what is now peninsular Florida. This structure allowed warm Gulf waters to flow northeastward across southern Georgia and provided a climate conducive to colonization by warm-water flora and fauna.

From Late Cretaceous to Middle Eocene time a climate similar to that of the present day Bahama Bank prevailed along the areas of South Georgia influenced by the Suwannee Channel, and the Florida Carbonate Banks developed to the south (Huddleston, 1993).

The Suwannee Channel seems to have begun filling up with sediments (both siliciclastics from the continent and near-shore carbonates) during the Middle Eocene.

At the end of the Eocene and during the Early Oligocene, sea level dropped several times (spaced between intermittent rises that occurred at progressively lower elevations each time). The Suwannee Channel continued to exist as a connection between the Atlantic and the Gulf through the late Eocene, probably finally filling in during Oligocene time.

The Florida Carbonate Bank became re-established during the Oligocene (Huddleston, 1993, Scott, 1988). At this time the Suwannee Current (Huddleston, 1993) was probably established in a depositional basin center further to the west, which is the Apalachicola Embayment-Gulf Trough area (Figure 5.3), and the area that had previously been the Suwannee Channel became part of the Florida Carbonate Banks. Carbonate sediments of the Suwannee Limestone were deposited at this time.

During the Early to Middle Miocene when sea level rose again, the Apalachicola Embayment-Gulf Trough continued to exist as a shallow-water sea-way between the mainland (Georgia to the north) and the "islands" which probably comprised present peninsular Florida.

Figure 5.1: Subdivisions of the Project Area

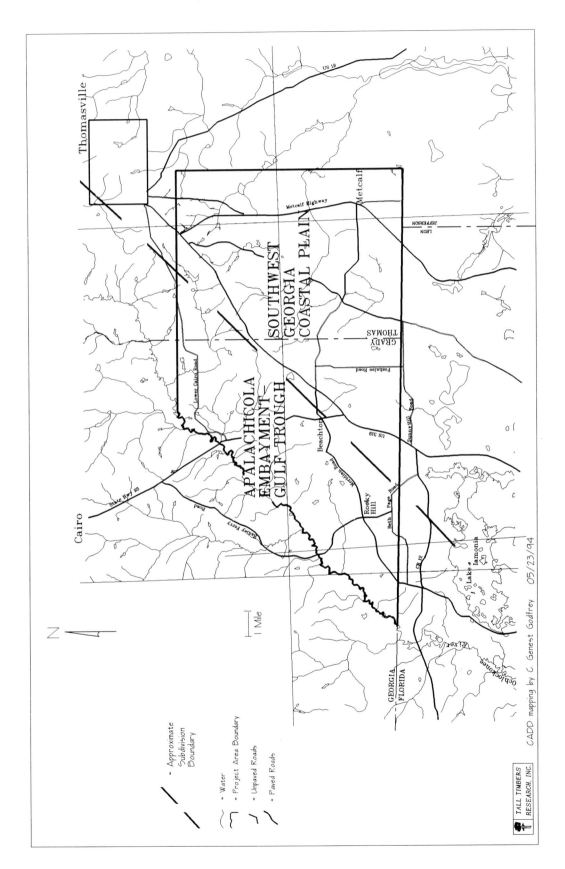

Figure 5.2: Late Eocene Paleogeography of Georgia and North Florida, from Huddleston, 1993. (Chattahoochee Embayment" is older term for Apalachicola Embayment.)

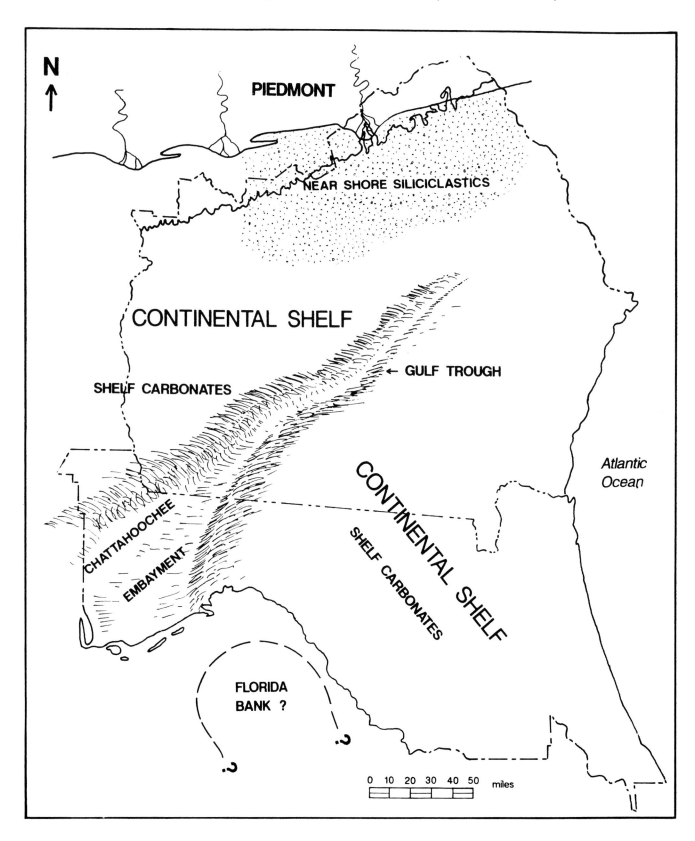

Figure 5.3:   Apalachicola Embayment-Gulf Trough During the Oligocene, from Huddleston, 1993.
(Chattahoochee Embayment" is older term for Apalachicola Embayment.)

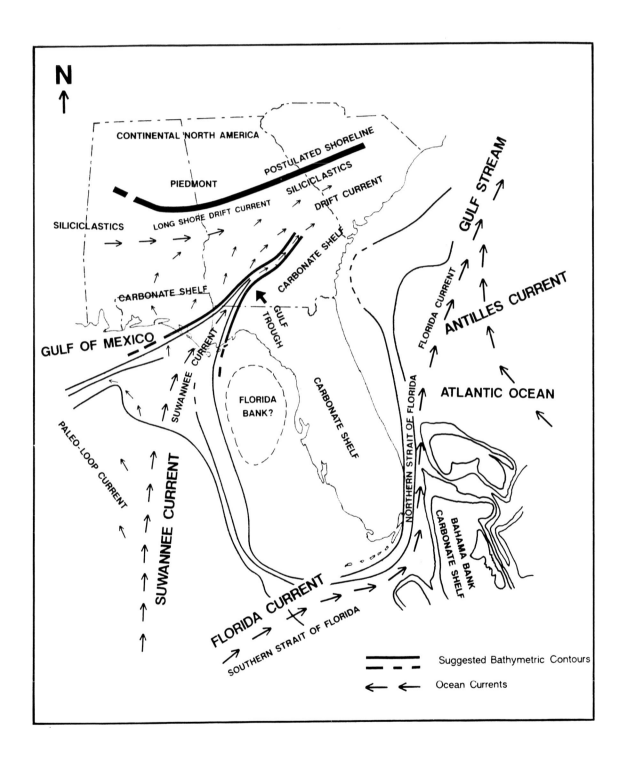

During the Miocene sea level continued to fluctuate. In the early Miocene, sediments of the Hawthorn Group were laid down during high stands of the sea. The sediments were especially thick within the Apalachicola Embayment-Gulf Trough, which had become a depositional center. When the shore line prograded (advanced seaward), an evaporitic basin-lagoon-tidal environment was present. In these brackish-water to tidal environments, palygorskite (attapulgite), sepiolite, phosphate and dolomites were deposited, with the greatest thicknesses being of Middle Miocene age. (Weaver and Beck, 1977)

By the close of the Miocene the Apalachicola Embayment-Gulf Trough was filled (Figure 5.4). Following the in-filling of the Apalachicola Embayment-Gulf Trough, the warm current from the Gulf no longer swept past the southern coast of Georgia; in fact, this current was redirected around a growing peninsula and through the Florida Straits (Huddleston, 1988; Scott, 1990). Thus, water temperatures cooled and the climate became less Mediterranean in nature. During the Pliocene, a large influx of clastic sediments blanketed the area (Miccosukee Formation) in a shallow marine or deltaic environment.

By the onset of the Pleistocene ice ages, the climate was rather humid and much cooler. Sea level continued to fluctuate, especially during the Pleistocene ice ages, when large areas of the present continental shelf were exposed on both the Atlantic and Gulf coasts. The study area has been emergent (above sea level) since the Pliocene sea fell (more than 1.6 m.a.). Since then, as shorelines advanced seaward, sediments of the study area have been subject to soil forming processes, or have been reworked by fluvial processes and redeposited in streams or river valleys (Huddleston, 1988).

The paleogeographic and environmental studies suggest an area gradually changing from marine and near-shore warm-tropical to arid environments, to an environment more typical of a continental land mass with the humid, sub-tropic climate that is found in present day south Grady and south Thomas counties.

Regional Stratigraphy

Southwest Georgia Coastal Plain

The majority of the project area (some of the Grady County and all of the Thomas County portion of the project area) falls predominantly within the Southwest Georgia Coastal Plain. The sedimentary thickness of most local importance (overlying the Floridan Aquifer) is Miocene to Recent in age and ranges from less than 100 feet just south of Thomasville to more than 200 feet along the eastern boundary of the Apalachicola Embayment-Gulf Trough east of the Ochlockonee River. These sediments were deposited on a shallow carbonate bank along the southern flank of the Apalachicola Embayment-Gulf Trough (Huddleston, 1993).

Surficial deposits generally range from undifferentiated alluvium of variable texture, sandy to sandy clay sediments of recent age (less than 10 thousand years of age, ka.) to surface outcrops of the Pliocene Miccosukee Formation (between 1.8 and 3.4 m.a.), containing conspicuous red to reddish orange sands with distinct white clay laminae and mottling (Puri and Vernon, 1964; Chen, 1965; Huddleston, 1988).

Figure 5.4:   Cross-Section Showing Deposition in the Apalachicola Embayment-Gulf Trough and
Adjacent North Florida and South Georgia from Lower Oligocene through Upper
Miocene Time, from Weaver and Beck, 1977. Section is E-W, from Lake Seminole,
through project area, to Atlantic coast.

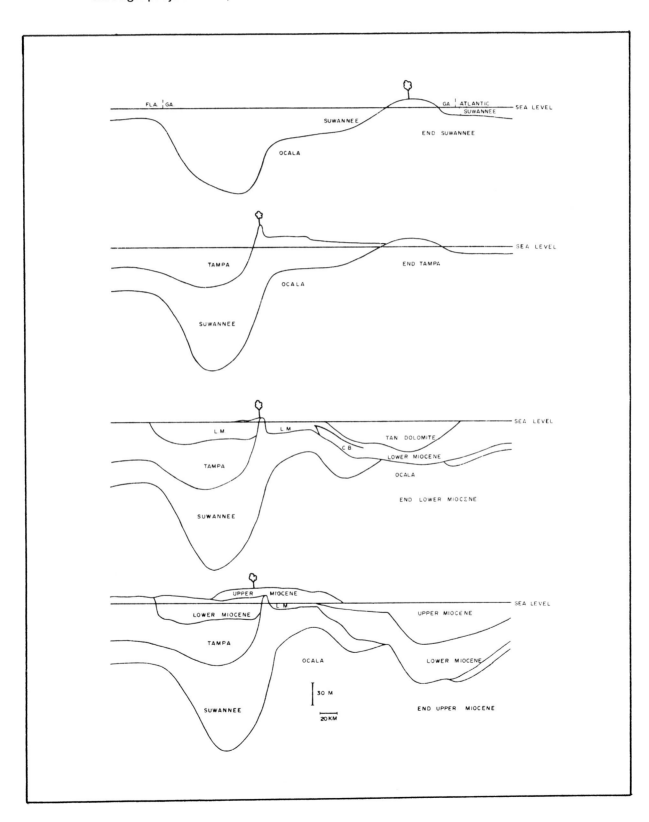

Stream valleys and sink holes are characterized by outcrops of Lower Miocene (13.5-23.7 m.a.) Hawthorn Group, (Torreya Formation in at least the south part of the area), an argillaceous (clayey), fine grained sand to sandy clay with varying amounts of usually calcitic or sometimes dolomitic limestones. Dominant clays are montmorillonite and attapulgite (palygorskite).

An erosional surface separates the Hawthorn Group from the underlying Chattahoochee Formation. The Chattahoochee may outcrop in deeper sink holes, but generally occurs in the sub-surface. This Lower Miocene formation represents the same geologic time interval as the rocks and sediments of Parachula Formation (found in the Trough-Embayment), but is not considered to be part of the Hawthorn Group by most workers (Puri and Vernon, 1964; Huddleston, 1988; Scott, 1988 and 1990; Kellam and Gorday, 1990).

The Chattahoochee is predominantly dolostone, a carbonate rock of dolomitic mineralogy, but may contain quartz sand, calcitic limestone, chert, mica, and heavy minerals. This unit is usually about 50-100 feet thick (Rupert, personal communication, 1994; Huddleston, 1988), but poor sub-surface control limits information on the formation in the project area.

Within the Southwest Georgia Coastal Plain part of the study area, the Upper Floridan Aquifer underlies the Chattahoochee Formation (although some early workers may include the Chattahoochee as part of the Upper Floridan). Here the Floridan is composed of deposits of the Lower Oligocene age limestones and dolostones (between 31 and 33.5 m.a.) to the underlying Upper Eocene saccaroidal and fossiliferous limestones of the Ocala Group at its base (about 33.5-36 m.a.), (Herrick and Vorhis, 1963; Bush and Johnston, 1988; Kellam and Gorday, 1990; Huddleston, 1993). In the Southwest Georgia Coastal Plain, the thickness of the Floridan ranges from about 850 feet south of Metcalf near the Georgia/Florida line to about 500 feet near the south flank of the Embayment-Trough system (Miller, 1986).

Apalachicola Embayment-Gulf Trough

The Grady County portion of the study area lies mainly within the Apalachicola Embayment-Gulf Trough. This is a northeast-trending linear sub-surface depressional feature continuous with the Gulf of Mexico (Figure 5.5).

The Gulf Trough and Apalachicola Embayment are believed to have been produced by the Suwannee Current, which connected the Gulf of Mexico and the Atlantic Ocean (Huddleston, 1990, from Kellam and Gorday, 1990). This current is interpreted by Huddleston to have inhibited sedimentation in the Embayment-Trough region during the Middle to Upper Eocene. An early Oligocene fall in sea level probably caused the cessation of the Suwannee Current. Sedimentation in the Embayment-Trough re-initiated during the Miocene Epoch and by the end of the Miocene, the Embayment-Trough was filled.

The Embayment-Trough is nearly 35 miles wide at the Georgia-Florida state line and exhibits nearly 200 feet of relief within the project area. Within the Embayment-Trough area, sediments overlying the Floridan Aquifer are somewhat thicker than the adjacent Georgia Coastal Plain Area, between 180 and 200 feet in most of this part of the study area (Kellam and Gorday, 1990).

The Apalachicola Embayment-Gulf Trough is filled with sediments which range from the Late Cretaceous Period (more than 66.5 m.a.) to the Holocene or Recent Epoch. (This report only addresses stratigraphy and lithology from the Eocene Epoch forward, that which includes the rocks

Figure 5.5:   Apalachicola Embayment-Gulf Trough, from Scott, 1990.

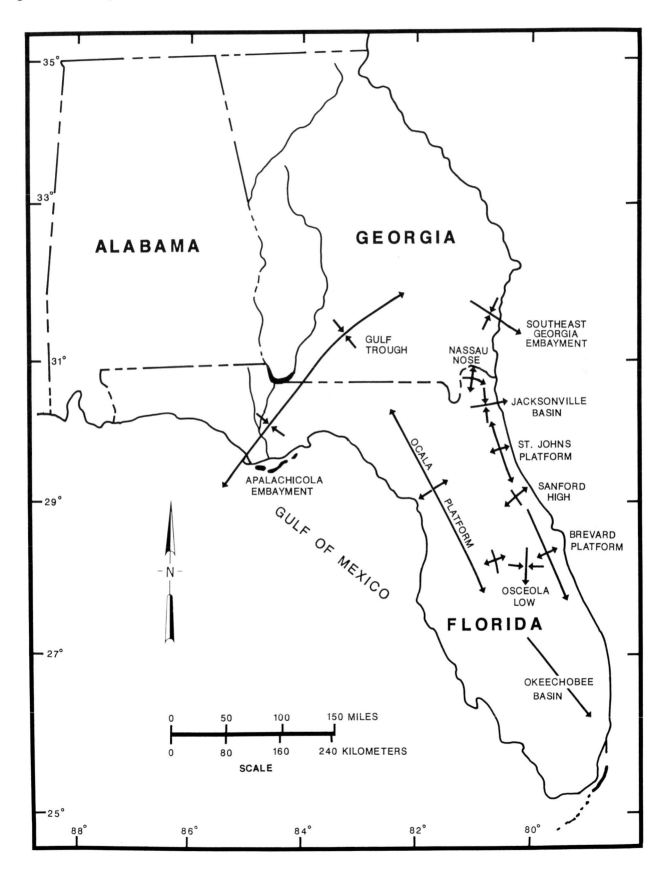

from the base of the Upper Floridan Aquifer to the land surface). In the Embayment-Trough, the total thickness of sediments overlying the limestones of the Floridan Aquifer ranges up to about 200 feet along the Ochlockonee River. These sediments are made up of sandy surficial deposits of Recent Age, sandy to clayey Miccosukee Formation outcrops of Pliocene age; and the oldest surface outcrops of the argillaceous sands to heavy clays (such as polygorskite, sepiolite and montmorillonite) of the Miocene Hawthorn Group (Weaver and Beck, 1977; Huddleston, 1988).

In the Trough area the Floridan system varies from dolomitic, calcitic, and clayey sands of the Parachula Formation (about 22-23.7 m.a.) found at the top of the Floridan Aquifer to the Lower Oligocene deposits of coarsely granular limestones overlying massively to thinly bedded granular limestones and dolomitic limestones that are underlain by undifferentiated Upper Eocene rocks (about 35.5-36 m.a.) (Huddleston, 1993). Some workers include these underlying carbonates in the Ocala Limestone (Miller, 1986). The thickness of sediments comprising the Floridan Aquifer ranges from about 600 feet southeast of Moncrief to about 400 feet along the east bank of the Ochlockonee River just south of Pine Park (Miller, 1986) (Figure 5.6).

All local geologic formations, their ages, and local equivalents are presented in chart-form on Figure 5.7. The sedimentary units of both subdivisions of the project area are provided and correlated. Those formations that are included in the Floridan Aquifer are indicated.

Geologic Structure

The Tertiary to Recent (last 65 million years) structure of the project area has long been a subject of controversy. Two basic schools of thought exist: One group (Applin and Applin, 1944; Herrick and Vorhis, 1963; Patterson and Herrick, 1971; Weaver and Beck, 1977; and Huddleston, 1993) believes that little or no tectonic activity has occurred in the project area since the Cretaceous period (more than 66.5 m.a.). The second school of thought adheres to the notion that faulting has resulted in vertical displacement in the Apalachicola Embayment-Gulf Trough area (Sever, 1962, 1964, and 1966; Gremillion, 1965; Tanner, 1966; Hendry and Sproul, 1966; Gelbaum, 1978; Miller, 1986). This faulting would cross Grady County, in a northeast-southwest direction, just north of the Ochlockonee River. In addition, this second group believes that uplift and folding occurred to the east of the project area and produced a feature Sever (1966) called the "Barwick Arch."

Patterson and Herrick (1971) noted that "the area extending north and northeast of the mouth of the Apalachicola River, as far as the Georgia-Florida line has been thought to be structurally depressed since Johnson (1892) proposed the "Chattahoochee Embayment of the Gulf of Mexico." Since Johnson's time the feature has been extended northeast into central Georgia (Toulmin, 1952) and has gone by many names including: "The Southwest Georgia Basin" (Murray, 1957), "The Apalachicola Embayment" (Puri and Vernon, 1964), and "The Gulf Trough of Georgia" (Herrick and Vorhis, 1963) which was later shortened to the "Gulf Trough" (Hendry and Sproul, 1966). This report follows the discussion by Kellam and Gorday (1990) and Scott (1990) which recognizes both Applin and Applin's name and that of Hendry and Sproul, calling the feature the Apalachicola Embayment-Gulf Trough System.

All workers seem to agree that there is some sort of structural depression in the surface of the Oligocene sediments in the area and that this linear feature is covered by thick Miocene sediments. It is the nature of the feature which excites the controversy. One theory proposes that the trough is the result of a "graben" (Figure 5.8), a down-dropped block bounded by normal faults (Sever, 1962, Gremillion, 1965; Tanner, 1966; Gelbaum, 1978; and Miller, 1986). Others simply see the

trough as a downfaulted area (Murray, 1961; Hendry and Sproul, 1966). Sever later (1964) suggested that the trough feature was a syncline and, in 1966, added a fault along the southeast side of the structure (Figure 5.9).

The second basic theory associated with the trough is that it is a sedimentary structure: either a huge solution valley in the thick Oligocene carbonates[1] (Patterson and Herrick, 1971) or the remnant of a submarine valley or strait (Dall and Harris, 1892; Rainwater, 1956; Scott, 1990; Huddleston, 1993) (Figure 5.10).

Huddleston's contention that it may be a remnant of the Cretaceous Suwannee Strait, which filled completely with sediments during the Miocene seems reasonable and explains the feature in the least complicated manner.

Another "structural" feature is often referred to in the literature as the "Barwick Arch." This feature, a "high" in the top of the Oligocene limestone, was first mapped by Sever, 1966. (see Figure 5.9). A search of the literature has found no mention of this high by most early workers, (Cooke, 1943; Applin and Applin, 1944 and 1967; Herrick and Vorhis, 1963) and a complete rejection of its presence in work done by Patterson and Herrick (1971) and Huddleston, 1993). The authors ecountered no clear evidence of a significant Oligocene (Suwannee Limestone) high.

Discussion

It seems likely that the only large-scale structure present is the Gulf Trough-Apalachicola Embayment, which lies along the northwestern part of the project area in Grady County. Minor local structural variations are present due to solution and collapse in the Oligocene Suwannee limestones. These features are discussed later in this report.

With the exception of local variations due to the presence of karst features, the sediments of Oligocene Age generally dip toward the northwest (into the Apalachicola Embayment-Gulf Trough) and toward the Gulf of Mexico to the south. Sediments above the Oligocene dip generally to the south-southeast over much of the project area.

---

[1] Limestones of the Floridan Aquifer

Figure 5.8: Proposed Graben Origin of Apalachicola Embayment-Gulf Trough, from Miller, 1986.

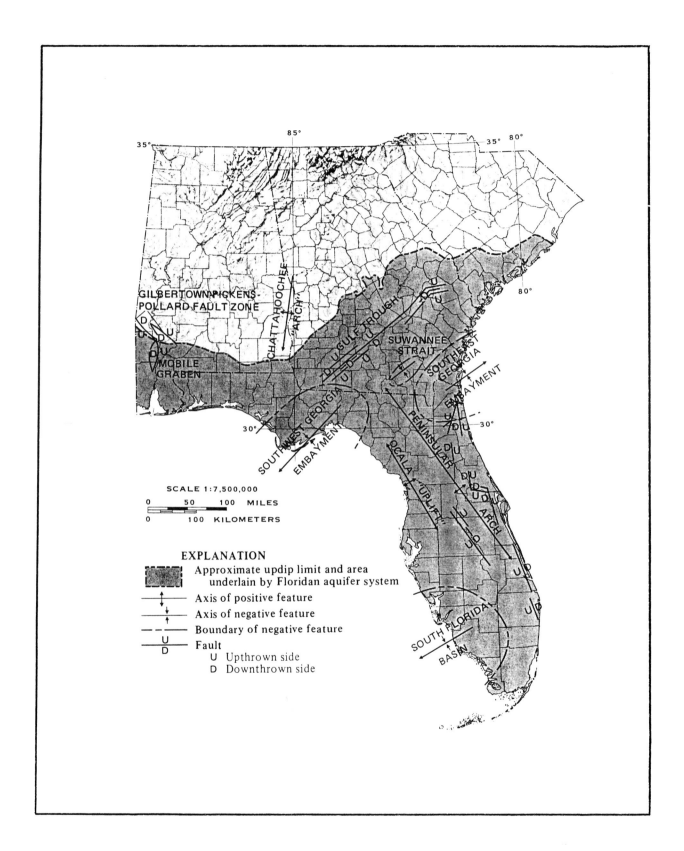

Figure 5.9: Proposed Ochlockonee Fault, by Sever, 1966.

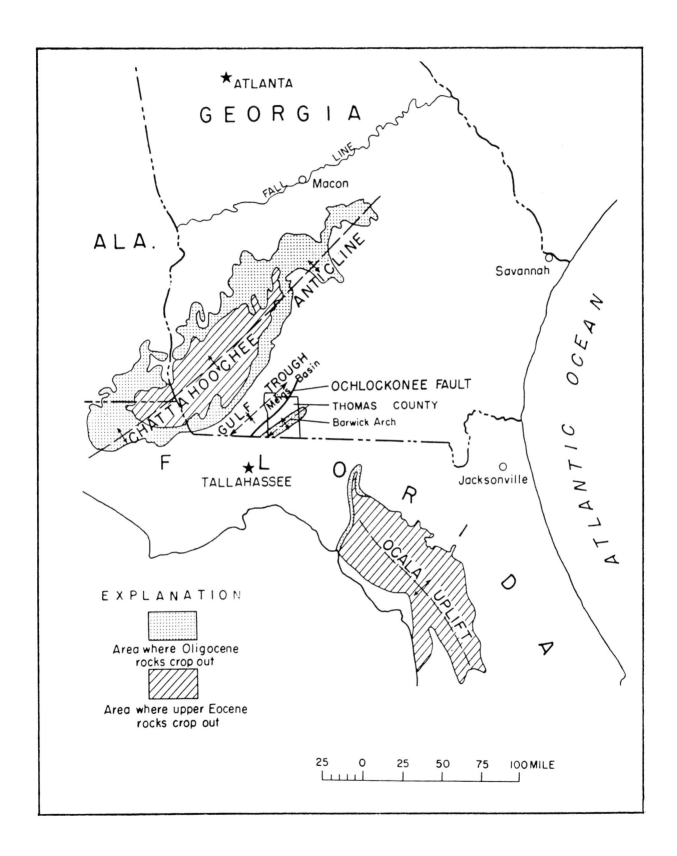

Figure 5.10: Non-Structural Origin of Apalachicola Embayment-Gulf Trough, from Huddleston, 1993.

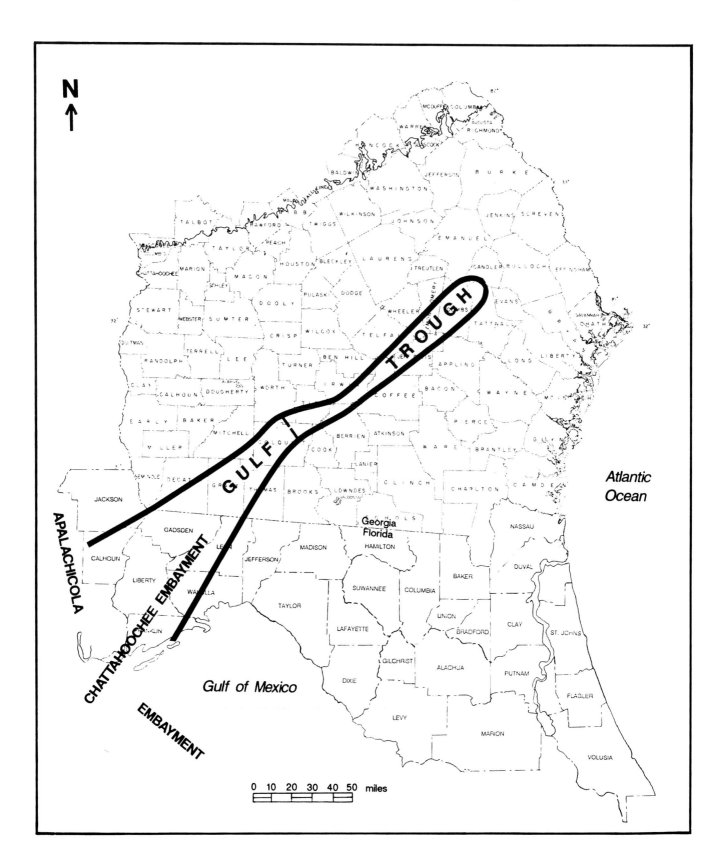

GENERAL HYDROLOGIC SETTING

The Floridan Aquifer

General

The Florida Aquifer system is a highly productive, regional aquifer system serving most of Florida, large areas of Georgia, and parts of Alabama and South Carolina (Miller, 1986). This aquifer system is composed of a thick sequence of highly permeable, carbonate rocks, ranging in age from Paleocene (more than 55 ma) to Miocene (more than 5 ma) (Kellam and Gorday, 1990). The Floridan Aquifer system is quite complex and is represented over large areas by three principal confining units and both an "Upper" and "Lower" Floridan system. Within the project area in southern Thomas and Grady counties, the Floridan is represented only by the "Upper Floridan" (referred to hereafter "the Floridan").

The Floridan system serves as the primary public and private water supply for nearly all users in the study area (Pierce, et al., 1982, Trent, et al., 1987). Locally, the Floridan Aquifer consists of permeable carbonates, limestones, and dolostones of Upper Eocene to Lower Oligocene age.

Geologic Framework

Throughout the project area the Floridan is overlain by Miocene age sediments of variable thickness and composition (Herrick and Vorhis, 1963; Weaver and Beck, 1977; Miller, 1986; Huddleston, 1988; Kellam and Gorday, 1990) (Figure 5.11).

Sediments range from thick sequences of clastics and low permeability carbonates in some parts of the Apalachicola Embayment-Gulf Trough area of Grady County to permeable carbonates and thin, breached or semi-confining clastics in Thomas County and the remainder of Grady County. The upper confining unit is primarily the Miocene age, Hawthorn Group (Huddleston, 1988; Scott, 1990), also known in the literature as the Hawthorn Formation (Puri and Vernon, 1964; Hendry and Sproul, 1966; Miller, 1986). These sands, clays and carbonates constitute the "upper confining unit" (Miller, 1986) of the Upper Floridan System within the study area. Hawthorn sediments vary in thickness from almost 200 feet south of Pine Park to less than 100 feet near Thomasville to about 140 feet at the Georgia-Florida line, near Tall Timbers Research Station. In general, the Hawthorn is thickest in a band trending diagonally across the study area along the flanks of the Gulf Trough.

Hawthorn rocks also vary greatly in age. They may be as old as the Aquitanian age (23.7 m.a.) or as young as the Serravallian age (between 15.2 and 10.5 m.a.). (Huddleston, 1988).

Miller (1986) and Bush and Johnston (1988) regard the upper confining unit as breached and the Floridan as "unconfined or semi-confined" where the Hawthorn is the thinnest. (Figure 5.12).

In these areas "much of the Hawthorn has been removed by erosion" (Miller, 1986) and/or has been breached by sink holes or other solution features. Sink holes, pipes and disappearing streams, common solution features, are found throughout much of the project area. These openings provide a direct connection between the Floridan and the surface. These features are apparently due to collapse of the thin overlying cover of clastic sediments into solution features in the underlying

Figure 5.11: General Thickness of Sediments Overlying the Floridan Aquifer, modified from Kellam and Gorday, 1990.

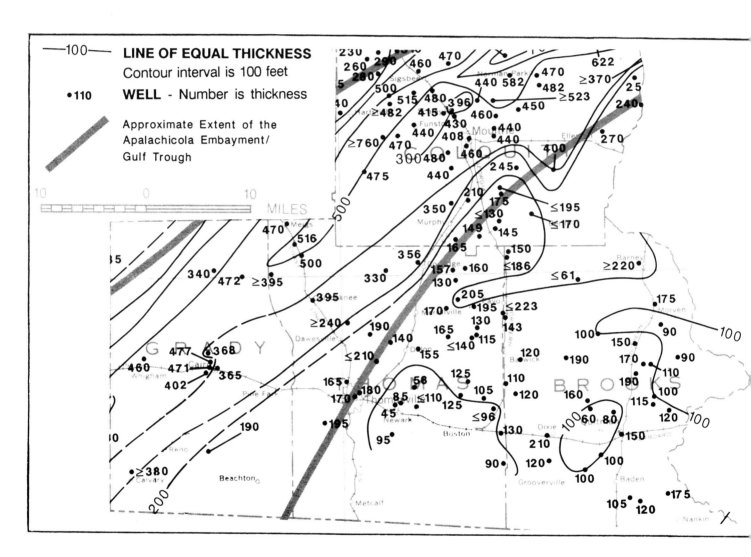

Figure 5.12: Areas Where the Floridan Aquifer is Unconfined or Semiconfined, modified from Miller, 1986.

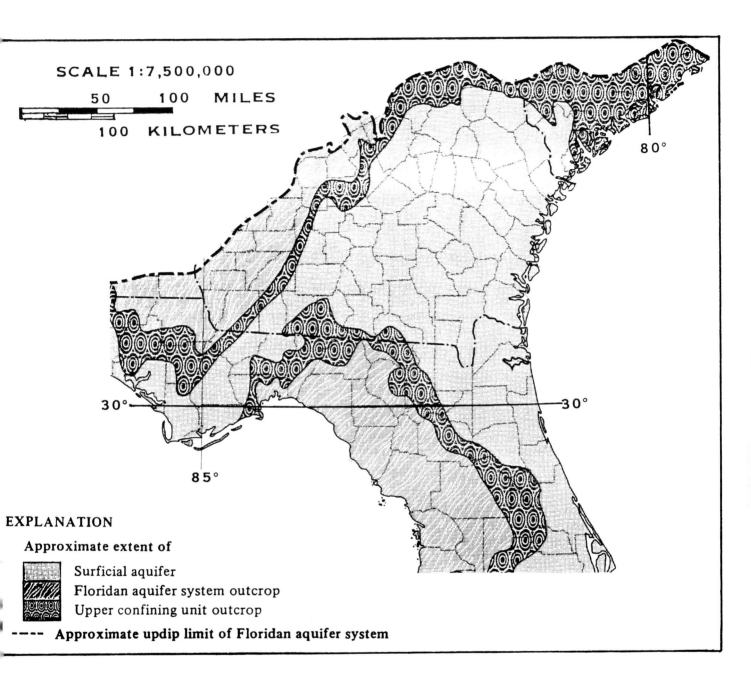

SCALE 1:7,500,000

50   100   MILES

100   KILOMETERS

80°

30°   30°

85°

EXPLANATION

Approximate extent of

Surficial aquifer
Floridan aquifer system outcrop
Upper confining unit outcrop

- - - - Approximate updip limit of Floridan aquifer system

cavernous limestone of the Floridan, and are not caused by solution of Miocene carbonates in the upper confining unit (Miller, 1986).

The Floridan Aquifer confines its waters in rocks that range in age from Oligocene (Suwannee and Bridgeboro Limestones) and Miocene (Parachula Formation) at its top (Huddleston, 1988; Kellam and Gorday, 1990; Huddleston, 1993), to Upper Eocene age rocks at its base (Miller, 1986; Bush and Johnston, 1988; Huddleston, 1988 and 1993). Suwannee Limestone predominates in the study area; however, the Parachula may occur in the sub-surface within the Apalachicola Embayment-Gulf Trough areas of Grady County (Huddleston, 1988). Bridgeboro Limestone is found as scattered limestone formations flanking the Apalachicola Embayment-Gulf Trough in Grady County and, also, lying parallel to the southern flank of the Embayment-Trough in Thomas County (Huddleston, 1993). The base of the Floridan is Eocene throughout the study area, and for the most part, is composed of the Ocala Group, which forms the base of much of the Upper Floridan. However, along the flanks of the Gulf Trough, the Floridan is often based in undifferentiated Upper Eocene Limestones, representing the same general time span as the Ocala Group Limestones (Miller, 1986; Bush and Johnston, 1988; Huddleston, 1988 and 1993; Kellam and Gorday, 1990).

Surficial Aquifers

Surficial aquifers are "water table" or "shallow" aquifers. The water table is the "top of the fresh ground water body" below which all pores or openings are filled (saturated) (Conover, et al. in Fernald and Patton, 1984).

Surficial aquifers are present throughout much of the project area, (Figure 5.13). Water infiltrates sandy and loamy unsaturated soil and sediments to the water table. Where these sediments are thin and highly permeable, surficial aquifers may transmit water through leaky confining beds to recharge the Floridan directly. In other places, where thick, clayey sediments confine the Floridan, the surficial aquifers are separated from the principal water supply source (Conover et al., 1984; Miller, 1986).

Precipitation (rainfall) waters may take several pathways once in contact with the land surface. They may run off directly, entering surface water systems such as lakes, streams and wetlands, but most of this water does not run off, it infiltrates. Once infiltration has occurred, the water may be held loosely, as soil water available for use by plants or in sediments or rocks as vadose water, or it may (and most does) percolate downward until it reaches the water table. At this point, there are still two pathways open to infiltrating water. The first pathway is to move laterally, supplying lakes, streams and wetlands. The second path is downward, slowly recharging the Floridan (Miller, 1986).

The water table "surface" is gently undulating, and tends to follow topographic highs and lows. However, it is much closer to the surface in low-lying areas, than beneath hills and uplands. Lakes, streams, ponds and wetlands are places where the water table or local surficial aquifer intersects the ground surface (Conover, et al., 1984).

Water levels within the surficial aquifers are not stable. They respond very quickly to forces which affect recharge and discharge, such as rainfall, drought and pumping. Seasonal variations may be as much as one to five feet in wetlands and up to 10 feet in upland areas (U.S.D.A.-SCS, 1979 and U.S.D.A.-SCS unpublished; Conover, et al., 1984; Miller, 1986).

Surficial aquifers are primarily found in sediments of Pliocene to Recent Age (less than 3 m.a.) or in recently reworked and redeposited older sediments. These are generally quite sandy, but in some

Figure 5.13: Occurrence of Shallow Aquifers, modified from Miller, 1986.

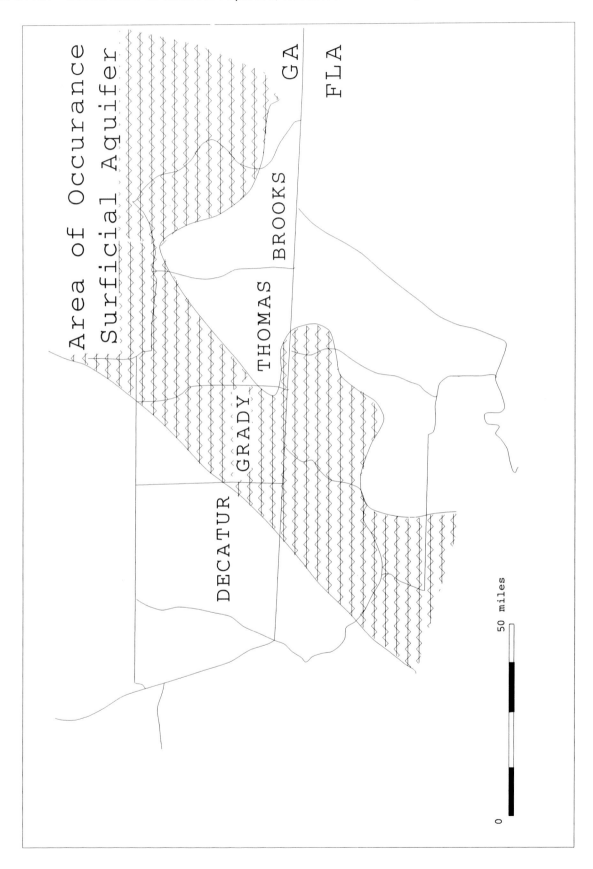

cases are perched, developing above shallow aquicludes of limited areal extent (Dunne and Leopold, 1978; U.S.D.A.- SCS, 1979 and unpublished).

Water tables serve as "source-sink" beds for deeper systems such as the Upper Floridan Aquifer System throughout the project area. Where the base of a local surficial aquifer is above the potentiometric surface of the Floridan, it serves to recharge the larger system, and is thus a "source" bed. In other places, the potentiometric surface of the Floridan may lie above the elevation of the base of surficial systems. In these "sinks" water flows upward into the water table, from the Floridan (Miller, 1986). These connections are directly dependent upon the thickness and permeability of the confining beds that separate the two systems.

Water tables do not provide important public sources of potable water in most of the project area. The local importance of these surficial aquifer systems lies in their use by rural land-owners as private domestic supplies in both the Thomas and Grady County parts of the study area. In addition, water tables serve as the principal source recharging local lakes and ponds, a major source of irrigation and livestock water in Grady County (see Trent, et al., 1987).

Finally, surficial aquifers are extremely sensitive to outside forces or stresses, responding rapidly to rainfall or drought. This sensitivity makes them very vulnerable to local contamination from pollutant discharges (Dunne and Leopold, 1978). These discharges may take a number of forms such as industrial waste; animal waste from farms; human waste from municipal systems or septic tanks; or surface water, laden with hydrocarbons and other toxins from roads and parking lots.

Recharge to and Transmission of Water Within the Floridan Aquifer System

Generally, groundwater moves from areas of high pressure to low pressure. In an artesian aquifer, as the Floridan is in most areas, the slope of the potentiometric surface determines the direction in which the water moves (Figure 5.14).

This slope is the difference in feet between points on adjacent contours divided by the distance between the contours. Groundwater movement tends to be perpendicular to the contour lines, and in the direction of the greatest slope.

Many factors affect the rate of water movement within and recharge to the Floridan. These include infiltration characteristics; the relative land surface, water table and potentiometric surface elevations; the geologic setting (nature of the rocks and sediments); and climatic conditions, such as local rainfall and evapotranspiration (Conover, et al., 1984).

The depth at which groundwater circulates depends upon groundwater pressure. Water circulation occurs at greatest depth below areas of high water pressure and is shallowest where groundwater pressure is lowest (at discharge areas such as springs or streams). Where the upper part of the system is characterized by sink holes and other large solution features, the speed of groundwater movement may approach that of surface water streams, but, in most cases, the rate of groundwater movement is less than a few hundred feet per year (Conover, et al., 1984).

Locally, the presence of the Apalachicola Embayment-Gulf Trough system exerts control over water recharge to and water transmission within the Floridan Aquifer. The southeast flank of this linear, sub-surface depression, filled with thick sediments, crosses the project area trending northeast, from a point north of the Grady-Thomas county corner, and approximately following the topographic high on which U.S. Highway 319 is built.

In general, to the south and east of the Embayment-Trough, recharge and transmissivities are high. Within the Embayment-Trough in the Grady County part of the project area, transmissivities are unknown; however, it is a matter of record that transmissivities within the local Embayment-Trough are variable, ranging from the extremely high rate of 430,000 feet^2/day between Cairo and Pine Park to the extreme low rate of 390 feet^2/day just west of the project area, at Reno. (Kellam and Gorday, 1990).

Aquifer recharge tends to occur in areas of high potentiometric values. (Figure 5.15). A local potentiometric high occurs along the eastern Embayment-Trough flank, passing just south of Thomasville and trending diagonally westward into Grady County between Pine Park and Beachton, more or less along the eastern side of the Ochlockonee River.

In southern Thomas County and in southeastern parts of the Grady County area of the project, numerous sink holes breach the upper confining unit (Hawthorn) of the Floridan Aquifer System. These sinks allow direct recharge into the deep aquifer (Miller, 1986). Sink holes are less prevalent to the west and virtually disappear northwest of U.S. Highway 319.

Some generalizations are possible, based upon available groundwater data and the local geologic characteristics of the Floridan System. Karst features, indicative of large scale secondary porosity, are responsible for the extremely high transmissivity values near Thomasville. Solution features, such as sink holes and disappearing streams, are typical of those parts of the project area where the Floridan Aquifer is unconfined or semi-confined (Figure 5.12) and where sediments overlying the Floridan are generally about 100 feet thick (or less) (Miller, 1986) in most of the project area (Figure 5.11) (Kellam and Gorday, 1990). Finally, in these areas, the Floridan lies near the surface, and the system is a single, vertically permeable unit, with the upper confining unit consisting of thin breached clastics and permeable carbonates.

Even though rather prevalent breaching of the upper confining beds certainly exists in a large part of the area, the potentiometric surface of the Floridan seems to be consistently above the top of the aquifer in much of the area. Thus, artesian conditions are maintained, albeit not to a great extent in some areas.

Water Availability and Use

Water Supply

Water movement through the Floridan is affected naturally by rainfall, runoff and evapotranspiration. Rainfall is equal to runoff, infiltration and evapotranspiration within the project area. This same balance existed before groundwater development in the Floridan occurred. Pumping induces recharge or reduces natural discharge from the Floridan, which causes capture from runoff and evapotranspiration; but water withdrawn that doesn't become part of a product ultimately returns to the hydrologic system.

The total regional impact of pumping is minimal, less than the equivalent of one inch of rainfall annually. In all probability the evapotranspiration has not been changed much by man's activities,

Figure 5.14: Potentiometric Surface of the Floridan Aquifer, from Johnston, et al., 1981.

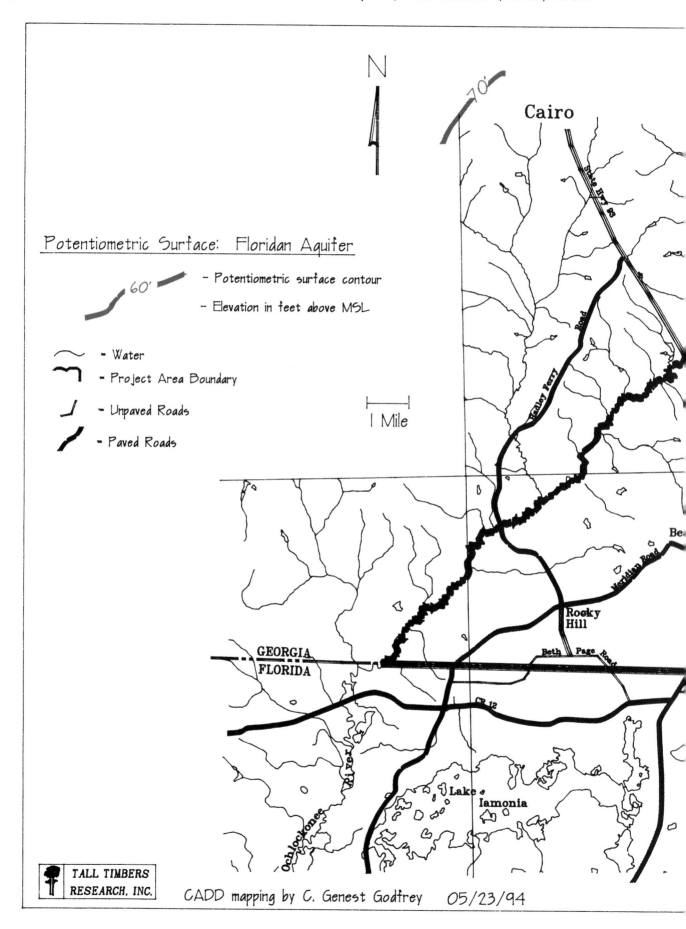

Figure 5.15: Local Recharge Rates of the Floridan Aquifer, from Bush and J

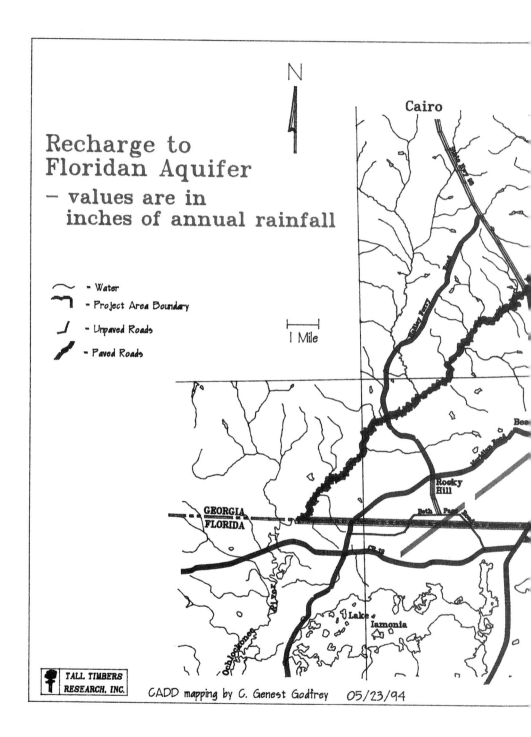

and there is no reason to suspect that there have been significant changes in rainfall over the past 1000 years. Thus it is assumed (by Bush and Johnston, 1988) that no appreciable changes in runoff have occurred since groundwater development began (ignoring local runoff changes due to land development).

Average rainfall is 51 inches for nearly all the project area. A very small corner of the Grady County part, between western Leon County, Florida and the Ochlockonee River, may have slightly higher average annual rainfall (up to 57 inches) (Figure 5.16).

In a normal year, there are two periods of relatively high and two periods of relatively low rainfall. These seasonal variations in rainfall are reflected in average water levels within the aquifer, although not dramatically. Rainfall maximums occur in late winter or early spring and then again in mid-summer. Conversely, the driest periods occur in the fall, generally in October, and again in mid-spring, usually in May. In response to these supply fluctuations, the highest water levels are usually found in late winter or early spring with the lowest water levels occurring in autumn.

Long term average runoff is variable; it may average as little as seven inches per year (in areas of well-developed karst topography) south and east of Thomasville, to as much as 17 inches per year in parts of west Thomas and east Grady Counties. The average is about 12 inches per year.

The most common features which affect runoff variability within a basin are topography and proximity of the water table to the surface. Thus flat swampy basins tend to have less runoff than areas with equal rainfall, but steeper topography and fewer wetlands.

Evapotranspiration (that water lost to evaporation from water surfaces and transpiration from plants) is not easily quantified. However regionally-developed estimates show that evapotranspiration can range from about 34 to 35 inches per year within the project area.

Hydrologic Budget

The hydrologic budget of the project area (Figure 5.17) was developed after Bush and Johnston (1986). The system characteristic that most strongly influences the distribution of natural recharge, flow and discharge is the degree of confinement of the Floridan Aquifer (see the discussion of the Floridan, above).

Groundwater Circulation

Before development, the flow system was in a state of long-term, dynamic equilibrium. This means that natural discharge and natural recharge were balanced, and there was no net change in the potentiometric surface (water level) in the Floridan Aquifer. The dominant features of the pre-development flow system are discharge from Floridan springs and direct aquifer discharge to streams and lakes. Although regional analysis of these factors exists, very little work has been done in quantifying these discharges within the project area watersheds. (See Groundwater Data from Georgia, USGS Open File Reports 88-223 and 89-408 for regional information).

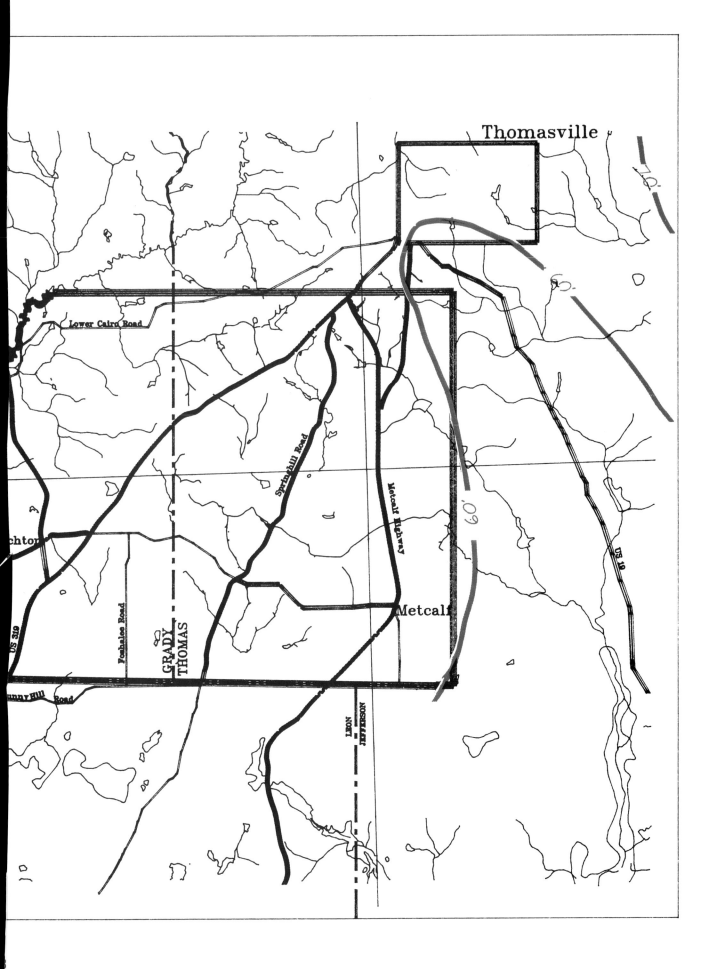

Thomasville

Lower Cairo Road

Springhill Road

Metcalf Highway

Metcalf

GRADY
THOMAS

Foabalee Road

chton

US 319

unny Hill Road

LEON
JEFFERSON

US 19

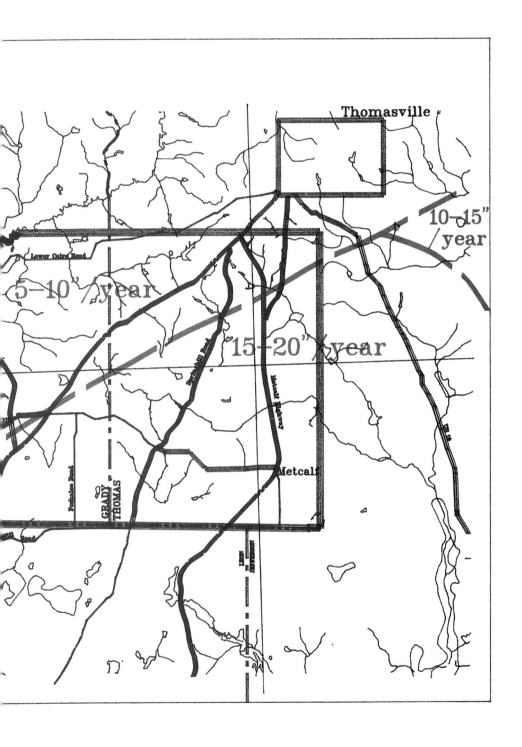

Method

U.S. Geological Survey 1:24,000 scale (7.5 minutes) topographic maps were used to locate all the sinks in the project area that were large enough and had sufficient topographic relief to be mapped at this scale (generally, one mile equals 2.65 inches). At this level, which was the most detailed available, the smallest sinks indicated were approximately 100 feet in diameter. Smaller ones (areally) were apparently below the level of either detection or effective map designation.

Using an elevation contour interval of 10 feet, all "closed" contours, indicating a local depression with no drainage outlet, were mapped as sink holes. This approach is considered quite conservative for two reasons:

1.   Sinks with a depth of less than the contour interval were not always indicated on the maps, and

2.   Topographic areas that could be interpreted as being of sink origin, but which erosion or later subsidence had altered to the extent that contours no longer closed, were omitted.

Only those features that met the "closed depression" criteria were mapped as sink holes. For this purpose, no consideration was given to whether or not the features were old or recent, actively subsiding or not, or holding water or not. Two exceptions were made in the floodplain of the Ochlockonee River, just south of the Florida state line; these two depressions were determined to be riverine features and not likely sinks.

The sink holes mapped in the described manner were delineated on the topographic maps and transferred to a standard project base map. For convenience, the sinks were indicated on the base map with standardized symbols, generally conforming to the (often irregular) areal extent of the individual features. The symbols used (circles) generally grouped the sinks into three sizes: approximately one-eighth mile in diameter (or less), approximately one-quarter mile in diameter, and approximately one-half mile in diameter (only one sink was located that exceeded the one-half mile designation (Original Pond Sink, about 2-½ miles west-southwest of Metcalf) and it was included with those having the half-mile designation). The sink holes are shown by symbols on Figure 5.18.

Results

Thus mapped, the U.S. Geological Survey topographic maps for the area indicated just under one-hundred sink holes in the specific project area. Nearly the same number (about 90) were indicated in areas immediately adjacent to the project area, especially east of Metcalf and slightly west of the Ochlockonee River, near the Florida state line.

Generally, the sinks mapped in this manner seemed to conform to three areas of concentration. One concentration was noted in the Metcalf area, extending across the project boundary to the east; a second concentration was apparent adjoining the project area on the southwest side. The largest concentration was found to parallel roughly U.S. Highway 319 and Meridian Road, in a band approximately three miles wide, extending southwestward from just south of Thomasville to (and across) the Florida state line. The largest number of sinks, as well as the most numerous large sinks were found in this latter area of concentration, which is almost exclusively to the southeast of the two highways.

In the area generally between U.S. Highway 319/Meridian Road, and the Ochlockonee River, sink holes are infrequently expressed at land surface. In fact, less than a dozen were indicated on the topographic maps of this entire portion of the project area, which covers over fifty square miles. In a general sense, the boundary between the area dominated by sinks and the area with very few sinks corresponds to U.S. Highway 319 from Thomasville southwest to its intersection with Meridian Road, thence Meridian Road southwest to the Florida state line.

The mapped sinks were verified in the field by visits to a representative sample of them. In no case (except, as mentioned, in the Ochlockonee River floodplain) were the sink depressions determined to be mapped in error. The sample examined (approximately 25%) is judged adequate to provide a reasonable level of confidence in this part of the effort.

Field observation and mapped features of the sinks indicated various degrees of topographic expression and water-holding capability. Some generalization of types was possible; however the types are often gradational. Many of the (areally) large sinks appear as wide, gentle depressions, somewhat saucer-shaped, with varying degrees of water-holding capability. Most seemed to hold water, at least at ground level, for some portions of the year, as indicated by wetland plant communities if not water itself. Typical examples of the large sinks are: Cherokee Sink, adjacent to the Georgia state line near Tall Timbers Research Station (Figure 5.19) and several large sinks along U.S. Highway 319 in the vicinity of Beachton in Grady County (Figure 5.20). Original Pond Sink, near Metcalf, is also an example. Topographic relief in these larger features ranged from ten to more than 30 feet.

Figure 5.19: Cherokee Sink

Figure 5.20: Sink Near Beachton on U.S. Highway 319

Small sinks, around 100 feet in diameter, were more diverse. Some were (relatively) quite deep, approaching 35 feet, and obviously did not hold water (Figure 5.21), and had solid bottoms with non-wetland vegetative growth. Others were observed to be taking water (from runoff and/or shallow groundwater) through obvious openings (Figure 5.22). Still other small sinks (Figures 5.23 and 5.24) were found with standing water, even during a relatively dry period, and were apparently intersecting the local, shallow, water table or were sealed by organic debris and/or other sediments.

Many of the small-to-medium size sinks would have been easily overlooked if not for the topographic maps. A number of these appear simply as "low, damp areas" or even abandoned fields (Figure 5.25). At ground level, it was difficult to detect the "closed" nature of the depressions, without careful observation. However, those that appear on the topographic maps are readily determined.

During the course of site visits, and even during transit from one area to another, one fact was quite obvious: a large number of sink holes (albeit mainly small ones) do not appear on the topographic maps. On virtually every trip to verify mapped sinks, un-mapped ones were located.

Some of the un-mapped sinks have occurred since publication of the topographic maps (generally in the 1980's). An excellent example is a small sink that occurred during early fall of 1993 adjacent to the southern boundary of the project on Mandalay Plantation (Figure 5.26).

The feature is small, perhaps 10 feet in diameter and five feet deep with vertical sides, but indicative of ongoing subsidence in the area. The "new" sink is in an area perhaps 200 yards across, containing at least four other, much older, sinks, one holding water, but none of them appear on the topographic map of the area.

5-34

Figure 5.21: Tall Timbers Sink

Figure 5.22: Small Sink, 0.25 Miles SW of Project

Figure 5.23: Small Sink on Arcadia Plantation

Figure 5.24: Sinkola Sink

Figure 5.25: Sink Along Sunny Hill Road, Foshalee Plantation

Figure 5.26: New Sink on Mandalay Plantation

Another example is on Mistletoe Plantation in the southwest corner of the project area. Here, a fairly large sink, about 50 feet deep and 400 feet in diameter, has existed for some time (mature hardwoods grow in the bottom), although the feature does not appear on the topographic map of the area. The sink is dry, at least most of the time, and has been farmed in the past (Figure 5.27).

Figure 5.27: Previously Unmapped Sink, Mistletoe Plantation

Cascades Sink, one-half mile south of the Georgia state line on Cherokee Plantation, is a striking feature: approximately 30-35 feet in diameter, over 40 feet deep, with nearly vertical sides and an obvious opening at the bottom (Figure 5.28). The feature was used in the past, in conjunction with ditches, to drain the local area. Apparently tree-cover may have obscured this feature or its small areal size may have prevented map designation.

Without question, the most impressive sink feature in the project area occurs on Arcadia Plantation, approximately two miles south of Thomasville, between the Metcalf Highway and Springhill Road. Reportedly, in 1985, a small sink opened at this site in the bottom of a 12 acre pond, draining it overnight. The sink was dammed off, and the pond refilled, only to have another, larger one open in the same area and, again, drain the pond overnight. The initial sink has since become clogged and holds water (Figure 5.29). The more recent one, however, is still extremely active.

Since formation, the more recent sink (designated "Wade Sink" herein) has grown to a size of about 150 feet wide and 40 feet deep, with nearly vertical sides and a distinct cavity opening at the bottom. In January 1994, local creek drainage into the feature was estimated to be at least 300,000 gallons per day and, even at this rate of flow, the sink transmits the water downward without even allowing a pool in the bottom. In addition, some 3,000 to 5,000 cubic yards of sediment have been transmitted to the sub-surface by this feature. (Figures 5.30, 5.31 and 5.32). The Wade Sink is too recent to appear on the topographic maps of the area and actually is shown on the maps as a pond.

Figure 5.28: Cascades Sink, Cherokee Plantation

Also apparent on Arcadia Plantation are a number of smaller, un-mapped, older sinks and another large sink feature capable of taking the entire flow of a local creek, at least during low water times. The larger feature was apparently clogged when the local topographic mapping was accomplished and appears on the topographic maps as a long pond, interrupting the flow of an intermittent stream. The sink is approximately 40 feet deep, perhaps 60 feet wide and has been substantially lengthened, probably by creek erosion. An obvious exit was observed in the bottom, easily taking a water flow of 10-20 gallons per minute in January 1994. The sink basin was full in February 1994, probably resulting from temporarily more flow in the creek than the sink would accept.

No attempt was made to locate and map all sink holes in the project area. If indeed possible, such an endeavor would require many months of on-the-ground investigation. Most of the sinks exist on the large plantation properties in the area and, even though plantation managers are acutely aware of the nature of the properties they oversee, they may not recognize some of the smaller depressions as sink holes; thus very detailed field work would be necessary to identify them all.

Figure 5.29: Blue Hole Sink, Arcadia Plantation

Although the sink holes that have been mapped and others that were detected in the field are numerous and often striking, the number of new and otherwise un-mapped sinks that exist in the area is equally impressive. Though a precise, documented calculation is not possible at this time, the number of previously un-mapped sinks detected during limited field work for this project seems to indicate that the actual number may exceed the mapped number by a very substantial margin. For example, Sinkola Plantation (about three miles southwest of Thomasville on the southeast side of U.S. Highway 319) has a total of five sink features that appear as closed depressions on the topographic maps. By the owner's estimate, there actually may be as many as seventy-five small sink holes on the property (Figure 5.33). (Based on a site inspection, the owner's estimate seems reasonable, if not conservative.)

However, even without locating any new or previously unmapped sink holes in the project area, the sinks apparent on the topographic maps would be adequate to show the prominence of these solution features in a major part of the area. Based only on the topographic maps, many parts of the area showed a local density of three to five sinks per square mile, with a maximum of about twelve in a

Figure 5.30: Wade Sink

square mile area immediately adjacent to the southwest corner of the study area. The true sink density certainly exceeds these levels.[2]

Surface Drainage Assessment

Stream patterns in any area normally bear a direct relationship to the underlying geologic material and, thus, areal difference in stream behavior often reflects changes in the thickness and lithology of local formations. In the project area, stream patterns coincide with prevalence of sink hole expression at the surface, for the most part, and help in indicating areas of internal drainage.

---

[2] The precise location, depth, and surface configuration of the sink holes mapped, and the location of additional sinks resulting from field work, are available, plotted on 1:24,000 topographic maps filed with Thomas College, Thomasville, Georgia.

Figure 5.31: Wade Sink

Method

Every mapped surface stream in the project area was outlined on the topographic maps, in order to detect typical drainage patterns. This effort was augmented by computer mapping capability at Tall Timbers Research Station, Tallahassee, Florida, which was able to isolate stream patterns from all other surface features (Figure 5.34). In some cases, the computer-generated configuration showed streams as more continuous than the topographic maps indicated. In the few instances of disagreement, the topographic maps were considered authoritative. Additionally, intermittent streams were not distinguishable from those with more constant flow on the computer map. Those streams referred to below as intermittent are shown as such on the topographic maps.

Figure 5.32: Wade Sink

Results

Stream patterns in the project area are easily separated into two distinct types that apparently conform to areal differences in sub-surface conditions.

<u>Northwest Area</u>:   In the area generally northwest of U.S. Highway 319/Meridian Road, stream patterns are well-developed and dendritic. Valley-heads tend to be relatively steep, narrow and "V"-shaped. With the exception of the Lee's Creek drainage basin, most of the creeks drain fairly small areas, and all ultimately drain to the northwest, emptying into the Ochlockonee River.

Northeast of the Beachton area, the local drainage divide is clearly U.S. Highway 319, with the upstream ends of many of the smaller drainages reaching almost to the highway. In only one minor case was drainage of any significance observed to cross the highway.

Figure 5.33: Small, Unmapped Sinks on Sinkola Plantation

Southwest of the Beachton area and northwest of Meridian Road, the drainage is virtually identical to areas further north, except for the area south of Hadley Mill Creek (onemile north of Rocky Hill). South of Hadley Mill Creek there are generally wide valleys, and not even intermittent streams are indicated, except for one small stream flowing northwest into the project area from Florida.

Stream density in the northwest portion of the project area ranges from (rarely) one stream course per square mile to as high as six or seven per square mile, with an average of about four. One exception was noted in the Beachton area where, locally, no streams are indicated; however, this area approximates the drainage divide. South of Hadley Mill Creek, as previously indicated, the mapped stream density is effectively zero. In measuring the stream density, tributaries to a main stream were considered separate stream courses and no distinction was made between intermittent and year-round streams.

The drainage pattern indicated in the area northwest of U.S. Highway 319/Meridian Road, from Hadley Mill Creek to the north, is consistent with streams underlain by at least moderately erodable clastic sediments. The streams appear to be actively eroding, but not rapidly. No deep gullies or other severe features were noted. Although some of the streams are indicated as intermittent, a significant number are shown as year-round features, indicating contribution to the streams from local, shallow groundwater. Figure 5.35 is an example of the topography and drainage pattern in this area.

Figure 5.34: Surface Drainage Patterns in the Project Area

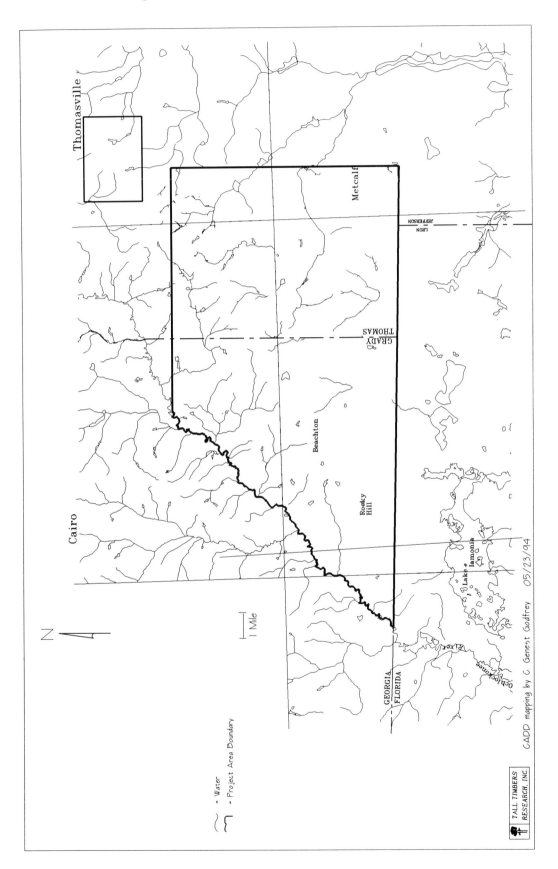

Figure 5.35: Typical Topography, Northwest Portion of Project Area

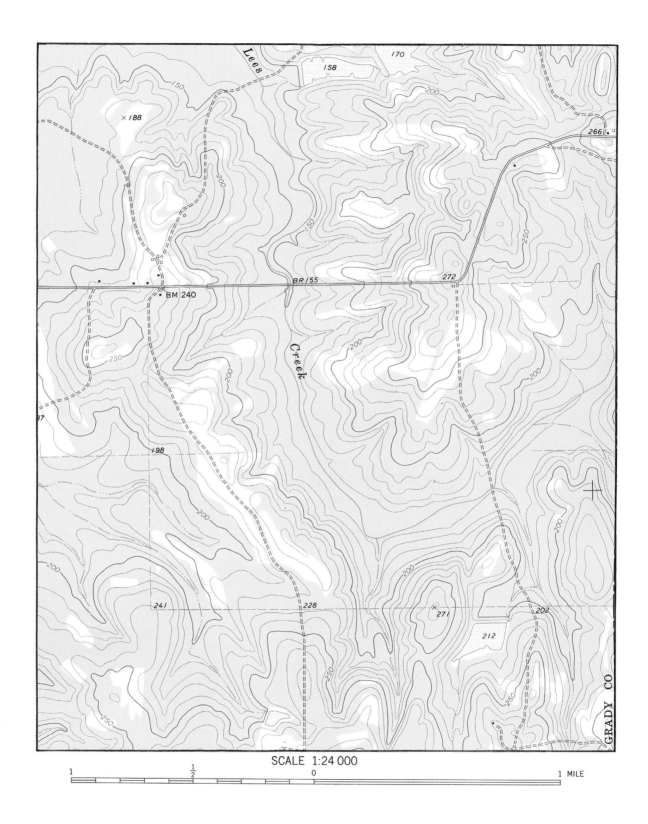

SCALE 1:24 000

Southeast Area: The portion of the project area to the southeast of U.S. Highway 319/Meridian Road, and south of Hadley Mill Creek on the northwest side, exhibits an entirely different drainage pattern (except for a small area southeast of U.S. Highway 319, just south of Thomasville, which is more typical of the drainage in the northwestern area). Drainage here is poorly developed and far from dendritic. Valley-heads are wide, rounded, and often encompass swampy areas and/or sink holes. Valley floors are often quite wide (up to about one-half mile), many are virtually flat, and most of the streams in them are designated as intermittent, with courses often interrupted by swampy areas with no definable channel. Two general drainage directions are indicated: one to the south-southeast into Florida, and the other to the east-southeast toward the Aucilla River. Wards Creek, with headwaters in Thomasville, and Pine Creek, two to three miles north of the Florida State line, are the only substantial drainage systems in the area, and even these are interrupted by swampy areas along their courses.

Most of the drainage in this southeastern area is characterized on the topographic maps by intermittent streams, many of which are prone to disappear. Even streams draining relatively large areas show very little flow. For example, Slater Branch virtually disappears as it approaches Springhill Road, after draining an area in excess of five square miles. In fact, with the obvious exception of Pine Creek and Wards Creek, a great number of the streams in this area effectively disappear—some after flowing for several miles and draining significantly large areas. An example of typical topography and drainage in this area is provided in Figure 5.36.

Some of the streams obviously flow into sink holes. For example, the entire flow of one branch of Wards Creek currently empties into the relatively young sink hole (Wade Sink) on Arcadia Plantation. During low water, at least, the entire flow of the creek crossing Springhill Road, about two miles south of U.S. Highway 319, is consumed by another large sink hole on Arcadia Plantation. Two streams that drain part of the Beachton area and an area near the intersection of U.S. Highway 319 and the Beachton-Metcalf Road, join after flowing separately for a mile or more, and then disappear about 0.2 miles north of a mapped sink hole. As another example, a small creek flowing southwest from the Metcalf area disappears into the Original Pond sink hole. This type of disappearance is exemplified slightly to the east of the project area, near Boston, where the Aucilla River disappears into Howell Sinks. Other small streams in the area simply seem to stop flowing, without the detectable presence of a sink hole. A good example is Titi Branch, which disappears less than a mile from the Florida state line, west of Original Pond (actually, it is referred to as "Dry Creek" from this point south).

A possibly more outstanding feature is the complete lack of any streams (based on the topographic maps) in an area of about 22 square miles, extending across the entire southern portion of Grady County (within the project area) and reaching as far to the north as Beachton. A similar area of at least eight square miles generally surrounds Metcalf and extends to the Florida state line. (This general lack of surface drainage is also quite evident in portions of Leon and Jefferson Counties, Florida, adjacent to the project area). The northern part of the project area east of U.S. Highway 319 has a somewhat higher stream density, ranging from zero to occasionally as many as five stream courses per square mile, with an average close to two per square mile.

Drainage of the nature described in this area, given over 50 inches of annual rainfall, must have a substantial internal component reaching the local aquifer(s) (i.e. either through sink holes or downward percolation through permeable sediments). During periods of high rainfall, there is obviously stream flow for at least short periods, and this has helped to lower the land surface by erosion. But, except in excessive cases, a large part of the rainfall not subject to evapotranspiration must drain locally to the sub-surface. In addition to the mapped sink holes, the generally low stream

Figure 5.36: Typical Topography, Southeast Portion of Project Area

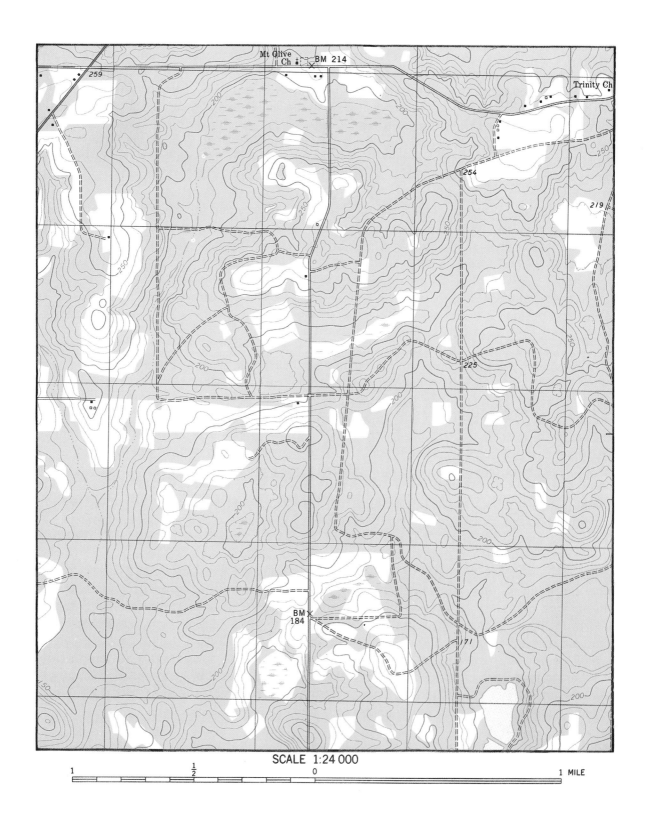

SCALE 1:24 000

density, disappearing streams, wide valleys, wide rounded valley-heads, and disorganized drainage pattern are very common in a karst landscape (sink hole area, underlain by limestone).

Local Geology, Reconnaissance

The surface geology (those formations exposed at land surface) is a major factor controlling topography, surface drainage, and downward movement of water to provide aquifer recharge. Exposed formations are normally mapped using the contacts between the formations as marker horizons, combined with outcrop descriptions, and correlated with sub-surface information (well data) where possible. Mapping in this manner can provide a general predictive capability for estimating the local depth to various sub-surface horizons (aquifer tops, for example), and also serves as one method of detecting geologic structure (faults, for instance) which may have a pronounced geologic effect locally. Documenting the characteristics of local formations during field work also allows some determination as to the capability of the sediments to transmit water downward to aquifers or, perhaps, to retard it.

Although previous sub-surface work had provided some information regarding generalized local depths to the top of the Floridan Aquifer, reconnaissance-level field mapping was chosen as a way to allow some local refinement of these estimates and provide a marker horizon. Although this horizon is certainly irregular, it is considered more consistent, area-wide, than the very sparse sub-surface (well) data that is available. The field mapping produced results that were very generally consistent with some of the previous results in Georgia and with more detailed mapping in adjoining areas of Florida. However, the local concentration of efforts produced more detailed information needed to refine the previous work in a number of areas and, in fact, to provide an improved sub-surface predictive capability.

Method

The only surface geologic mapping horizon available in the project area is the contact between the Torreya Formation of Lower Miocene age (mapped as Hawthorn Group, Undifferentiated) and the Miccosukee Formation of Upper Pliocene age. The two formations make up virtually all of the surface exposure in the area, except where they may be overlain sporadically by thin veneers of Pleistocene or recent alluvial deposits.[3] In general, most of the higher elevations in the project area are at least capped with sediments of the Miccosukee Formation, while valley floors are often below the Miccosukee, in the Hawthorn Group sediments.

Both of the formations have the advantage of having been the subject of rather intensive investigation (and description) in Gadsden, Leon, and Jefferson counties, Florida (for example, see: Yon, 1966; Rupert, 1990; Hendry and Sproul, 1966; and Scott, 1988). Surface exposures, well cuttings, and cores have been described to the extent that the two formations can be distinguished fairly

---

[3] Lateral (northward) extent of the Torreya Formation posed a problem in northern parts of the project area, both in Thomas and in Grady County. In this general area, the Torreya may interfinger with another (equivalent) formation of the Hawthorn Group, but the precise relationship has not been determined. Hence, "Hawthorn Group, Undifferentiated" is used on the surface geologic map of the area (Figure 5.43) for the sediments that directly underlie the Miccosukee Formation. In the southern part of the project area, these are clearly of the Torreya Formation, to the north the relationship is questionable.

consistently in the outcrop, and the contact between them can be correlated with sub-surface occurrences. All three Florida counties which are adjacent to the project area have surface geologic maps delineating areas of exposure of the formations at a scale of ½ inch = 1 mile.

Less local field work has been accomplished in the project area itself, although some work on the formations Sever (1966), and Huddleston (1988) has provided good information on the area of occurrence, age, stratigraphic correlation and significance of the formations.[4] Sub-surface information is available (McFadden, et al., 1986, for example), but the data on the two formations is very sparse in the project area. Previous surface geologic mapping is represented in the Geologic Map of the State of Georgia (1976), and the Miccosukee Formation and the Hawthorn Group are indicated in the project area. However, the scale of this map makes it more useful for regional studies than specific site investigations.

Given the available descriptions of the formations, it was expected that their lithologic characteristics were distinct enough and areally consistent enough to allow a reconnaissance-level, local mapping effort, with some degree of reliability. However, it should be emphasized, at this point, that no attempt was made to carry out a detailed study of the two formations. Project efforts did not involve re-description of the lithology, correlations with other units, or interpretation of environments of deposition and other characteristics.

Rather, the two formations were addressed from the standpoint of developing a useful marker horizon (the contact) and information that would relate to the local groundwater regime. Existing descriptions and interpretations were generally accepted and seemed reliable for the level of use. General lithology, and more specific information adjacent to formation contacts, was compiled in the field for comparison to the published information.

Finally, a major advantage of using the two formations was that they often could be distinguished based on gross lithologic characteristics. This allowed for fairly rapid field work, which was desirable under the time constraints of the project.

Established Formation Descriptions

Torreya Formation: The Torreya Formation was previously described as "Hawthorn Formation" in Florida (see Yon, 1966, and Hendry and Sproul, 1966). It outcrops in Jefferson County, Florida, as variously colored (normally grays) sandy, phosphatic clay and fine to medium, clayey, phosphatic, quartz sands. Chert and thin layers of sandy limestone are sometimes found associated with both lithologies. Based on surface geology and well data, the Torreya varies in thickness from 30-40 feet to about 90 feet in the northern part of the Jefferson County, where it was deposited on an uneven surface and, later, subjected to erosion (Yon, 1966).

In Florida Geological Survey Core Hole Wooten No. 2 (FGS Core 6927) north of Monticello (see Figure 5.37), the formation consists of 73 feet of generally phosphatic beds of sandy clay and clayey sand (see Johnson, 1986, for records of Florida cores). The clay predominates through most of the section. FGS Core Hole Sasser No. 1 (FGS Core 6933) in the northwest portion of the county, north of Lake Miccosukee, encountered 55 feet of Torreya, consisting mainly of sandy silt and clay in the bottom 35 feet, with sandy clay, clayey sand, and one five-foot bed of partially recrystallized

---

[4] These authors are by no means the only ones to address the project area. Others are listed in the reference section.

limestone above. Other thin limestone, dolomite and dolomitic limestone is evident at intervals throughout, but not predominant. Surface exposures of the Torreya are limited to the lower elevations in portions of the county adjacent to the project area, with an upper contact level of about 150' MSL[5] in northwest Jefferson County.

In northern Leon County, Florida, the Torreya was also previously mapped as Hawthorn and is generally composed of sandy, phosphatic limestone, overlain by sandy, phosphoritic clays, overlain, in turn, by sandy, clayey, phosphoritic silt, with the entire section becoming more calcareous to the west (Hendry and Sproul, 1966). In weathered outcrops, the Torreya was found difficult to distinguish from the overlying Miccosukee Formation and some areas of Torreya exposure were mapped (projected) by extending sub-surface structure contours to the land surface.

Hendry and Sproul (1966) provided a maximum Torreya thickness of about 90 feet in northern Leon County and Scott (1988) found slightly in excess of this amount. The elevation of the contact with beds of the overlying Miccosukee Formation was projected by Scott (1988) to be 200 feet MSL in extreme north-central Leon County; however, the Tall Timbers Core (FGS Core 16736) cuts eighty feet of Torreya with the upper contact at 170 feet MSL in this same area (Rupert, 1994, unpublished). Rupert (1990) describes a generally similar Torreya section in Gadsden County, Florida, consisting of fine to medium clayey sand and sandy clay, with variable amounts of limestone, dolomite and phosphate grains (p. 26). Fuller's earth (palygorskite) is mined from the Torreya in this area and to the north in Georgia, west of the Ochlockonee River. Rupert provides a thickness of about 150 feet in extreme northeastern Gadsden County, adjacent to the project area and an upper contact elevation of about 175' MSL. This section (thickness) reflects the thickening of Miocene sediments in the Apalachicola Embayment-Gulf Trough area.

In the project area, the Torreya Formation has somewhat more surface exposure than in much of the adjacent portions of Florida. Huddleston, (1988) shows its area of occurrence covering the southern two-thirds of both Grady and Thomas Counties, with the northward extent uncertain. The local lithology is described as a clayey, fine sand or finely sandy clay, variously calcareous and dolomitic. Fine quartz sand is the dominant component of the formation. In the sub-surface, both limestone and dolomite are common, with the calcite portion diminishing and disappearing to the north. Where it outcrops, leaching by groundwater has removed the limestone/dolomite component in most cases, and the formation appears as a fine sand to sandy clay, with indistinct layers (Huddleston, 1988, p. 55). Huddleston did not describe a thickness in the project area; however, he confirms a thickness of 50-100 feet in adjacent portions of Florida.

Sub-surface information on the Torreya Formation in the project area is limited at best. GGS Well 801, about six miles south of Cairo and 1-½ miles northwest of the Ochlockonee River (project boundary), penetrated 170 feet of Hawthorn Group, Undifferentiated, consisting predominantly of limestone, with sand, clay and some dolomite. The formation rests on the Suwannee Limestone and is overlain by Pleistocene fluvial sediments (McFadden, et al., 1986). This well is within the Apalachicola Embayment-Gulf Trough, however, and the consequent Hawthorn thickness is judged too great to be representative of the Torreya in areas further east. GGS Well 914, about two miles southwest of Thomasville on U.S. Highway 319, penetrated at least 55 feet of Hawthorn Formation, consisting primarily of a fine sand with "abundant limestone." However, this interval is overlain by 70 feet of fine sand (with limestone) that is designated as "Miccosukee/Hawthorn Undifferentiated" (i.e. the top of the Hawthorn is undistinguishable in this well). Here, the Hawthorn overlies the Chattahoochee Formation at a depth of 125 feet. GGS Well 807, slightly east of the project area and

---

[5] MSL: above (or below) mean sea level

Figure 5.37: Location of Wells Used for Sub-surface Control

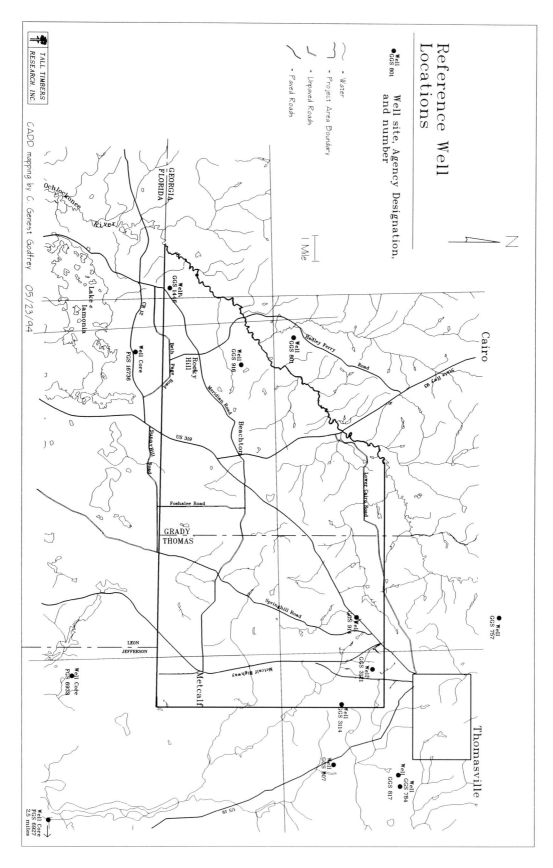

just south of the Lower Boston Road, penetrates 55 feet of Hawthorn, consisting of fine, slightly phosphatic, silty sand, with limestone. In this well, the Hawthorn overlies the Suwannee Limestone and is overlain by a 40 foot sand thickness designated as Miccosukee Formation (McFadden, et al., 1986).

It is apparent that sub-surface control on the Torreya Formation (Hawthorn Group) is inadequate to provide much information on the thickness of the formation in the project area; however, the contact with underlying formations seems fairly definitive. The Tall Timbers Core, though slightly south of the project, probably provides the best sub-surface description, including thickness, especially when viewed in concert with other Florida sub-surface information further to the east.

Miccosukee Formation: The Miccosukee Formation contains sediments previously described as Hawthorn (Miocene age) or Citronelle Formation (Pliocene age) and was formally named and described by Hendry and Yon (1967). A Pliocene age for the formation is generally accepted now (see Huddleston, 1988). In the general area of the project, the Miccosukee Formation consists of all sediments lying above the Hawthorn Group, exclusive of Pleistocene or later sediments that may overlie them in some areas. The Miccosukee deposits have been described by various authors (for example, see Vernon [1951] and Yon [1966]) as river delta sediments deposited on top of the near-shore, more massive marine sediments of the Hawthorn. Huddleston (1988 and personal communication, 1994) describes the sediments as shallow marine.

In Jefferson County, Florida, the formation is distinctive, and consists of moderately to poorly sorted, coarse to fine grained, clayey, quartz sand in a variety of colors (often red), and sandy clays. The sands are often cross-bedded and otherwise display prominent irregular bedding. The feature most diagnostic of the surface exposures is thin, white to light-gray clay laminae, often cross-bedded, which occur in the sands. The sediments are extremely variable, from outcrop to outcrop; however, the general lithology and, especially, the clay laminae are persistent (Yon, 1966). Yon found thicknesses up to 160 feet of Miccosukee Formation in Jefferson County, but erosion has removed substantial amounts in some areas. The contact with the underlying Hawthorn Group was/is poorly exposed in the county and may or may not be conformable (Scott, 1988, describes the contact as disconformable, with a contact elevation of about 150 feet (MSL) in the northwestern corner of Jefferson County).

In Leon County, Florida, Hendry and Sproul (1966) describe Miccosukee Formation sediments quite similar to those in Jefferson County, with prominent light-colored clay laminae. Also in this area, the formation was found to contain frequent sandstone lenses and sandstone float. Maximum thicknesses of about 90 feet were reported for northern Leon County.

Hendry and Sproul (1966) also document considerable post-depositional slumping of the formation, as shown by abundant joints, small faults, abnormal dips and wavy bedding (p. 86).

In Gadsden County, the formation caps the higher elevations east of Little River and descriptions by Rupert (1990) seem to accommodate those in Leon County.

In Georgia, the formation is recognized throughout the project area, and maintains many of the lithologic characteristics of the Florida portion of the outcrop area. Huddleston (1988) describes the dominantly thin-bedded nature and clay laminae, with some few clay layers reaching as much as one foot in thickness. Clay breccia is common, and local exposures may have coarse to gravelly sand lenses and stringers, probably representing tidal channel scour and fill (Huddleston, 1988, p. 126). Burrowing and bioturbation are common. Typical in all descriptions, both in Florida and Georgia, is a lack of calcareous material, chert, and phosphatic material — all common in the underlying Hawthorn Group (though the phosphatic material seems less prevalent in the Georgia Hawthorn section).

Field Mapping

In field situations in the project area (mainly in road-cuts and some sink holes), the gross lithologies of the Hawthorn and Miccosukee Formations generally were distinct enough to allow consistent mapping, even when the actual contact between the two was not clear. The Torreya Formation (mapped as Hawthorn Group) appears in most exposures as a fairly massive, fine to medium clayey sand. Formation color ranges from light brown to tan to yellowish gray, and some exposures exhibit borings and mottling (Figure 5.38). Thin layers of limestone fragments, silicified limestone fragments and chert fragments and nodules are present, sporadically, and are important keys to formation identification.

Figure 5.38: Typical Hawthorn Exposure

For mapping purposes, the Miccosukee Formation was distinguished by its thin-bedded and often distorted nature, light-colored clay laminae, often abundant clay flakes on the outcrop surface, clay clasts, cross-bedding and clay-filled joints (Figure 5.39). Color varied, but red was very common. The dominant lithology is fine sand with variable amounts of clay.

Some medium to coarse sand and sporadic gravel is present also. In a number of exposures, the formation has weathered to a deep red, near ground surface, and limonite was common in these instances, especially near the contact with the Hawthorn.

Figure 5.39: Typical Miccosukee Formation Exposure

In some local areas, indurated sandstone ledges were prominent in the outcrops, especially in the area west and southwest of Metcalf (Figure 5.40). The formation was often more massive and fine-grained near the bottom, but at least weak bedding was normally observable throughout.

These field characteristics were correlated with sub-surface and surface data in areas adjacent to the southern side of the project area and, where possible, with sub-surface information within the project area. The Geologic Map of Georgia (1976) was also used as a general guide. Initially, a southeasterly dip of about five to ten feet per mile was assumed for the contact between the formations. Although this was useful in projecting possible contact areas, the contact itself proved to be an irregular surface.

The Hawthorn-Miccosukee contact was mapped, wherever it could be distinguished, on all public roads in the project area. Location of the contact was extrapolated from known points when exposures were too weathered or indefinite.

Nature of the Contact

A peculiarity of the area of contact between the Hawthorn and Miccosukee sediments is fairly consistent distortion of the sediments. This occurrence was always noted when exposures were large enough and a clay bed (from one to several feet in thickness) was present at the base of the Miccosukee section. The distortion was normally gentle folding (wavy nature of the beds). The folding was rarely evident in upper Torreya sediments and was sometimes difficult to distinguish in the basal Miccosukee sediments in areas where cross-bedding exists. It is not unlikely that the more massive nature of the Torreya sediments and the cross-bedded nature of the Miccosukee sediments both tend to mask the post-depositional distortion in the absence of a definite marker bed. The

Figure 5.40: Sandstone Ledges in the Miccosukee Formation, West of Metcalf

distortion is attributed to post-depositional slumping of the beds and is more likely the rule than the exception (others have reached the same conclusion; see Rupert [1990], for example).

In areas to the northwest of U.S. Highway 319, the lower Miccosukee clay bed was more-or-less uniformly present in the contact areas. It was also detected in areas along Foshalee Road. A clay bed is also evident at the top of the Torreya section in the Tall Timbers Core; here, it is 7.7 feet thick.

In most areas, the Hawthorn/Miccosukee contact was placed at the base of normally red sands typified by thin bedding, light-colored clay laminae, clay clasts, and (sometimes) cross bedding, overlying more massive, tan to yellowish-gray, fine-to-medium, clayey sands of the Hawthorn. When present in the outcrop, chert or limestone fragments were used as definitive Hawthorn indicators. In many instances, whether the lower Miccosukee clay bed was noticeable or not, the contact occurred at, or just above, a local break in slope.

Examples of the contact areas are:

- Meridian Road, 1.3 miles north of the Florida state line.
- Hilltop exposure, 0.9 miles northwest of Rocky Hill on Hadley Ferry Road, south side of Hadley Mill Creek (Figure 5.41).
- One mile south of Metcalf-Beachton road on Foshalee Road.
- 0.2 miles west of Lee's Creek on Lower Cairo Road, about six miles west of Thomasville.
- 2.4 miles southeast of Ochlockonee River on Highway 93, on northwest side of creek crossing.
- General area of creek crossing 2.5 miles south of U.S. Highway 319, on Springhill Road.

Neither carbonates nor chert nor shell material were detected in any exposure of the Miccosukee Formation. Limestone fragments, chert, and some silicified limestone, however, are not uncommon in the Hawthorn, at various levels. Large limestone boulders were evident, weathering out of the sediments 50 feet below the top of the Hawthorn (Torreya) on Foshalee Road (Figure 5.42). Fist-size limestone fragments were noted in the Hawthorn near the Ochlockonee River in the vicinity of Highway 93 on the Lower Cairo Road, and a substantial limestone ledge outcrops along the Ochlockonee River on Mistletoe Plantation in the southwest corner of the project area. The only shell bed detected was a small, thin layer of Ostrea (sp.) fragments near the top of the Hawthorn sediments on Highway 93, just southeast of the Ochlockonee River. Nodular chert fragments were evident in the Hawthorn in the recent sink hole (Wade Sink) on Arcadia Plantation, south of Thomasville, and in an area near Lee's Creek on the Lower Cairo Road, west-southwest of Thomasville.

Figure 5.41: Miccosukee/Hawthorn Contact, Northwest of
Rocky Hill

Figure 5.42: Limestone Boulders in the Torreya Formation, Foshalee Road

The outcrop patterns of the Miccosukee Formation and Hawthorn Group are shown on Figure 5.43, Reconnaissance-Level Geologic Map.

Implications

The Hawthorn/Miccosukee contact elevations indicate a generalized dip of about ten feet per mile to the south-southeast in a large part of the project area, ranging from about 160 feet MSL near Metcalf to approximately 210 feet MSL just south of Thomasville and on Highway 93, between Beachton and the Ochlockonee River (Figure 5.44). Though there are probably other undetected disruptions, the only readily apparent regional change in dip is a flattening of the contact in the area just north of the Florida state line, and two low elevations (180 feet MSL) in the northwest part of the area. These northwestern measurements may indicate an erosional feature in the top of the Hawthorn sediments. A higher-than-expected contact elevation in the vicinity of Foshalee Road may also indicate no more than differential erosion prior to Miccosukee deposition. Additionally, the overall contact attitude in the southern part of the area is generally consistent with results by Rupert (1990), Hendry and Sproul (1966), and Yon (1966) in Gadsden, Leon, and Jefferson Counties (Florida) respectively. The contact strike (250° to 270°) is at a large angle to the trend of the Apalachicola Embayment-Gulf Trough (about 215°-225°) and this agrees with the suggestions of Kellam and Gorday, Huddleston, Schmidt and others that the final filling of the trough was accomplished by sediments of the Hawthorn Group. In any case, the base of Miccosukee sediments in the project area probably shows no indication of the influence of any trough activity.

Generally stated, the Miccosukee Formation occupies the higher elevations in the area, at least capping the ridges in the northern part and occupying the hill-tops and the sides of many valleys in the southern part. All of the major valley floors appear to be developed in the Hawthorn sediments

Figure 5.44: Representative Elevations of the Miccosukee/Hawthorn Contact

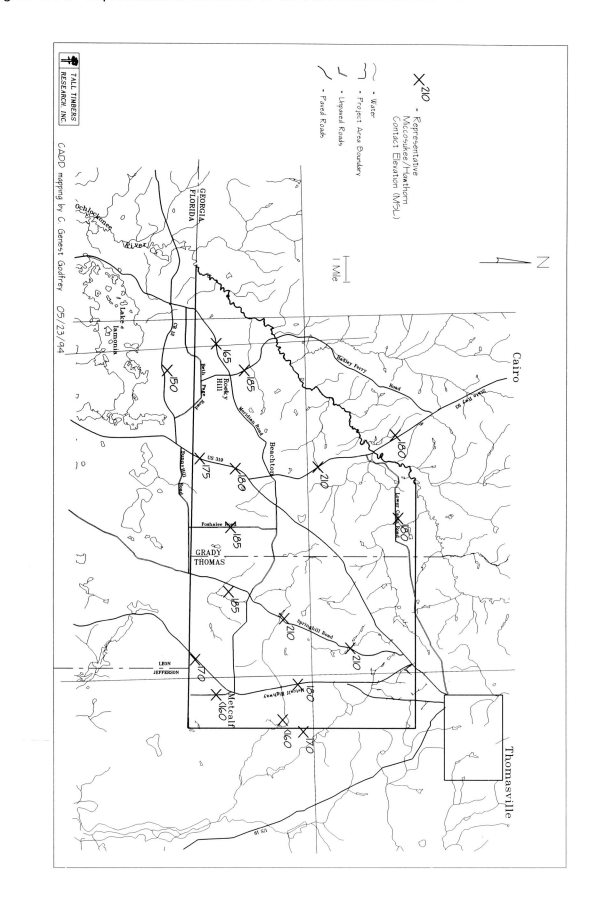

area-wide, and these sediments occupy some higher positions on the valley sides to the north andto the west, where erosion by the Ochlockonee drainage system has generally lowered the landscape, and in the general area of Foshalee Road.

Sink holes are expressed at the surface in outcrop areas of both formations. Of the sinks located from topographic maps, about half were expressed in surface exposures of each formation. Noteworthy, though not without exception, is the fact that a substantial number of the (areally) larger sink holes occur in valley-floor areas where the Hawthorn sediments are exposed or very near the surface. In the case of the few large sinks that do occur in Miccosukee exposures, the bottom elevations of the surface expressions approximate the top of the Hawthorn.

Obvious distortion of many of the contact exposures, combined with the very common development of joint systems that are easily apparent in Miccosukee exposures, above the Hawthorn, is taken as evidence of general, post-depositional subsidence over much of the area. The probable explanation for the subsidence is dissolution of limestone at depth (probably concentrated in the upper part of the Suwannee Limestone-see Miller, 1986), followed by slumping and differential compaction of the overlying beds of the Hawthorn and Miccosukee sediments. The local prevalence of sink holes makes it unlikely that this factor is not a major cause of the distortion, although some un-related differential compaction may have occurred as a result of partial dewatering of clay sediments caused by pressure (Huddleston, personal communication, March 1994).

Use of Surface and Sub-surface Geologic Data

Previous work (See Kellam and Gorday, 1990,and Miller, 1986) has provided estimates of the thickness of sediments overlying the Floridan Aquifer (down to top of the Suwannee Limestone) in the project area. This was accomplished by the use of thicknesses of material measured between ground surface and the Suwannee Limestone in very widely-spaced local reference wells. These treatments provided "thickness-of-overburden" contours based on the well data and (probably due to the regional scope of the investigations) did not take into account the effect of local topography in reducing the thickness of the sediments above the Floridan.

For example, in one location (a creek bottom), about two miles east of GGS Well 914, on U.S. Highway 319, south of Thomasville, the thickness of sediments overlying the Floridan Aquifer (top of Suwannee Limestone) is at least 80 feet less than the thickness indicated at the well (170 feet) and used for previous generalization in the area. This reduces the generalized "overburden" by about half at that location.

As another example, the Tall Timbers (Florida) Core (FGS Core 16736) indicates a local overburden thickness of 190 feet (this core was not available for use by previous authors). If employed in the previous, generalized manner, this information would mask the fact that in a creek bottom and a sink hole, about one mile north of the core location, on the Georgia state line, the actual thickness of overlying sediments has been reduced by nearly 70 feet (to approximately 120 feet total thickness) by erosion. As a result, the development of a more locally adaptable method was appropriate for the project area.

In evaluating well logs and other information in adjacent areas of Florida, and in four wells (GGS Wells 914, 807, 284, and 1446) and outcrops in the project area, an average maximum thickness of 140 feet was determined for sediments lying between the base of the Miccosukee Formation and the top of the Suwannee Limestone (in much of the project area this corresponds to the combined thickness of the Hawthorn and Chattahoochee sediments). Although the thickness is likely less in some areas (especially in the northern part of the area), the figure seems reasonable based on the available information. However, since it is known that sediments of this interval thicken rapidly westward into the Apalachicola Embayment-Gulf Trough, (Kellam and Gorday, 1990), the average maximum 140 foot thickness is considered applicable only to that portion of the project area lying east of U.S. Highway 319 and in the eastern part of the area between Meridian Road and U.S. Highway 319.

Representative thicknesses that were used in computing the average maximum thickness between the Suwannee and Miccosukee formations are given below (see well locations, Figure 5.37).

* GGS Well 914 (Thomas County). 125 feet: 70 feet of Chattahoochee Formation, overlain by (at least) 55 feet of Torreya. (The upper contact of the Torreya Formation in this well is not specific, although the approximation seems reasonable, based on surface exposures in the area). Well data is from McFadden, et al. (1986).

* GGS Well 807 (Thomas County). 100 feet: McFadden, et al. (1986) gives only 55 feet of Torreya, with the Chattahoochee Formation absent. Extension of surface mapping into the area of this well gives a greater Hawthorn thickness above the Suwannee.

* GGS Well 784 (Thomas County). 110 feet: This thickness is based on presence of only Torreya sediments between the Suwannee Limestone and the Miccosukee Formation (from McFadden, et al., 1986), with the Miccosukee/Hawthorn contact elevation based on surface mapping. Nearby, GGS Well 817, if accurate, indicates only about 50-foot thickness between the Suwannee and the Miccosukee Formation (based on the well log and surface mapping). However, GGS Well 817 indicates the top of the Suwannee Limestone to be 65 feet higher than in GGS Well 784, which is only 0.4 miles to the east. The higher contact elevation in Well Log 817, while providing a much thinner overburden calculation, is considered suspect unless later sub-surface information proves its accuracy.

* GGS Well 1446 (Grady County). 230 feet: This thickness of undifferentiated sediments (Hawthorn and probably Chattahoochee Formation) is based on a Suwannee contact at -70 feet MSL (McFadden, et al., 1986) and a projected Miccosukee Formation contact at 160 feet MSL. This well is obviously on the southeast flank of the Apalachicola Embayment-Gulf Trough and serves only to limit the area where the 140 foot thickness may be applicable.

* FGS Core 6933 (Jefferson County). 176 feet: Johnson (1986) describes 121 feet of St. Marks Formation overlying the Suwannee Limestone, overlain in turn by 55 feet of Hawthorn sediments below the Miccosukee contact.

* FGS Core 16736 (Leon County, Tall Timbers). 142 feet: Rupert (1994, unpub.) describes 17 feet of St. Marks Formation overlying the Suwannee Limestone, overlain in turn by 43 feet of Chattahoochee Formation, overlain by 82 feet of Torreya (Hawthorn) sediments under the Miccosukee contact.

Given the fact that the St. Marks Formation has not been detected in the project area (see Huddleston, 1988, for example) and appears to pinch out just north of the Tall Timbers core, the only sediments recognized between the Suwannee Limestone and the Miccosukee Formation in the project area are attributable to the Chattahoochee Formation and the overlying Hawthorn sediments. Based on only one well description in the project area, the Chattahoochee Formation is of uncertain areal extent, though thicknesses of 40 to 70 feet may be present in some areas. The average described thickness of Hawthorn sediments is about 80 feet in and south of the project area; however, the greater thicknesses of Hawthorn are described where the Chattahoochee Formation is apparently absent, due to non-deposition or erosion prior to Hawthorn deposition, or possibly due to inclusion of Chattahoochee sediments as part of the Hawthorn by previous workers.

Based on the above, a generalization of 140 feet (maximum) between the Suwannee Limestone and the base of the Miccosukee Formation seems reasonable as a "rule-of-thumb" in the designated area. Although this thickness estimate may be reasonable and useful, given the relative lack of sub-surface information, it should be viewed with caution for specific areas and always subject to local refinement.

Use of the base of the Miccosukee Formation as a marker horizon and the generalized thickness of 140 feet between that horizon and the Suwannee Limestone (top of the Floridan Aquifer) provides an improved capability to estimate depth to the Floridan Aquifer in the designated part of the project area. In this vicinity, all outcrop areas of the Hawthorn sediments (areas where the Hawthorn is exposed at the surface and the overlying Miccosukee Formation is absent) may be generally assumed to have a thickness of no more than 140 feet of sediments overlying the Floridan (see Reconnaissance-level Geologic Map, Figure 5.43). In fact, viewed in this manner, virtually all of the Hawthorn outcrop areas are below the top of the Hawthorn and, hence, may have considerably less than 140 feet, depending on the amount of Hawthorn sediments that have been removed locally by erosion.

For example, using the method described yields the following "overburden" thicknesses in the indicated locations, based on ground elevation from the topographic maps (stated differently, this is the approximate local depth to the top of the Floridan Aquifer, since all locations below lie within Hawthorn outcrop areas).

- Large, shallow sink, 0.5 miles west of U.S. Highway 319, adjacent to the Florida state line: approximately 75 feet.

- Large, shallow sink 1.3 miles north of the Florida state line on east side of U.S. Highway 319 (Hutchinson Plantation): approximately 85 feet.

- Valley floor of Titi Branch/Dry Creek at Springhill Road (Springhill Plantation): approximately 110 feet.

- Valley floor of Pine Creek at Springhill Road (Long Pine Plantation): approximately 90 feet.

- Bottom of dry sink adjacent to Sinkola Sink (approximately 1.5 miles southeast of U.S. Highway 319 on Sinkola Plantation): 70 to 80 feet.

- Valley floor (un-named drainage) on Springhill Road 2.5 miles south of U.S. Highway 319 (Arcadia Plantation): approximately 120 feet.

- Bottom of sink in same un-named drainage, 0.5 miles south of Arcadia location above (Arcadia Plantation): approximately 70 feet.

- Valley floor of Pine Creek, two miles north of Metcalf on Highway 122 (Milestone Plantation): approximately 80 feet.

- Bottom of 1985 sink hole, 0.5 miles west of Highway 122, about two miles south of Thomasville (Arcadia Plantation): approximately 90 feet (local measurements indicate that this is closer to 70 feet).

Maximum thicknesses of all sediments (above the Floridan) in areas of Miccosukee Formation outcrops correspond to the hilltops and are illustrated by the following examples:

- Hilltop areas between Beth Page Road and Rocky Hill: approximately 220 feet.

- Hilltop area 0.75 miles south of the Beachton-Metcalf road, on Foshalee Road: approximately 210 feet.

- Area along U.S. Highway 319 in vicinity of Thomasville School, about two miles southwest of Thomasville: approximately 210 feet.

Between U.S. Highway 319/Meridian Road and the Ochlockonee River, the generalized maximum thickness between the Miccosukee Formation and Suwannee Limestone is in excess of values to the east, as the thickness of these sediments increases progressively westward toward the axis of the Apalachicola Embayment-Gulf Trough (Kellam and Gorday, 1990). However, sub-surface data is generally lacking in this area of the project. The Miccosukee Formation has been removed by erosion in much of this area and, although the Miccosukee/Hawthorn contact could be projected through the area with some accuracy, the critical datum is the top of the Suwannee Limestone-which is dependably reported in only one well within this portion of the project, near the Florida state line (Mistletoe Plantation, GGS Well 1446).

Some information may be extrapolated from GGS Well 1446, GGS Well 801 (west of the Ochlockonee River) and GGS Well 757 (northwest side of Thomasville). GGS Well 757 is certainly within the trough area (Kellam and Gorday, 1990), albeit only by about 3-4 miles. This well reached a total depth of 240 feet and bottomed in Hawthorn (although, based on Kellam and Gorday's structure map, the Suwannee contact should be close to the elevation of the bottom of the well). The well penetrated 185 feet of Hawthorn sediments, beneath the Miccosukee contact (McFadden, et al., 1986).

GGS Well 801, west of the Ochlockonee River (just outside the project area), penetrated 190 feet of sediments over the Suwannee Limestone (McFadden et al., 1986); however, the Miccosukee Formation has been removed locally by erosion (and likely the upper part of the Hawthorn as well). GGS Well 1446, (in McFadden, et al., 1986) shows only a Suwannee contact at approximately minus 70 feet MSL. Using a projected Miccosukee contact elevation of approximately 160 feet MSL in the well gives a thickness of 240 feet of (probably) Chattahoochee and Hawthorn sediments at this site. Total thickness of overlying sediments (including Miccosukee) is 310 feet — obviously the well is within the influence of the Embayment-Trough.

Based on (short distance) extrapolation of the elevation of the top of the Suwannee Limestone in reference wells, and the general location of the axis of the Apalachicola Embayment-Gulf Trough as shown by Kellam and Gorday (1990), the minimum local thickness of all sediments overlying the Suwannee Limestone (Floridan Aquifer top) in the area between U.S. Highway 319/Meridian Road and the Ochlockonee River exists beneath the river channel itself (lowest topographic point). Examples are as follows:

- River channel north of Rocky Hill: 125-foot thickness (estimated maximum)

- River channel at the Georgia-Florida state line: 160-foot thickness (estimated minimum)

- River channel west of Thomasville: 130-foot thickness (estimated minimum)

It should be evident, however, that in most of this part of the project area, to the east of the Ochlockonee River floodplain, thicknesses of overlying sediments certainly exceed those estimated below the river channel.

One additional well is available for sub-surface reference between the Ochlockonee River and Meridian Road. The well log for GGS Well 916 indicates the top of the Suwannee Limestone at an elevation of 163 feet MSL (McFadden, et al., 1986). This places the Suwannee contact approximately 240 feet higher than Well 1446, which is about four miles to the south, about 70 feet higher than in GGS Well 914, and nearly 200 feet higher than the described contact in GGS Well 801. The described Suwannee contact in GGS Well 916, if projected for no more than a mile, would easily crop out in the Ochlockonee River valley to the west and in Hadley Mill Creek to the south. Yet, no published report has indicated any sediments below the Hawthorn Group to be exposed in these two drainages, and surface geologic mapping for this report reached the same conclusion. Based on the apparently substantial elevation anomaly and the lack of corroboration by any field mapping effort, the log for this well is perhaps arguably suspect. Kellam and Gorday (1990) accepted the log in their work on the Gulf Trough, and, if the log is accurate it would necessitate rather substantial revision of thickness estimates in this report. Given the local topography, it would also indicate surface exposure of the Floridan Aquifer in the area — which is not indicated at any other location in the project area. The well log was not accepted as reliable for use herein.

As a means of comparing approaches, the thickness of sediments overlying the Floridan Aquifer was also estimated, area-wide, by subtracting the elevations of a modified version of Kellam and Gorday's "top of Floridan" structure map from surface elevations available on the local topographic maps. Representative thicknesses of overlying sediments, thus derived, are presented in Figure 5.45.

Soils

General

Three broad groups of soils occur across the project area in southern Thomas and Grady Counties. These are differentiated by occurrence, based on relative position of the landform. They are:

Nearly level soils on bottom lands and on stream terraces or low uplands; nearly level to gently sloping soils on uplands, along drainage ways, in depressions or on flats; and finally, nearly level to sloping upland soils.

Typically these groups are then subdivided into soil complexes for general soil maps of an area, and further subdivided in smaller individual soil map units for detailed soil survey maps. These smaller units are delineated based on differences in observable soil characteristics such as soil texture (particle size distribution), structure, consistence (relative hardness), permeability, drainage (relative wetness), and presence of, and depth to, soil water table.

This report concentrates on only one of these characteristics, permeability, as an indicator of likelihood of rapid transmission of fluids through the soil and subsoil.

Figure 5.45: Representative Thicknesses of Sediments Overlying the Florida Aquifer

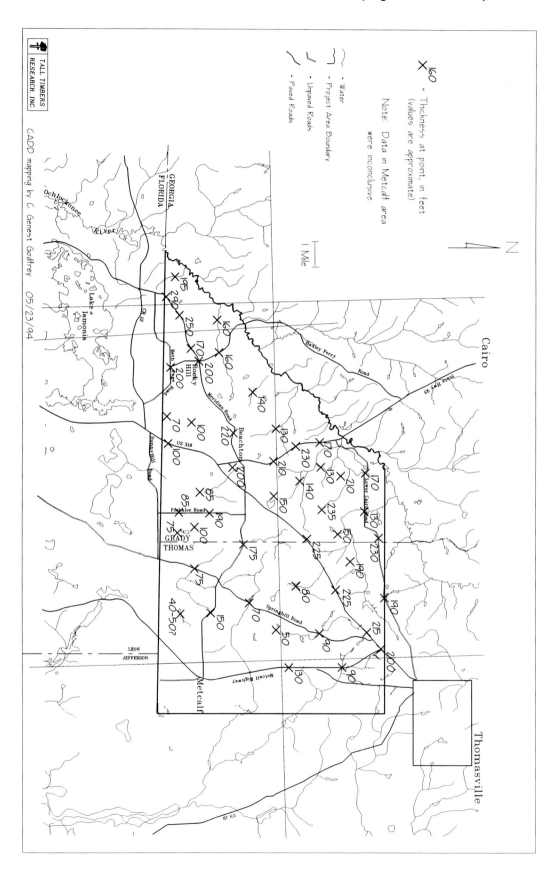

Method

Soil survey atlases of Thomas County (May, 1979, Soil Survey of Brooks and Thomas County, Georgia) and Grady County (unpublished advance copies of soil survey atlases and soil descriptions and interpretations) were obtained from the local offices of the Soil Conservation Service in Thomasville and Cairo, Georgia. These maps and soil data were evaluated and interpreted. Three basic units were delineated using soil survey aerial atlases as base maps. These units were differentiated solely on the basis of subsoil permeability.

In developing an interpretive map some decisions regarding placement of a map unit in a group were necessarily arbitrary, particularly in those cases where map units included areas that might normally fall into more than one permeability grouping. In these cases, if a significant part of the unit was much more permeable than the remainder, the entire unit was grouped with that part of the unit. In addition, the Grady County soil survey is incomplete. This results in three problems in the interpretation and evaluation of the Grady County data. First, in some areas, there are no soil units delineated; these areas are designated as "unmapped areas" on the soil permeability maps, Figures 5.46 and 5.47.

Secondly, matching and correlation of Grady County Soil Map Units with those of adjacent counties is incomplete; where this occurs there are conflicting soil boundaries at the Grady/Thomas county line. These areas are designated by a "?" question mark symbol, indicating the incomplete nature of the data and the preliminary nature of the Grady County Soil Map. Finally, only soil series descriptions and interpretations were available for Grady County. The specific map unit descriptions and information regarding significant inclusions in map units were unavailable. Thus, Grady County's soil permeabilities are strictly associated with the regional soil series interpretations, and not as specific to Grady County as those data that were used to develop the Thomas County soil interpretations.

Soil Permeability Classes

The soils of Thomas and Grady Counties are divided into three broad interpretative groups. As previously indicated, these are based solely on subsoil permeabilities. Each soil series was evaluated based on the permeability of the most restrictive subsoil layer. The most restrictive layer was used in order to identify that part of the subsoil in which water is predicted to move most slowly. This means that less-restrictive layers probably lie above and/or below the part of the soil used to differentiate the soil group. Soils were classed as having high, moderate or low permeability (see Table 2).

Table 5.2
Soil Permeability Classes

Soil Legend and	Interpretation	Comments
Symbol	Permeability (in/hr)	
L	Low 0.06-0.6	v. slow to slow percolation within sub-soil
M	Medium 0.6-2.0	moderate percolation with sub-soil water
H	High > 2.0-20.0	rapid to excessive percolation within sub-soil

Areas with high permeability are for the most part sandy. They may be sandy uplands, but in most instances occur on low-lying stream terraces. In Grady County these occur primarily adjacent to and along the Ochlockonee River. These soils make up a little less than five percent of the Thomas County area and about 20 percent of the Grady County part of the project area.

Soils with moderately permeable subsoils were by far the most significant in occurrence and distribution, comprising about 40 percent of the area in Grady County, and about 70 percent of the project area in Thomas County. They are generally sloping to nearly level loamy soils and usually occur on uplands, but may occasionally be found along drainage ways.

Slowly permeable soils comprise a significant part in both Grady and Thomas County project areas. These soils have thick clayey layers, or are characterized by iron oxide cementation in the subsoil, restricting water movement and sometimes creating perched or temporary water tables. They are generally nearly level to gently sloping soils and may occur on uplands, along drainage ways, in depressions or on flats. Soils in this category comprise about 25 percent of the Thomas County section and about 40 percent of the Grady County part of the project area. The project area is made up of predominantly moderately permeable soils, but contains significant areas of both low permeability and high permeability soils.[6]

---

[6] See Appendix V: Table V-1 (Soil Permeability Groups by Map Symbol and Map Unit Name, Thomas County); Table V-2 (Soil Permeability Groups by Map Symbol and Map Unit Name, Grady County); Table V-3 (Physical and Chemical Properties of Soils, Brooks and Thomas Counties); Table B-4 (Physical Properties of Soils, Decatur and Grady Counties).

Synthesis

Summary of Conditions

The project area is a fairly typical coastal plain location, in most respects. Sub-surface geologic formations that have some effect on surface activities are limited to a relatively thick limestone (Floridan Aquifer), overlain by generally thin layers of clastic sediments, with some carbonates included in the lower part.

In most of the project areas, the sub-surface layers dip fairly gently to the southeast with some local irregularities. In western portions of the area, dips of the deeper formations are locally to the northwest, the limestone surface occurs progressively lower, and the thickness of overlying clastic sediments increases. This is due to the influence of a trough-like feature, centered further west, which ceased to exist (filled up) prior to deposition of the uppermost clastic sediments.

Although local lithology of the clastic sediments may vary at times, the thickness overlying the Floridan Aquifer remains generally consistent over the eastern and southern parts of the area, averaging about 140 feet between the bottom of the uppermost sedimentary layer (Miccosukee Formation) and the limestone. To the west, toward the trough, the thickness increases. The entire thickness of clastic sediments above the limestone ranges from sand to clayey sand, to sandy clay, to clay, with fine clayey sand perhaps the dominant lithology. Thin clay beds (and some carbonates) are fairly common in lower parts of the clastic sediments.

The clastic sediments are divided into two geologic units, both of which have substantial surface exposures that cover almost the entire land surface of the area. The two units (The Miccosukee Formation, above, and the Hawthorn) are often distinct in the outcrop and the contact between the two can be mapped locally without special difficulty. Beneath the clastics, but above the major (Floridan) limestone, a thin, dense limestone (Chattahoochee Formation) has been mapped in the sub-surface of some parts of the area and may extend to others.

Topographically, the eastern and southern portions of the area are dominated by sink holes, disappearing streams, otherwise poorly-developed surface drainage, and other karst features. The sinks and disappearing streams have most likely resulted from solution-cavity development in the upper part of the Floridan Aquifer and subsidence that followed.

Areas high in soil permeability are characterized by rapid to excessively rapid percolation and have very high to high potential to transmit fluids and thus pollution through the soil profile. Those parts of the project area mapped as moderately permeable transmit fluids more slowly, but are still subject to seepage and are capable of transmitting contaminants into groundwaters, but not as fast and efficiently as the highly permeable areas. Areas with low permeability soils are much less efficient in transmitting water from the soil to underlying geologic materials. In general, these areas are less susceptible to seepage and can be quite impermeable. Where the slowly permeable soils occur near sink holes, they may perch fluids and then assist in transmitting them laterally, on top of the low permeability (or slowly permeable) layers, acting as conduits into the sink and in these instances, probably directly into the Floridan. The larger amount of low permeability soils in Grady County corresponds, at least generally, to a larger area of Hawthorn outcrop and certainly has a bearing on reduced recharge in northwest portions of the project area.

Recharge to the Floridan has been calculated to be a rather low five to ten inches per year in the northwest part of the area and fifteen to twenty inches per year in the remainder of the area (an amount not exceeded in the Floridan Aquifer in the Southeastern United States). Groundwater flow direction in the Floridan varies locally, but is generally to the southeast within the project area. The potentiometric level is above the top of the aquifer in much of the area, indicating artesian conditions. Well yields from the aquifer are good in the east and south and decrease rather substantially to the northwest. The aquifer shows little to no effect from local withdrawals within or immediately adjacent to the project area.

Composite of Conditions and Implications

The east and south part of the project area is underlain by a very productive, generally under-utilized, limestone aquifer at shallow depths. Though partially confined, the aquifer is directly connected to the surface via sink holes, as well as receiving apparently rapid downward percolation of water through the overlying sediments. To the west, the aquifer is generally less productive, deeper, and overlain by a greater sequence of sediments; general soil permeability is lower in this area, as well. Recharge is low in the west and sink holes are generally rare, indicating a greater degree of local protection for the aquifer.

The implications are simple and straight-forward: To the east of U.S. Highway 319 and in at least a portion of the area between U.S. Highway 319 and Meridian Road, the Floridan Aquifer is a good, albeit rather fragile resource. Conditions in the aquifer are directly impacted by the quality of water occurring as surface drainage and as shallow groundwater—both of which reach the aquifer rapidly and in substantial amounts. Based on surface features, that portion of the western part of the project area south of Hadley Mill Creek seems perhaps equally vulnerable.

In western parts of the area, west of U.S. Highway 319/Meridian Road the aquifer is deeper, less productive and apparently better protected by overlying sedimentary thicknesses. Surface waters reaching the aquifer have been calculated to be less than half of the comparable amount to the east, and, correspondingly, a greater amount of both surface and shallow groundwater drains to the Ochlockonee River. Recharge rates are, hence, relatively slow. The degree of vulnerability of the Florida Aquifer in this area, though obviously less than to the east, is uncertain, as evidenced by the presence of some, albeit much fewer, sink features.

Limitations of Information

Geologic information in the project area is quite limited. Of the logged wells available for use in and immediately adjacent to the project, only one has a complete, measured section beginning in the Miccosukee Formation and extending into the Suwannee Limestone (upper part of the Floridan Aquifer), and this well lies more than a mile south of the project, in Florida. One of the remaining wells in the area (GGS Well 916), is considered too suspect for use. Of the others, two give fairly complete Sections (GGS 914 and 801), but one of these is too far to the west to have much applicability to the project area. However, the formation descriptions in a majority of the wells seemed consistent with surface mapping efforts and, hence, had definitive value.

Sub-surface data are inconclusive as to the extent of the previously-mapped structural anomalies in the project area, specifically the "Barwick Arch" and the "Ochlockonee Fault." Surface geologic mapping did not serve to confirm the Barwick Arch or the surface exposures of Suwannee Limestone that have been attributed to it (Sever, 1966).

Additionally, the lateral change in geologic conditions, from the south and east to the northwest, though apparent in the topography and in calculated recharge rates, is difficult to define in the sub-surface. Simply stated, precise location of the southeast edge of the Apalachicola Embayment-Gulf Trough (or Sever's Ochlockonee Fault), where sediments overlying the Floridan Aquifer begin to thicken rapidly to the west, is not possible based on existing sub-surface data—though some generalizations are warranted.

The top of the Floridan Aquifer (top of the Suwannee Limestone) is certainly an irregular surface in adjacent parts of Florida and is assumed to be so in the project area. However, the extent of irregularity is difficult to define, based on existing information, and will certainly have some effect (both plus and minus) on the local accuracy of estimates of sediment thickness overlying the Floridan Aquifer, and, hence, its extent of vulnerability.

Local recharge rates for the Floridan Aquifer, calculated by the U.S. Geological Survey for a regional-scale investigation, could be refined substantially by specific investigations involving aquifer tests and local calculation of rainfall versus evapotranspiration and surface run-off. Based on field observations, very local recharge rates in excess of those previously calculated would not be unexpected.

Very little is known about the local hydraulic characteristics of the Floridan Aquifer, except in the Thomasville area. Based on local usage, the aquifer is assumed to be more than adequate to supply an increased demand in most areas. However, this assumption can be documented only by the appropriate aquifer tests. Similar documentation is also lacking on the effectiveness of the local confining beds for the Floridan.

Incompatibility in level-of-detail between soils maps in Thomas and Grady Counties leads to some uncertainty in comparisons, though general conclusions are possible. Future work in Grady County will help to alleviate the existing problem.

General Conclusion

Near-surface geology in the project area is understood generally, but local specifics are often lacking. The Floridan Aquifer, which supplies groundwater to the area, is quite adequate for current (and probably future) uses, and no existing special problems with it were detected during the course of this investigation. Given continuation of current land usage in the area, no specific groundwater problem can be predicted for the near future. The aquifer is, however, quite vulnerable to changes in water quality originating at land surface in areas east and southeast of U.S. Highway 319/Meridian Road and possibly south of Hadley Mill Creek as well. The northwestern portion of the area does not exhibit the same vulnerability, though the local extent is uncertain

Additional definition of the aquifer system, and the geology that relates to it, especially in the sub-surface, is rather urgently needed in order to make adequate determinations of aquifer capabilities, limits, and local contamination potential (see Future Study Needs, Appendix VI). In the interim, a local regulatory approach toprotect the more sensitive areas of the aquifer system would probably be of significant value.

Finally, the remainder (east part) of the Red Hills area in Georgia is generally similar to the subject of this report. The existing state of knowledge of the area in comparable, and the need for "base-line" information to use in land use and other local determinations is equally pressing. A similar study would be instrumental in meeting these needs and, by adding information on adjacent areas, it would certainly enhance the current effort.

REFERENCES

Note: The references herein are provided in two sections, using different formats, as follows:

- Annotated References. This section concentrates on those references considered most useful in preparing this report. The entries are ordered by topic and title (rather than author) and a brief summary of each is included. This presentation was selected to provide a general guide for further examination of ideas developed in the report.

- Selected References. Standard citation by author is used to present all sources of information consulted in preparation of this report.

Annotated References

A. Water Resources
1. *U. S. Geological Survey Professional Papers 1403A-C.* This series provides a detailed analysis of the Floridan Aquifer System which serves Florida and parts of Georgia, South Carolina and Alabama. Those parts of the 1403 series helpful to the study of southern Thomas and Grady Counties are:

  * *USGS Professional Paper 1403-A: Summary of the Hydrology of the Floridan Aquifer System in Florida and in Parts of Georgia, South Carolina, and Alabama.* Johnston, R.H. and Bush, P.W. (1988). 24 p.

    An overview of the regional analysis (1403 series); a brief summary of previous work; a regional-scope summary of the geology and hydrology of the Floridan Aquifer System. The hydrogeology section touches on hydraulic properties, regional flow system, groundwater development, and groundwater chemistry.

  * *USGS Professional Paper 1403-B: Hydrogeologic Framework of the Floridan Aquifer System in Florida and in Parts of Georgia, Alabama, and South Carolina.* Miller, G.A. (1986). 91 p.

    A regional look at the setting, stratigraphy and geologic structure of the rock units comprising the Floridan System. Includes numerous maps and figures.

    USGS Professional Paper 1403-C: Groundwater Hydrau-lics, Regional Flow, and Groundwater Development of the Floridan Aquifer System in Florida and in Parts of Georgia, South Carolina, and Alabama. Bush, P.W. and Johnston, R.H. (1988). 80 p.

    Hydraulic properties of the aquifer system are the principle emphasis of this section. In addition, Bush and Johnston discuss the regional flow system in terms of a 3-dimensional finite-difference flow model. Recharge and discharge are addressed as important components of the regional flow system. Water quality in the region is mentioned briefly. Contains numerous maps and figures.

*   *USGS Professional Papers 1403-D through 1403-H*: These are detailed investigations of local water problems in five sub-areas: 1403-D - *South Carolina, Southeast Georgia and Northeast Florida*, 1403-E- *East- Central Florida*, 1403-F- *West-Central Florida*, 1403-G- *South Florida*, 1403-H- *Western Panhandle, Florida*.

(South Georgia and the Big Bend area of Florida are <u>not</u> covered individually. However, these areas are discussed within the regional framework in 1403-B, 1403-C and 1403-I).

*   *USGS Professional Paper 1403-I: Geochemistry of the Floridan Aquifer System in Florida and in parts of Georgia, South Carolina and Alabama*. Sprinkle, C.L. (1985).

Describes the geochemistry of the Floridan Aquifer System, including the principle chemical processes operating in the groundwater flow system.

2.   *Water Resource Atlas of Florida*: Fernald, E.A. and Patton, D.J. (Eds) (1984). 291 p.

A full treatise on water resources of Florida, both ground and surface, and the management of these resources. A regional perspecitve is used throughout, but the information provided has applicability to the southern part of the project area.

3.   *Georgia Geological Survey Information Circular 85: Water Use in Georgia by County for 1987*. Trent, V.P, Fanning, G. L. and Doonan, GA, (1990). 111 p.

A cooperative publication with the USGS. Provides water - use for Georgia by use- category for each county. This is one of a series of periodically updated water use circulars. The data used in generating the reports is part of a centralized database, the Georgia Water-User Data System (GWUDS).

4.   *Georgia Geological Survey Information Circular 34: Reconnaissance of the Groundtwater and Geology of Thomas County, Georgia*. Sever, C.W. (1966). 9 p.

Brief overview of Thomas County, Georgia geologic formations and structures. Also includes discussion of the water quality and hydraulic properties of the Floridan locally.

5.   *Georgia Geological Survey Information Circular 36: Hydraulics of Aquifers at Alapha. Coolidge, Fitzgerald, Montezuma and Thomasville, Georgia*. Sever, C.W. (1969). 16 p.

Summary data for the above cities includes: performance tests, pumping effects, hydraulic properties of the aquifer and chemical water quality.

6. *USGS Water Supply Paper 1809-Q: Groundwater Resources and Geology of Seminole, Decator and Grady Counties, Georgia*. Sever, C. W. (1965). 30 p.

> Discussion of water quantity and quality for Seminole, Decator and Grady counties. Includes brief overview of stratigraphy and structure, but concentrates on water quantity and quality data.

7. *Florida Geological Survey Special Publication 32: Florida's Groundwater Quality Monitoring Program: Hydrogeologic Framework*. ed. by Scott, T.M.; Lloyd, G. M. and Maddox, G. (1991). 97 p.

> Details of the hydrogeologic framework of Florida. Specific attention paid to the Floridan Aquifer. Divided by water management district boundaries. Includes stratigraphy and structure, and a brief geologic history.

8. *Florida Geological Survey Special Publication 34: Florida's Groundwater Quality Monitoring Program: Background Hydrogeochemistry*. ed. by Maddox, G.L., Lloyd, G.M., Scott, T.M.; Upchurch, S.B.; Copeland, R. (1992). 364 p.

> Detailed water quality background data statewide. Data organized by water management district boundaries. Includes some brief stratigraphy, but primarily concentrates on establishing background values for water-borne substances. Discusses general water quality of the water in all Florida's aquifer systems, but again emphasizes the Floridan which serves most of Florida's citizens. Water chemistry data includes both naturally-occurring substances and pollutants.

9. *Georgia Geological Survey Bulletin 94: Hydrogeology of the Gulf Trough - Apalachicola Embayment Area, Georgia*. Kellam, M.F. and Gorday, L.L. (1990). 74 p.

> Examines the effects of the Apalachicola Embayment - Gulf Trough on water quality and quantity for a band of Georgia counties which stretches diagonally from the Florida Line (Decatur, Grady, Thomas, Brooks) to the Atlantic coast (Screven and Effingham). Includes hydraulic conductivities, water chemistry and brief overview of associated stratigraphy.

10. *Georgia Geological Survey Information Circular - 56: Geologic Data of the Gulf Trough Area, Georgia*. McFadden, S.S.; Hetrick, G.H.; Kellam, M.F.; Rodenbeck, S.A. and Huddleston, P.F. (1986), 345 p.

> This is essentially a well-log data report which is the basis for the discussion found in the Kellam and Gorday, GGS Bulletin #94, and covers the same counties. This data was also used by Huddleston, in his stratigraphic work (1988 and 1993) in GGS Bulletin #104 and 105.

11. *Georgia Geological Survey Information Circular - 18: Source and Quality of Ground Water in Southwestern Georgia*. Wart, R.L. (1960). 74 p.

> One of the very first groundwater quality investigations. It contains general stratigraphic information, but concentrates primarily on chemical parameters. Used municipal wells for its data sources.

B. <u>Geologic Framework, Paleogeography, Soils, Stratigraphy and Structure</u>

1. *American Association of Petroleum Geologists. Bulletin Volume 28, No. 12: Regional Subsurface Stratigraphy and Structure of Florida and Southern Georgia.* Applin, P.L. and E.R. (1944). 84 p.

    An early important work of regional scope, this paper addresses Lower Cretaceous to Recent deposits. Concentrates on paleontological correlations.

2. *USGS Bulletin 941: Geology of the Coastal Plain of Georgia.* Cooke, C.W. (1943). 121 p.

    A very early overview of the stratigraphy and structure of Georgia from the "Fall Line" south. Includes stratigraphic units which encompass the Floridan Aquifer System.

3. *Georgia Geological Survey Information Circular 25: Subsurface Geology of the Georgia Coastal Plain.* Herrick, M. and Vorhis, R.C. (1963). 78 p.

    Stratigraphy of Georgia from the Fall Line south and eastward. Includes paleontological evidence, along with isopach maps and geologic sections. Timeframe: Upper Cretaceous to Recent.

4. *Georgia Geological Survey Information Circular 41: Chattahoochee Anticline, Apalachicola Embayment, Gulf Trough and Related Structural Features, Southwestern Georgia, Fact or Fiction.* Patterson, S.M. and Herrick, M.. (1971). 16 p.

    An evaluation of the hypothetical structural features of the southwestern Georgia Coastal Plain. Gives a brief history of the structures which have been proposed for the area. Includes some maps and figures.

5. *Florida Geological Survey Special Publication 5: Summary of the Geology of Florida and a Guidebook to the Classic Exposures.* Puri, H.S. and Vernon, R.O. (1964). 312 p.

    Detailed stratigraphy of Florida, including detailed lithologic descriptions of classic and/or representative outcrops. Includes type sections. This publication also has location maps and field guide references.

6. *Sedimentary Geology, Volume 17, No 1/2: Miocene of the S.E. United States: A Model for Chemical Sedimentation in A Peri-marine Environment.* Weaver, C.E. and Beck, K.C., (1977). 234 p.

    Detailed investigation of Miocene clay deposits of north Florida and south Georgia. Includes regional setting, structure, stratigraphy and chemistry. Also, paleogeographic interpretations. Many figures, maps, logs and electron micrographs.

7. *Florida Geological Survey Bulletin 48*: *Geology of Jefferson County, Florida.* Yon, G. W., (1966). 119 p.

    Detailed local geology includes physiography, stratigraphy, structure, geologic history and economic geology. Includes some Floridan data.

8. *Florida Geological Survey Bulletin 47*: *Geology and Groundwater Resources of Leon County, Florida.* Hendry, C.W. and Sproul, C.R., (1966). 178 p.

    Similar to Bulletin #48, but for Leon County, Florida. This bulletin is about 50% stratigraphy and structure, and 50% hydrogeology.

9. *Florida Geological Survey Bulletin 59*: *Lithostrati-graphy of the Hawthorn Group (Miocene) of Florida.* Scott, T.M.,(1988). 148 p.

    Detailed discussion of Miocene Hawthorn; traces nomenclature changes. Includes lithologic unit descriptions, cross-sections, maps, etc. Defines Hawthorn sediments as a Group as proposed by Huddleston (1988).

10. *Georgia Geological Survey Bulletin 104. A Revision of the Lithostratigraphic Units of the Coastal Plain of Georgia; the Miocene through Holocene.* Huddleston, P.F., (1988). 162 p.

    Miocene to Recent stratigraphy and structure. Detailed descriptions of lithostratigraphic units; maps delineating areal extent in outcrop or subcrop. Includes: stratigraphic correlation chart, stratigraphic cross -sections and locations of type localities and reference sections.

11. *Georgia Geological Survey Bulletin 105*: *A Revision of the Lithostratigraphic Units of the Coastal Plain of Georgia; The Oligocene.* Huddlestun, P.F. (1993). 152 p.

    Oligocene stratigraphy, structure, paleoenvironment and paleogeography. Contains detailed lithostratigraphy, areal distribution maps, Oligocene correlation chart, and stratigraphic cross sections.

12. *USDA - SCS. Soil survey of Brooks and Thomas Counties.* (1979).

    Detailed soil maps, interpretations and descriptions. Includes aerial photographs, and data tables identifying physical and chemical properties of mapped soils and discusses land use limitations by soil series or map unit type.

Selected References

American Geophysical Institute, 1980, *Glossary of Geology*.

Applin, P.L. and E.R., 1944, *Regional Subsurface Stratigraphy and Structure of Florida and Southern Georgia*: Bull. Am. Assoc. Pet. Geol., Vol. 28, No. 12, p. 1673-1753.

_____,1967, *The Gulf Series in the Subsurface in Northern Florida and Southern Georgia*: U.S. Geological Survey Professional Paper 524-G, 35 p.

Bush, P.W. and Johnston, R.H., 1988, *Groundwater Hydraulics, Regional Flow and Groundwater Development of the Floridan Aquifer System in Florida, and in Parts of Georgia, South Carolina, and Alabama*: U.S. Geological Survey Professional Paper 1403-C, 80 p.

Chen, C.S., 1965, *The Regional Lithostratigraphic Analysis of Paleocene and Eocene Rocks of Florida*: Florida Geological Survey Bull. 45, 105 p.

Clark and Zisa, 1976, *Physiography of Georgia*: Georgia Geological Survey.

Cooke, C.W., 1943, *Geology of the Coastal Plain of Georgia*: U.S. Geological Survey Bulletin 941, 121 p.

Dall, W.H. and Harris, G.D., 1892. *Correlation Papers, Neocene*: U.S. Geological Survey Bull. 84, 349 p.

Dunne, T. and Leopold, L.B., 1978, *Water in Environmental Planning*: W.H. Freeman and Co., N.Y., 88 p.

Fernald, E.A. and Patton, D.J., eds., 1984, *Water Resource Atlas of Florida*: Florida State University, 291 p.

Gelbaum, C.S., 1978, *Geology and Groundwater of the Gulf Trough, in Georgia*: Georgia Geological Survey, Bull. 93, p. 38-49.

_____ and Howell, J., 1979, *Geohydrology of the Gulf Trough, in Georgia*: Georgia Geological Survey Inf. Cir. #53, p. 140-153.

Georgia Geological Survey, 1976, *Geologic Map of Georgia*.

Gremillion, L.R., 1965, *The Origin of Attapulgite in the Miocene Strata of Florida and Georgia*: Thesis, Florida State University, Tallahassee, FL, 139 p.

Hendry, Jr., C.W. and Sproul, C.R., 1966, *Geology and Groundwater Resources of Leon County, Florida*: Florida Geological Survey Bull. 47, 178 p.

Hendry, Jr., C.W. and Yon, Jr., J.W., 1967, *Stratigraphy of Upper Miocene Miccosukee Formation in Jefferson and Leon Counties, Florida*: American Association Pet. Geol. Bull., Vol. 51, No. 2, p. 250-256.

Herrick, S.M. and Vorhis, R.C., 1963, *Subsurface Geology of the Georgia Coastal Plain*: Georgia Geological Survey Inf. Cir. 25, 78 p.

Huddleston, P.F., 1988, *A Revision of the Lithostratigraphic Units of the Coastal Plain of Georgia: The Miocene through the Holocene*: Georgia Geological Survey Bull. 104, 162 p.

_____, 1993, *A Revision of The Lithostratigraphic Units of the Coastal Plain of Georgia: The Oligocene*: Georgia Geological Survey, Bull. 105, 152 p.

Johnson, L.C., 1892, *The Chattachoochee Embayment*: G.S.A. Bull. Vol. 3, p. 128-132.

Johnson, R.A., 1986, *Shallow Stratigraphic Core Tests on File at the Florida Geological Survey*: Florida Geological Survey Inf. Cir. 103, 431 p.

Johnston, R.H. and Bush, P.W., 1988, *Summary of the Hydrology of the Floridan Aquifer System in Florida and in Parts of Georgia, South Carolina and Alabama*: U.S. Geological Survey Prof. Paper 1403-A, 24 p.

Kellam, M. F. and Gorday, L.L., 1990, *Hydrogeology of the Gulf Trough-Apalachicola Embayment Area, Georgia*: Georgia Geological Survey Bull. 94, 74 p.

Maddox, G.L., Lloyd, J.M., Scott, T.M., Upchurch, S.B., and Copeland, R. ed., 1993, *Florida's Groundwater Monitoring Program, Background Geochemistry*: Florida Geological Survey Sp. Pub. 34, 364 p.

McFadden, S.S., Hetrick, J.H., Kellam, M.F., Rodenbeck, S.A., and Huddlestun, P.F., 1986, *Geologic Data of the Gulf Trough Area, Georgia*: Georgial Geological Survey Inf. Cir. 56, 345 p.

Miller, J.A., 1986. *Hydrogeologic Framework of the Floridan Aquifer System in Florida, and in Parts of Georgia, South, Carolina and Alabama*: U.S. Geological Survey Professional Paper 1403-B, 91 p.

Murray, G.E., 1957, *Geologic Occurrence of Hydrocarbons in the Gulf Coast Province of the United States*: Gulf Coast Assoc. Geol. Socs. Trans., Vol. 7, p. 253-299.

_____, 1961, *Geology of the Atlantic and Gulf Coastal Province of the United States*: New York, Harper, 692 p.

Pascale, C.A. and Wagner, J., 1982, *Water Resources of the Ochlockonee River Area, Northwest Florida*: U.S. Geological Survey Inv. OFR-81-1121, 114 p.

Patterson, S.H. and Herrick, S.M., 1971, *Chattahoochee Anticline, Apalachicola Embayment, Gulf Trough and Related Structural Features, Southwestern Georgia, Fact or Fiction*: Georgia Geological Survey Inf. Cir 41, 16 p.

Pierce, R.R., Barker, N.L. and Stiles, H.R., 1982. *Water Use in Georgia by County for 1981*: Georgia Geological Survey Inf. Cir. 59, 180 p.

Puri, H.S. and Vernon, R.O., 1964, *Summary of the Geology of Florida and A Guidebook to the Classic Exposures*: Florida Geological Survey Sp. Pub. 5, 312 p.

Rainwater, E.H., 1956, *Geology of Jackson County, Florida*: by Wayne Moore (a review: in) Am. Assoc. Petrol. Geol. Bull., Vol 40, No. 7, p. 1727-1729.

Rupert, F.R., 1990, *Geology of Gadsden County, Florida*: Florida Geological Survey Bull. 62, 61 p.

_____, 1994, Unpublished Report - Florida Geological Survey Well Core 16736 - Tall Timbers, Leon County, Florida.

_____, and Yon, J.W., 1993, *Geologic Map of Jefferson County, Florida*: Florida Geological Survey, OF-MS-31.

Schmidt, W., 1985, *Stratigraphy and Geological History of the Apalachicola Embayment*: Florida Geological Survey Bull. 58, 146 p.

Scott, T.M., 1988, *Lithostratigraphy of the Hawthorn (Miocene) of Florida*: Florida Geological Survey Bulletin 59, 148 p.

_____, 1990, *A Brief Overview of Miocene Lithostratigraphy -Northern Florida and Eastern Georgia*: Florida Geological Survey OFR - 31, 6p.

_____, 1993, *Geologic Map of Gadsden County, Florida*: Florida Geological Survey, OF-MS-22.

_____, 1993, *Geologic Map of Leon County, Florida*: Florida Geological Survey, OF-MS-28.

_____, Lloyd, J.M., Maddox, G., 1991, *Florida's Water Quality Monitoring Program, Hydrogeological Framework*: Florida Geological Survey Sp. Pub. 32, 97 p.

Sever, C.W., 1965, *Groundwater Resources and Geology of Seminole, Decatur and Grady Counties, Georgia*: U.S. Geological Survey - Water Supply Paper, 1809-Q, 30 p.

_____, 1966a, *Miocene Structural Movements in Thomas County, Georgia*: USGS Professional Paper 550-C, 4p.

_____, 1966b, *Reconnaissance of the Groundwater and Geology of Thomas County, Georgia*: Georgia Geological Survey Inf. Cir. 34, 14 p.

_____, 1969, *Hydraulics of Aquifers at Alapaha, Coolidge, Fitzgerald, Montezuma and Thomasville, Georgia*: Georgia Geological Survey Inf. Cir 36, 16 p.

Sprinkle, C.L., 1989, *Geochemistry of the Floridan Aquifer in Florida, Parts of Georgia, Alabama and South Carolina*: U.S. Geological Survey Professional Paper 1403-I.

Tanner, W.F., 1966. *Late Cenozoic History and Coastal Morphology of the Apalachicola River Region, Western Florida*: In: Deltas. Houston Geological Society, Houston, TX, pp. 83-98.

Toth, J., 1963, *A Theoretical Analysis of Groundwater Flow in Small Drainage Basins*: Jour. of Geophysical Res., Vol., 68, No. 16, p. 4795-4812.

Toulmin, L.D., 1955, *Cenozoic Geology of Southeastern Alabama, Florida and Georgia*: Am. Assoc. Petrol. Geol. Bull., Vol. 39, pp. 207-235.

Trent, V.P., Fanning, G.C., Dunnan, G.A., 1990, *Water Use in Georgia by County for 1987*: Georgia Geological Survey Inf. Cir. 85, 111 p.

USDA - Soil Conservation Service, 1979, *Soil Survey of Brooks and Thomas County, Georgia*.

_____, 1979, *General Soil Map of Thomas County, Georgia*.

_____, 1977, *Soil Associations and Land Use Potentials of Georgia Soils*.

Vernon, R.O., 1951, *Geology of Citrus and Levy Counties, Florida*: Florida Geological Survey Bull. 33, 256 p.

Wagner, J.R., 1982, *Groundwater Resources of the Little River Basin and Vicinity, N.W. Florida*: Northwest Florida Water Management District, Water Res. Sp. Rpt. 82-2.

Wagner, J.R. and Musgrove, R.J., 1983, *Hydrologic Assessment of Lake Iamonia and Iamonia Sink, Leon County, Florida*: Northwest Florida Water Management District Water Resources Sp. Rpt. 83-1, 50 p.

Wait, R.L., 1960, *Source and Quality of Groundwater in Southwestern Georgia*: Georgia Geological Survey Inf. Cir. 18, 74 p.

Weaver, C.E. and Beck, K.C., 1977, *Miocene of the S.E. United States: A Model for Chemical Sedimentation in a Perimarine Environment*: Sed. Geol., Vol. 17, No. 1 and 2, 234 p.

Yon, J.W., Jr., 1966. *Geology of Jefferson County, Florida*: Florida Geological Survey, Bull. 48, 115 p.

APPENDICES

APPENDIX I

TALL TIMBERS PLANT LIST

<u>**CLASS DICOTS**</u>

FAMILY ACANTHACEAE
Dyschoriste oblongifolia
Elytraria caroliniensis
Justicia ovata var. lanceolata
Ruellia caroliniensis

FAMILY ACERACEAE
Acer rubrum

FAMILY ACERACEAE
Mullugo verticillata
Sesuvium aritimum

FAMILY AMARANTHACEAE
Amaranthus hybridus
Amaranthus viridis

FAMILY ANACARDIACEAE
Rhus copallina
Toxicodendron radicans
Toxicodendron toxicarium

FAMILY ANNONACEAE
Asimina incarna
Asimina longifolia
Asimina parviflora
Asimina triloba

FAMILY AQUIFOLIACEAE
Ilex opaca
Ilex vomitoria

FAMILY ARALIACEAE
Aralia spinosa

FAMILY ASCLEPIADACEAE
Asclepias amplexicaulis
Asclepias tuberosa
Asclepias variegata
Asclepias verticillata

FAMILY BERBERIDACEAE
Nandina domestica

FAMILY BETULACEAE
Betula nigra
Carpinus caroliniana
Ostrya virginiana

FAMILY BIGNONIACEAE
Bignonia capreolata
Campsis radicans

FAMILY CABOMBACEAE
Brasenia schreberi   Cabomba caroliniana

FAMILY CALLITRICHACEAE
Callitriche peploides

FAMILY CAMPANULACEAE
Lobelia floridana   Lobelia puberula
Lobelia georgiana   Triodanis biflora
Lobelia glandulosa   Triodanis perfoliata

FAMILY CAPRIFOLIACEAE
Lonicera fragrantissime   Viburnum nudum
Lonicera sempervirens   Viburnum obovatum
Sambucus canadensis   Viburnum rufidulum
Viburnum dentatum

FAMILY CARYOPHYLLACEAE
Cerastium glomeratum   Silene antirrhina
Sagina decumbens   Stellaria media

FAMILY CELASTRACEAE
Euonymus americanus

FAMILY CHENOPODIACEAE
Chenopodium ambrosioides

FAMILY CISTACEAE
Helianthemum carolinianum   Lechea mucronata
Lechea minor   Lechea pulchella

FAMILY COMPOSITATE
Ageratina aromatica   Ambrosia artemisiifolia
Aster dumosus   Aster lateriflorus
Aster sagittifolius   Aster tortifolium
Aster vimineus   Baccharis halimifolia
Bidens bipinnata   Bidens discoidea
Bidens mitis   Boltonia diffusa
Calyptocarpus vialis   Chrysopsis mariana
Cirsium nuttallii   Cnicus benedictus
Conoclinium coelestinum   Conyza bonariensis
Conyza canadensis   Conyza canadensis
   ₃opsis lanceolata   Coreopsis tripteris
Croptilon divaricatum   Elephantopus carolinianus
Elephantopus elatus   Elephantopus nudatus
Elephantopus tomentosus   Erechtites hieracifolia
Erigeron strigosus   Eupatorium album
Eupatorium capillifolium   Eupatorium compositifolium
Eupatorium hyssopifolium   Eupatorium leptophyllum
Eupatorium perfoliatum   Eupatorium rotundifolium

Eupatorium semiserratum
Facelis retusa
Gaillardia aestivalis
Gnaphalium falcatum
Gnaphalium pensilvanicum
Gnaphalium spicatum
Helianthus angustifolius
Helianthus resinosus
Helianthus strumosus
Hieracium floridanum
Hypochaeris tweedii
Krogia virginica
Lactuca canadensis
Liatris elegans
Liatris spicata
Mikania scandens
Pityopsis aspera
Pluchea foetida
Pterocaulon pycnostachym
Senecio glabellus
Solidago bootii
Solidago fistulosa
Solidago nemoralis
Solidago petiolaris
Solidago tortifolia
Sonchus asper
Verbesin aristata
Verbesina angustifolia
Xanthium strumarium

Euthamia minor
Fleischmannia incarnata
Gnaphalium americanum
Gnaphalium obtusifolium
Gnaphalium purpureum
Helenium amarum
Helianthus hirsutus
Helianthus simulans
Heterotheca subaxillaris
Hypochaeris glabra
Krigia cespitosa
Kuhnia eupatorioides
Lactuca graminifolia
Liatris graminifolia
Melanthera niva
Pityopsis adenolepis
Pluchea camphorata
Polymnia uvedalia
Pyrrhipappus carolinianus
Silphium simponsonii
Solidago canadensis
Solidago leavenworthii
Solidago odora
Solidago rugosa
Soliva pterosperma
Tetragonotheca helianthoides
Verbesina virginica
Verbesina gigantea
Youngia japonica

FAMILY CONVOLULACEAE
Cuscuta indecora
Ipomoea lacunosa
Ipomoea quamoclit
Stylisma humistrata

Dichondra carolinensis
Ipomoea pandurata
Jacquemontia tamifolia

FAMILY CORNACEAE
Cornus asperifolia

Cornus florida

FAMILY CRUCIFERAE
Cardamine hirsuta
Lepidium virginicum

Coronopus didymus
Raphanus raphanistrum

FAMILY CUCURBITACEAE
Citrullus vulgaris

Melothria pendula

FAMILY CYRILLACEAE
Cyrilla racemiflora

FAMILY DROSERACEAE
Drosera brevifolia

FAMILY EBENACEAE
Diospyros virgininana

FAMILY ELAEAGNACEAE
Elaeagnus umbellata

FAMILY ERICACEAE
Leucothoe racemosa
Oxydendron arboreum
Vaccinium arboreum
Vaccinium darrowii
Vaccinium stamineum

Lyonia lucida
Rhododendron canescens
Vaccinium corymbosum
Vaccinium elliottii

FAMILY EUPHORBIACEAE
Acalypha gracilens
Chamaesyce maculata
Chidoscolus stimulosus
Euphorbia discoidalis
Phyllanthus tenellus
Sebastinania fruticosa

Chamaesyce hyssopifolia
Chamaesyce nutans
Croton glandulosus
Euphorbia heterophylla
Phyllanthus urinaria
Tragia urens

FAMILY FAGACEAE
Castanea pumila
Quercus acutissima
Quercus falcata
Quercus margaretta
Quercus michauxii
Quercus nigra
Quercus pumila
Quercus velutina

Fagus grandifolia
Quercus alba
Quercus hemisphaerica
Quercus marilandica
Quercus minima
Quercus phellos
Quercus stellata
Quercus virginiana

FAMILY FUMARIACEAE
Corydalis micrantha

FAMILY GENTANACEAE
Sabatia angularis

Sabatia dodecandra

FAMILY GUTTIFERAE = HYPERICACEAE
Hypericum brachyphyllum
Hypericum galioides
Hypericum hypericoides
Hypericum nitidum
Triadenum tubulosum
Triadenum walteri

Hypericum crux-andreae
Hypericum gentianoides
Hypericum mutilum
Hypericum pseudomaculatum
Triadenum virginicum

FAMILY HALORAGACEAE
Myriophyllum heterophyllum
Proserpinaca palustris

Myriophyllum pinnatum

FAMILY HAMAMELIDACEAE
Liquidambar styraciflua

FAMILY HYDROPHUYLLACEAE
Hydrolea quadrivalvis

FAMILY JUGLANDACEAE
Carya cordiformis
Carya tomentosa

Carya glabra
Juglans nigra

FAMILY LABIATAE
Hyptis alata
Lycopus angustifolius
Pysnanthemum albescens
Scutellaria incana
Teucrium canadense

Lamium amplexicaule
Monarda punctata
Pycnanthemum flexuosum
Scutellaria integrifolia
Trichostema dichotomum

FAMILY LEGUMINOSAE
Amorpha fruticosa
Baptisia albescens
Chamaecrista aspera
Chamaecrista nictitans
Crotalaria pallida
Dalea carnea var. carnea
Desmodium ciliare
Desmodium glutinosum
Desmodium lineatum
Desmodium nudiflorum
Desmodium paniculatum
Desmodium viridiflorum
Galactia macreei
Lespedeza angustifolia
Lespedeza cuneata
Lespedeza intermedia
Lespedeza repens
Lespedeza stuevei
Lespedeza virginica
Medicago lupulina
Rhynchosia reniformis
Senna (Cassia) obtusifolia
Stylosanthes biflora
Tephrosia virginiana
Trifolium carolinianum
Trifolium incarnatum
Trifolium repens
Vicia dasycarpa

Amphicarpaea bracteata
Centrosema virginianum
Chamaecrista fasiculata
Clitoria mariana
Crotalaria spectabilis
Dalea pinnata var. pinnata
Desmodium floridanum
Desmodium laevigatum
Desmodium marilandicum
Desmodium obtusum
Desmodium tortuosum
Erythrina herbacea
Galactia mollis
Lespedeza bicolor
Lespedeza hirta
Lespedeza procumbens
Lespedeza striata
Lespedeza thunbergii
Medicago arabica
Melilotus indica
Schrankia microphylla
Sesbania macrocarpa
Tephrosia spicata
Trifolium campestre
Trifolium dubium
Trifolium reflexum
Vicia angustifolia
Vicia grandiflora

Vicia sative subsp. angustifolia
Vicia sativa x cordata
Vicia sativa x serratifolia

FAMILY LENTIBULBARIACEAE
Utricularia biflora
Utricularia inflata
Utricularia foliosa
Utricularia purpurea

FAMILY LINACEAE
Linum striatum

FAMILY LOGANIACEAE
Gelsemium rankinii
Metreola sessilifolia
Spigelia marilandica
Gelsemium sempervirens
Polypremum procumbens

FAMILY LYTHRACEAE
Rotala ramosior

FAMILY MAGNOLIACEAE
Liriodendron tulipifera
Magnolia pyramidata
Magnolia grandiflora
Magnolia virginiana

FAMILY MALVACEAE
Hibis aculeatus
Hibiscus moscheutos
Sida elliottii
Hibiscus militaris
Modiola caroliniana
Sida rhombifolia

FAMILY MELASTOMATACEAE
Rhexia mariana

FAMILY MORACEAE
Morus rubra

FAMILY MYICACEAE
Myrica cerifera
Myrica heterophylla

FAMILY NYMPHAEACEAE
Nuphar luteum
Nymphaea odorata

FAMILYOLEACEAE
Chionanthus virginicus
Ligustrum lucidum
Osmanthus americanus
Fraxinus pennsylvanica
Ligustrum sinense

FAMILY ONAGRACEAE
Ludwigia alata
Ludwigia decurrens
Ludwigia linearis
Ludwigia sphaerocarpa
Ludwigia alternifolia
Ludwigia leptocarpa
Ludwigia maritima
Ludwigia suffruticosa

Oenothera biennis
Oenothera laciniata

Oenothera fruticosa
Oenothera speciosa

FAMILY OROBANCHACEAE
Conopholis americana

FAMILY OXALIDACEAE
Oxalis corniculate

Oxalis dillenii

FAMILY PASSIFLORACEAE
Passiflora incarnata

FAMILY PHRYMACEAE
Phryma leptostachya

FAMILY PHYTOLACCACEAE
Phytolacca americana

FAMILY PLANTAGINACEAE
Plantago aristate

Plantago virginica

FAMILY POLYGALACEAE
Polygala balduinii
Polygala cymosa
Polygala polygama

Polygala boykinii
Polygala nana

FAMILY POLYGONACEAE
Polygonum hydropiperoides
Polygonum punctatum
Polygonum setaceum
Rumex hastatulus

Polygonum pensylvanicum
Polygonum scandens
Rumex crispus
Rumex pulcher

FAMILY PYROLACEAE
Monotropa uniflora

FAMILY RANUNCULACEAE
Clematis catesbyana
Ranunculus platensis

Clematis crispa
Ranunculus pusillus

FAMILY RHAMNACEAE
Ceanothus americanus

FAMILY ROSACEAE
Agrimonia microcarpa
Crataegus pulcherrima
Duchesnea indica
Prunus americana
Prunus caroliniana
Prunus umbellata
Rosa carolina

Crataegus aestivalis
Crataegus spathulata
Malus angustifolia
Prunus angustifolia
Prunus serotina
Pyracantha coccinea
Rosa laevigata

Rubus betulifolius
Rubus trivialis

Rubus cuneifolius

FAMILY RUBIACEAE
Cephalanthus occidentalis
Diodia virginiana
Galium hispidulum
Galium triflorum
Hedyotis procumbens
Richardia scabra

Diodia teres
Galium aparine
Galium pilosum
Hedyotis crassifolia
Hedyotis uniflora

FAMILY SALICACEAE
Salix caroliniana

FAMILY SAXIFRAGACEAE
Itea virginica

FAMILY SCROPHULARIACEAE
Agalinis fasciculata
Aureaolaria flava
Buchnera floridana
Gratiola ramosa
Linaria canadensis
Lindernia dubia
Micranthemum umbrosum
Veronica arvensis

Agalinis purpurea
Bacopa caroliniana
Gratiola floridana
Gratiola virginiana
Lindernia anagallidea
Mecardonia acuminata
Penstemon australis
Veronica peregrina

FAMILY SOLANACEAE
Physalis arenicola
Physalis virginiana

Physalis heterophylla
Solanum carolinense

FAMILY STERCULIACEAE
Melochia corchorifolia

FAMILY STYRACACEAE
Styrax americanum

FAMILY SYMPLOCACEAE
Symplocos tinctoria

FAMILY THEACEAE
Gordonia lasianthus

FAMILY TILIACEAE
Corchorus aestuans

FAMILY TURNERACEAE
Piriqueta caroliniana

FAMILY ULMACEAE
Celtis laevigata   Ulmus americana

FAMILY UMBELLIFERAE
Apium leptophyllum   Centella asiatica
Chaerophyllum tainturieri   Daucus pusillus
Eryngium baldwinii   Eryngium prostratum
Hydrocotyle umbellata   Sanicula canadensis
Sanicula marilandica   Sanicula smallii
Spermolepis divaricata

FAMILY URTICACEAE
Boehmeria cylindrica   Pilea pumila

FAMILY VERBENACEAE
Callicarpa americana   Clerodendrum indicum
Glandularia pulchella   Lantana montevidensis
Stylodon carneus   Verbena brasiliensis
Verbena canadensis   Verbena urticifolia

FAMILY VIOLACEAE
Viola affinis   Viola primulifolia
Viola triloba

FAMILY VITACEAE
Amelopsis arborea   Parthenocissus quinquefolia
Vitis aestivalis   Vitis rotundifolia

CLASS GYMNOSPERMS

FAMILY CUPRESSACEAE
Juniperus silicicola

FAMILY PINACEAE
Pinus echinata   Pinus glabra
Pinus palustris   Pinus taeda

FAMILY TAXODIACEAE
Taxodium distinchum

CLASS MONOCOTS

FAMILY AGAVACEAE
Polianthes virginica

FAMILY ALISMATACEAE
Sagittaria engelmanniana
Sagittaria latifolia
Sagittaria stagnorum
Sagittaria graminea
Sagittaria montevidensis

FAMILY AMARYLLIDACEAE
Hymenocallis duvalensis
Narcissus jonquilla
Hymenocallis occidentalis

FAMILY ARACEAE
Arisaema dracontium
Arisaema triphyllum
Arisaema quinatum

FAMILY BROMELIACEAE
Tillandsia usneoides

FAMILY BURMANNIACEAE
Apteria aphylla
Burmannia biflora

FAMILY COMMELINACEAE
Commelina communis
Commelina erecta
Tradescantia ohiensis
Commelina diffusa
Commelina virginica
Tradescantia subaspera

FAMILY CYPERACEAE
Bulbostylis barbata
Carex albotutescens
Carex debilis
Carex howei
Carex lupulina
Carex seora
Cyperus croceus
Cyperus esculentus
Cyperus haspan
Cyperus odoratus
Cyperus retrorsus
Cyperus sesquiflorus
Cyperus surinamensis
Cyperus tetragonus
Eleocharis baldwinii
Eleocharis obtusa
Fimbristylis autumnalis
Fuirena squarrosa
Rhynchospora corniculata
Rhynchospora fascicularis
Rhynchospora perplexa
Rhynchospora wrightiana
Scirpus ciliata
Scirpus oligantha
Scirpus reticularis
Bulbostylis ciliatifolia
Carex complanata
Carex digitalis
Carex intumenscens
Carex physorhyncha
Cyperus brevifolius
Cyperus cuspidatus
Cyperus filiculmis
Cyperus lutescens
Cyperus polystachyos
Cyperus rotundus
Cyperus strigosus
Cyperus tenuifolius
Cyperus virens
Eleocharis equisetoides
Eleocharis vivipara
Fimbristylis miliacea
Rhynchospora caduca
Rhynchospora debilis
Rhynchospora globularis
Rhynchospora rarifloria
Scirpus cyperinus
Scirpus hirtella
Scirpus pauciflora
Scirpus triglomerata

FAMILY DIOSCOREACEAE
Dioscorea quaternata

Dioscorea villosa

FAMILY ERIOCAULACEAE
Lachnocaulon engleri

Lachnocaulon minus

FAMILY GRAMINEAE
Agrostis hiemalis

Agrostis scabra

Andropogon gerardii

Andropogon glomeratus

Andropogon gyrans

Andropogon ternarius

Andropogon virginicus

Aristida longespica

Aristida purpurescens

Arundinaria gigantea

Arundo donax

Brachiaria plantaginea

Brachiaria ramosa

Briza minor

Bromus unioloides

Cenchrus echinatus

Chasmanthium laxum

Chasmanthium sessiliflorum

Coelorachis rugosa

Dactyloctenium aegyptium

Digitaria ciliaris

Digitaria filiformis

Digitaria ischaemum

Digitaria villosa

Echinochloa colonum

Echinochloa walteri

Eleusine indica

Eragrostis amabilis

Eragrostis hirsuta

Eragrostis spectabilis

Erianthus alopecuroides

Erianthus contortus

Erianthus giganteus

Erianthus strictus

Eustachys floridana

Festuca pratensis

Gymnopogon ambiguus

Heteropogon melanocarpus

Hordeum pusillum

Leersia hexandra

Leersia virginica

Lolium perenne

Muhlenbergia schreberi

Oplismenus setarius

Panicum aciculare

Panicum acuminatum

Panicum anceps

Panicum angustifolium

Panicum boscii

Panicum commonsonianum

Panicum consanguineum

Panicum dichotomiflorum

Panicum erectifolium

Panicum gymnocarpon

Panicum hemitomon

Panicum hians

Panicum lanuginosum

Panicum laxiflorum

Panicum maximum

Panicum rhizomatum

Panicum rigidulum

Panicum scoparium

Panicum sphaerocarpon

Panicum verrucosum

Panicum villosissimum

Panicum virgatum

Paspalum bifidum

Paspalum boscianum

Paspalum dilatatum

Paspalum dissectus

Paspalum floridanum

Paspalum notatum

Paspalum plicatulum

Paspalum setaceum

Paspalum urvillei

Pennisetum purpureum

Phalaris caroliniana

Stipa avenacea

Poa annua

Sacciolepis striata

Schizachyrium tenerum

Setaria geniculate

Setaria pumila

Sorghastrum elliottii

Sorghastrum nutans

Sphenopholis obtusata

Sporobolus clandestinis   Sporobolus indicus
Tridens flavus   Tripsacum dactyloides
Vulpia octoflora

FAMILY HYDROCHARITACEAE
Limnobium spongia

FAMILY IRIDACEAE
Sisyrinchium atlanticum
Sisyrinchium nashii

FAMILY JUNCACEAE
Juncus acuminatus   Juncus dichotomus
Juncus elliottii   Juncus marginatus
Juncus repens   Juncus scirpoides
Juncus tenuis

FAMILY LEMNACEAE
Lemna valdiviana   Spirodela polyrhiza
Wolffia columbiana

FAMILY LILIACEAE
Aletris obovata
Allium canadense
Amianthium muscaeoxicum
Lilium superbum
Medeola virginiana
Melanthium virinicum
Polygonatum biflorum

FAMILY ORCHIDACEAE
Corallorhiza wisteriana   Habenaria quinqueseta
Habenaria repens   Malaxis unifolia
Ponthieva racemosa   Spiranthes vernalis
Tipularia discolor

FAMILY PONTEDERIACEAE
Pontederia cordata

FAMILY POTAMOGETONACEAE
Potamogeton diversifolius   Potamogeton illinoensis
Potamogeton pulcher   Potamogeton pusillus

FAMILY SMILACAEAE
Smilax bona-nox   Smilax glauca
Smilax herbacea   Smilax pumila
Smilax smallii   Smilax tamnoides

FAMILY TRILLIACEAE
Trillium underwoodii

FAMILY XYRIDACEAE
Xyris difformis   Xyris jupicai

CLASS PTERIDOPHYTES

FAMILY ASPLENIACEAE
Asplenium platyneuron

FAMILY AZOLIACEA
Azolla caroliniana

FAMILY BLECHNACEAE
Woodwardia areolata

FAMILY DENNSTAEDTIACEAE
Pteridium aquilinum var. pseudocaudatum

FAMILY DRYOPTERIACEAE
Polystichum acrostichoides

FAILY LYCOPODIACEAE
Lycopodiell caroliniana

FAMILY OPHIOGLOSSACEAE
Botrychium biternatum   Botrychium dissectum
Botrychium virginianum

FAMILY OSMUNDACEAE
Osmunda cinnamomea   Osmunda regalis var. spectabilis

FAMILY POLYPODIACEAE
Onoclea sensibilis   Polypodium polypodioides

FAMILY SCHIZAEACEAE
Lygodium japonicum

FAMILY THELYPTERIDACEAE
Thelypteris hexagonoptera   Thelypteris hospidula
Thelypteris quadrangularis   Thelypteris torresiana

FAMILY WOODSIACEAE
Athyrium filix-femina subsp. asplenioides

APPENDIX II

TALL TIMBERS ANIMAL LIST

Reptiles and Amphibians Documented at Tall Timbers Research Station

COMMON NAME	SCIENTIFIC NAME
Oak toad	Bufo quercicus
Southern toad	Bufo terrestris
Woodhouse's toad	Bufo woodhousei
Greenhouse toad	Eleutherodactylus ricordi
Eastern narrowmouth toad	Gastrophryne carolinensis
Eastern spadefoot toad	Scaphiopus holbrookii holbrookii
Northern cricket frog	Acris crepitans
Southern cricket frog	Acris gryllus
Bird-voiced tree frog	Hyla avivoca
Cope's gray tree frog	Hyla chrysoscelis
Green tree frog	Hyla cinerea
Spring peeper	Hyla crucifer
Pine-woods tree frog	Hyla femoralis
Barking tree frog	Hyla gratiosa
Squirrel tree frog	Hyla squirella
Little grass frog	Limnaoedus ocularis
Southern chorus frog	Pseudacris nigrita
Upland chorus frog	Pseudacris triseriata
Gopher frog	Rana areolata
Bullfrog	Rana catesbeiana
Pig frog	Rana grylio
River frog	Rana heckscheri
Pickerel frog	Rana palustris
Southern leopard frog	Rana utricularia
Carpenter frog	Rana virgatipes
Flatwoods salamander	Ambystoma cingulatum
Spotted salamander	Ambystoma maculatum
Mole salamander	Ambystoma talpoideum
Two-toed amphiuma	Amphiuma means
Dusky salamander	Desmognathus fuscus
Seal Salamander	Desmognathus monticola
Southern dusky salamander	Desmognathus auriculatus
Dwarf salamander	Eurycea quadridigitata
Long-tailed salamander	Eurycea longicauda
Georgia blind salamander	Haideotriton wallacei
Four-toed salamander	Hemidactylium scutatum
Slimy salamander	Plethodon glutinosus glutinosus
Red salamander	Pseudotriton ruber
Many-lined salamander	Stereochilus marginatus
Eastern newt	Notophthalmus viridescens
Striped newt	Notophthalmus perstriatus
Dwarf siren	Pseudobranchus striatus

Greater siren	Siren lacertina
Gulf Coast waterdog	Necturus beyeri
Box Turtle	Terrapene carolina
Striped mud turtle	Kinosternon bauri
Eastern mud turtle	Kinosternon subrubrum subrubrum
Loggerhead musk turtle	Sternotherus minor
Stinkpot	Sternotherus odoratus
Florida softshell	Apalone ferox
Smooth softshell	Trionyx muticus
Gulf Coast softshell	Trionyx spinifer
Cooter	Chrysemys concinna
Coal skink	Eumeces anthracinus
Red-tailed skink	Eumeces egregius
Five-lined skink	Eumeces fasciatus
Southern fence lizard	Sceloporus undulatus undulatus
Island glass lizard	Ophisaurus compressus
Worm lizard	Rhineura floridana
Broadhead skink	Eumeces laticeps
Worm snake	Carphophis amoenus
Racer	Coluber constrictor
Ringneck snake	Diadophis punctatus
Indigo snake	Drymarchon corais
Rainbow snake	Farancia erytrogramma
Eastern hognose snake	Heterodon platyrhinos
Mole snake	Lampropeltis calligaster
Scarlet kingsnake	Lampropeltis triangulum elapsoides
Eastern coachwhip	Masticophis flagellum flagellum
Red-bellied water snake	Natrix erythrogaster
Northern water snake	Natrix sipedon
Brown water snake	Natrix taxispilota
Rough green snake	Opheodrys aestivus
Pine snake	Pituophis melanoleucas
Striped swamp snake	Regina alleni
Glossy crayfish snake	Regina rigida
Red-bellied snake	Storeria occipitomaculata
Crowned snake	Tantilla coronata
Eastern garter snake	Thamnophis sirtalis sirtalis
Rough earth snake	Virginia striatula
Smooth earth snake	Virginia valeriae valeriae
Coral snake	Micrurus fulvius
Copperhead	Agkistrodon contortrix
Eastern diamondback rattlesnake	Crotalus adamanteus
Pygmy rattlesnake	Sistrurus miliarius

Birds Documented at Tall Timbers Research Station

SCIENTIFIC NAME	COMMON NAME
Podilymbus podiceps	Pied-billed Grebe
Podiceps auritus	Horned Grebe
Phalacrocorax auritus	Double-crested Cormorant
Anhinga anhinga	Anhinga
Botaurus lentiginosus	American Bittern
Ixobrychus casmerodius	Least Bittern
Ardea herodias	Great Blue Heron
Casmerodius albus	Great Egret
Egretta thula	Snowy Egret
Egretta caerulea	Little Blue Heron
Egretta tricolor	Tricolored Heron
Bubulcus ibis	Cattle Egret
Butorides striatus	Green-backed Heron
Nycticorax violaceus	Yellow-crowned Night-Heron
Eudocimus albus	White Ibis
Mycteria americana	Wood Stork
Aix sponsa	Wood Duck
Anas crecca	Green-Winged Teal
Anas rubripes	American Black Duck
Anas discors	Blue-winged Teal
Anas clypeata	Northern Shoveler
Anas strepera	Gadwall
Anas americana	American Wigeon
Aythya americana	Redhead
Aythya collaris	Ring-necked Duck
Aythya affinis	Lesser Scaup
Lophodytes cucullatus	Hooded Merganser
Mergus serrator	Red-breasted Merganser
Oxyura jamaicensis	Ruddy Duck
Coragyps atratus	Black Vulture
Cathartes aura	Turkey Vulture
Haliaeetus leucocephalus	Bald Eagle
Circus cyaneus	Northern Harrier
Accipiter striatus	Sharp-shinned Hawk
Accipiter cooperii	Cooper's Hawk
Buteo lineatus	Red-shouldered Hawk
Buteo jamaicensis	Red-tailed Hawk
Falco sparverius	American Kestrel
Meleagris gallopavo	Wild Turkey
Colinus virginianus	Northern Bobwhite
Porzana carolina	Sora
Porphyrula martinica	Purple Gallinule
Gallinula chloropus	Common Moorhen
Fulica americana	American Coot
Charadrius vociferus	Killdeer
Tringa solitaria	Solitary Sandpiper

Actitis macularia	Spotted Sandpiper
Gallinago gallinago	Common Snipe
Scolopax minor	American Woodcock
Columba livia	Rock Dove
Zenaida macroura	Mourning Dove
Columbina passerina	Common Ground-Dove
Coccyzus erythropthalmus	Black-billed Cuckoo
Coccyzus americanus	Yellow-billed Cuckoo
Tyto alba	Common Barn-Owl
Bubo virginianus	Great Horned Owl
Strix varia	Barred Owl
Chordeiles minor	Common Nighthawk
Caprimulgus carolinensis	Chuck-will's-widow
Chaetura pelagica	Chimney Swift
Archilochus colubris	Ruby-throated Hummingbird
Selasphorus rufus	Rufous Hummingbird
Ceryle alcyon	Belted Kingfisher
Melanerpes erythrocephalus	Red-headed Woodpecker
Melanerpes carolinus	Red-bellied Woodpecker
Sphyrapicus varius	Yellow-bellied Sapsucker
Picoides pubescens	Downy Woodpecker
Picoides villosus	Hairy Woodpecker
Picoides borealis	Red-cockaded Woodpecker
Colaptes auratus	Northern Flicker
Dryocopus pileatus	Pileated Woodpecker
Contopus virens	Eastern Wood-Pewee
Empidonax flaviventris	Yellow-bellied Flycatcher
Empidonax virescens	Acadian Flycatcher
Empidonax alnorum	Alder Flycatcher
Empidonax traillii	Willow Flycatcher
Empidonax minimus	Least Flycatcher
Sayornis phoebe	Eastern Phoebe
Myiarchus crinitus	Great Crested Flycatcher
Tyrannus tyrannus	Eastern Kingbird
Progne subis	Purple Martin
Tachycineta bicolor	Tree Swallow
Riparia riparia	Bank Swallow
Hirundo pyrrhonota	Cliff Swallow
Hirundo rustica	Barn Swallow
Cyanocitta cristata	Blue Jay
Corvus brachyrhynchos	American Crow
Corvus ossifragus	Fish Crow
Parus carolinensis	Carolina Chickadee
Parus bicolor	Tufted Titmouse
Sitta canadensis	Red-breasted Nuthatch
Sitta carolinensis	White-breasted Nuthatch
Sitta pusilla	Brown-headed Nuthatch
Certhie americana	Brown Creeper
Thryothorus ludovicianus	Carolina Wren
Troglodytes aedon	House Wren

Troglodytes troglodytes	Winter Wren
Regulus satrapa	Golden-crowned Kinglet
Regulus calendula	Ruby-crowned Kinglet
Polioptila caerulea	Blue-gray Gnatcatcher
Sialia sialis	Eastern Bluebird
Catharus fuscescens	Veery
Catharus minimus	Gray-cheeked Thrush
Catharus ustulatus	Swainson's Thrush
Catharus guttatus	Hermit Thrush
Hylocichla mustelina	Wood Thrush
Turdus migratorius	American Robin
Dumetella carolinensis	Gray Catbird
Mimus polyglottos	Northern Mockingbird
Toxostoma rufum	Brown Thrasher
Bombycilla cedrorum	Cedar Waxwing
Lanius ludovicianus	Loggerhead Shrike
Sturnus vulgaris	European Starling
Vireo griseus	White-eyed Vireo
Vireo solitarius	Solitary Vireo
Vireo flavifrons	Yellow-throated Vireo
Vireo gilvus	Warbling Vireo
Vireo philadelphicus	Philadelphia Vireo
Vireo olivaceus	Red-eyed Vireo
Vermivora pinus	Blue-winged Warbler
Vermivora chrysoptera	Golden-winged Warbler
Vermivora peregrina	Tennessee Warbler
Vermivora celata	Orange-crowned Warbler
Vermivora ruficapilla	Nashville Warbler
Parula americana	Northern Parula
Dendroica petechia	Yellow Warbler
Dendroica pensylvanica	Chestnut-sided Warbler
Dendroica magnolia	Magnolia Warbler
Dendroica tigrina	Cape May Warbler
Dendroica caerulescens	Black-throated Blue Warbler
Dendroica coronata	Yellow-rumped Warbler
Dendroica virens	Black-throated Green Warbler
Dendroica fusca	Blackburnian Warbler
Dendroica dominica	Yellow-throated Warbler
Dendroica pinus	Pine Warbler
Dendroica discolor	Prairie Warbler
Dendroica palmarum	Palm Warbler
Dendroica castanea	Bay-breasted Warbler
Dendroica striata	Blackpoll Warbler
Dendroica cerulea	Cerulean Warbler
Mniotilta varia	Black-and-white Warbler
Setophaga ruticilla	American Redstart
Protonotaria citrea	Prothonotary Warbler
Helmitheros vermivorus	Worm-eating Warbler
Limnothlypis swainsonii	Swainson's Warbler
Seiurus aurocapillus	Ovenbird

Seiurus noveboracensis	Northern Waterthrush
Seiurus motacilla	Louisiana Waterthrush
Oporornis agilis	Connecticut Warbler
Oporornis philadelphia	Mourning Warbler
Geothlypis trichas	Common Yellowthroat
Wilsonia citrina	Hooded Warbler
Wilsonia pusilla	Wilson's Warbler
Wilsonia canadensis	Canada Warbler
Icteria virens	Yellow-breasted Chat
Piranga rubra	Summer Tanager
Piranga olivacea	Scarlet Tanager
Cardinalis cardinalis	Northern Cardinal
Pheucticus ludovicianus	Rose-breasted Grosbeak
Guiraca caerulea	Blue Grosbeak
Passerina cyanea	Indigo Bunting
Passerina ciris	Painted Bunting
Spiza americana	Dickcissel
Pipilo erythrophthalmus	Rufous-sided Towhee
Aimophila aestivalis	Bachman's Sparrow
Spizella passerina	Chipping Sparrow
Spizella pallida	Clay-colored Sparrow
Spizella pusilla	Field Sparrow
Pooecetes gramineus	Vesper Sparrow
Passerculus sandwichensis	Savannah Sparrow
Ammodramus savannarum	Grasshopper Sparrow
Ammodramus henslowii	Henslow's Sparrow
Ammodramus leconteii	Le Conte's Sparrow
Passerella iliaca	Fox Sparrow
Melospiza melodia	Song Sparrow
Melospiza lincolnii	Lincoln's Sparrow
Melospiza georgiana	Swamp Sparrow
Zonotrichia albicollis	White-throated Sparrow
Zonotrichia leucophrys	White-crowned Sparrow
Junco hyemalis	Dark-eyed Junco
Dolichonyx oryzivorus	Bobolink
Agelaius phoeniceus	Red-winged Blackbird
Sturnella magna	Eastern Meadowlark
Euphagus carolinus	Rusty Blackbird
Quiscalus quiscula	Common Grackle
Molothrus ater	Brown-headed Cowbird
Icterus spurius	Orchard Oriole
Icterus galbula	Northern Oriole
Carpodacus purpureus	Purple Finch
Carduelis pinus	Pine Siskin
Carduelis tristis	American Goldfinch
Coccothraustes vespertinus	Evening Grosbeak
Passer domesticus	House Sparrow

Mammals Documented at Tall Timbers Research Station

COMMON NAME	SCIENTIFIC NAME
Virginia Opossum	Didelphis virginiana
Southeastern Shrew	Sorex longirostris
Southern Short-tailed Shrew	Blarina carolinensis
Least Shrew	Cryptotis parva
Eastern Mole	Scalopus aquaticus
Southeastern Bat	Myotis austroriparius
Eastern Pipistrelle	Pipistrellus subflavus
Big Brown Bat	Eptesicus fuscus
Hoary Bat	Lasiurus cinereus
Red Bat	Lasiurus borealis
Seminole Bat	Lasiurus seminolus
Yellow Bat	Lasiurus intermedius
Evening Bat	Nycticeius humeralis
Brazilian Free-tailed Bat	Tadarida brasiliensis
Eastern Cottontail	Sylvilagus floridanus
Gray Squirrel	Sciurus carolinensis
Fox Squirrel	Sciurus niger
Southern Flying Squirrel	Glaucomys volans
Eastern Woodrat	Neotoma floridana
Hispid Cotton Rat	Sigmodon hispidus
Eastern Harvest Mouse	Reithrodontomys humulis
Marsh Rice Rat	Oryzomys palustris
Oldfield Mouse	Peromyscus polionotus
Cotton Mouse	Peromyscus gossypinus
Golden Mouse	Ochrotomys nuttalli
Pine Vole	Microtus pinetorum
Round-tailed Muskrat	Neofiber alleni
House Mouse	Mus musculus
Black Rat	Rattus rattus
Norway Rat	Rattus norvegicus
River Otter	Lutra canadensis
White-tailed Deer	Odocoileus virginianus
Gray Fox	Urocyon cinereoargenteus
Raccoon	Procyon lotor
Bobcat	Felis rufus
Nine-banded Armadillo	Dasypus novemcinctus
Beaver	Castor canadensis
Coyote	Canis latrans

APPENDIX III

LIST OF ANIMAL SPECIES OBSERVED ON PLANTATIONS WITHIN AND ADJACENT TO THE STUDY AREA BY WILSON BAKER

Observed Reptile and Amphibian List

COMMON NAME	SCIENTIFIC NAME
Cope's gray treefrog	Hyla chrysoscelis
Green treefrog	Hyla cinerea
Spring peeper	Hyla crucifer
Eastern narrowmouth toad	Gastrophryne carolinensis
Bullfrog	Rana catesbeina
Pig frog	Rana grylio
Southern leopard frog	Rana utricularia
American alligator	Alligator mississippiensis
Box turtle	Terrapene carolina
Gopher tortoise	Gopherus polyphemus
Florida softshell	Apalone ferox
Green anole	Anolis carolinensis
Broadhead skink	Eumeces laticeps
Southern fence lizard	Sceloporus undulatus undulatus
Southern black racer	Coluber constrictor pripus
Gray rat snake	Elaphe obsoleta spiloides
Eastern coachwhip	Masticophis flagellum flagellum
Eastern garter snake	Thamnophis sirtalis sirtalis
Cottonmouth	Agkistrodon piscivorus
Eastern diamondback rattlesnake	Crotalus adamanteus

Observed Mammal List

COMMON NAME	SCIENTIFIC NAME
Eastern pipistrelle	Pipistrellus subflavus
Evening bat	Nycticeius humeralis
Eastern mole	Scalopus aquaticus
Nine-banded armadillo	Dasypus novemcinctus
Eastern cottontail	Sylvilagus floridanus
Gray squirrel	Sciurus carolinensis
Fox squirrel	Sciurus niger
Southern flying squirrel	Glaucomys volans
Southeastern pocket gopher	Geomys pinetus
Beaver	Castor canadensis
Eastern woodrat	Neotoma floridana
Marsh rice rat	Oryzomys palustris
Round-tailed muskrat	Neofiber alleni
Nutria	Myocastor coypus
Raccoon	Procyon lotor

River otter	Lutra canadensis
Coyote	Canis latrans
Bobcat	Felis rufus
Wild hog	Sus scrofa
White-tailed deer	Odocoileus virginianus

Observed Bird List

COMMON NAME	SCIENTIFIC NAME
Common Loon	
Pied-billed Grebe	Podilymbus podiceps
Double-crested Cormorant	Phalacrocorax auritus
Anhinga	Anhinga anhinga
Great Blue Heron	Ardea herodias
Great Egret	Casmerodius albus
Little Blue Heron	Egretta caerulea
Cattle Egret	Bubulcus ibis
Snowy Egret	Egretta thula
Green-backed Heron	Butorides striatus
White Ibis	Eudocimus albus
Wood Stork	Mycteria americana
Wood Duck	Aix sponsa
Green-winged Teal	Anas crecca
American Black Duck	Anas rubripes
Mallard	Anas platyrhynchos
Northern Pintail	Anas acuta
Blue-winged Teal	Anas discors
American Wigeon	Anas americana
Ring-necked Duck	Aythya collaris
Hooded Merganser	Lophodytes cucullatus
Turkey Vulture	Cathartes aura
Osprey	Pandio haliaetus
Bald Eagle	Haliaeetus leucocephalus
Northern Harrier	Circus cyaneus
Sharp-shinned Hawk	Accipiter striatus
Cooper's Hawk	Accipiter cooperii
Red-shouldered Hawk	Buteo lineatus
Broad-winged Hawk	Buteo platypterus
Red-tailed Hawk	Buteo jamaicensis
American Kestrel	Falco sparverius
Wild Turkey	Meleagris gallopavo
Northern Bobwhite	Colinus virginianus
Purple Gallinule	Porphyrula martinica
Common Moorhen	Gallinula chloropus
Sandhill Crane	Grus canadensis
Killdeer	Charadrius vociferus
Common Snipe	Gallinago gallinago
American Woodcock	Scolopax minor

Rock Dove	Columba livia
Mourning Dove	Zenaida macroua
Common Ground-Dove	Columbia passerina
Yellow-billed Cuckoo	Coccyzus americanus
Eastern Screech-Owl	Otus asio
Great Horned Owl	Bubo virginianus
Barred Owl	Strix varia
Chuck-will's-widow	Caprimulgus carolinensis
Chimney Swift	Chaetura pelagica
Ruby-throated Hummingbird	Archilochus colubris
Belted Kingfisher	Ceryle alcyon
Red-headed Woodpecker	Melanerpes erythrocephalus
Red-bellied Woodpecker	Melanerpes carolinus
Yellow-bellied Sapsucker	Sphyrapicus varius
Downy Woodpecker	Picoides pubescens
Hairy Woodpecker	Picoides villosus
Red-cockaded Woodpecker	Picoides borealis
Common Flicker Northern Flicker	Colaptes auratus
Pileated Woodpecker	Dryocopus pileatus
Eastern Wood-Pewee	Contopus virens
Acadian Flycatcher	Empidonax virescens
Eastern Phoebe	Sayornis phoebe
Great Crested Flycatcher	Myiarchus crinitus
Eastern Kingbird	Tyrannus tyrannus
Purple Martin	Progne subis
N. Rough-winged Swallow	Stelgidopteryx serripennis
Barn Swallow	Hirundo rustica
Blue Jay	Cyanocitta cristata
American Crow	Corvus brachyrhynchos
Fish Crow	Corvus ossifragus
Carolina Chickadee	Parus carolinensis
Tufted Titmouse	Parus bicolor
White-breasted Nuthatch	Sitta carloinensis
Brown-headed Nuthatch	Sitta pusilla
Carolina Wren	Thryothorus ludovicianus
House Wren	Troglodytes aedon
Sedge Wren	Cistothorus platensis
Golden-crowned Kinglet	Regulus satrapa
Ruby-crowned Kinglet	Regulus calendula
Blue-grey Gnatcatcher	Polioptila caerulea
Eastern Bluebird	Sialia sialis
Hermit Thrush	Catharus guttatus
Wood Thrush	Hylocichla mustelina
Veery	Catharus fuscescens
American Robin	Turdus migratorius
Gray Catbird	Dumetella carolinensis
Northern Mocking bird	Mimus polyglottos
Brown Thrasher	Toxostoma rufum
Water Pipit	Anthus spinoletta
Cedar Waxwing	Bombycilla cedrorum

Loggerhead Shrike	Lanius ludovicianus
European Starling	Sturnus vulgaris
White-eyed Vireo	Vireo griseus
Solitary Vireo	Vireo solitarius
Yellow-throated Vireo	Vireo flavifrons
Red-eyed Vireo	Vireo olivaceus
Black-and-white warbler	Mniotilta varia
Northern Parula	Parula americana
Yellow-rumped Warbler	Dendroica coronata
Yellow-throated Warbler	Dendroica dominica
Orange-crowned Warbler	Vermivora celata
Pine Warbler	Dendroica pinus
Palm Warbler	Dendroica palmarus
Prothonotary Warbler	Protonotaria citrea
Prairie Warbler	Dendroica discolor
Ovenbird	Seiurus aurocapillus
Louisiana Waterthrush	Seiurus motacilla
Kentucky Warbler	Oporornis formosus
Common Yellowthroat	Geothlypis trichas
Hooded Warbler	Wilsonia citrina
Wilson's Warbler	Wilsonia pusilla
Yellow-breasted Chat	Icteria virens
Summer Tanager	Piranga rubra
Northern Cardinal	Cardinalis cardinalis
Rose-breasted Grosbeak	Pheucticus ludovicianus
Blue Grosbeak	Guiraca caerulea
Indigo Bunting	Passerina cyanea
Purple Finch	Carpodacus purpureus
American Goldfinch	Carduelis tristis
Rufous-sided Towhee	Pipilo erythrophthalmus
Bachman's Sparrow	Aimophila aestivalis
Dark-eyed Junco	Junco hyemalis
Chipping Sparrow	Spizella passerina
Field Sparrow	Spizella pusilla
Vesper Sparrow	Pooecetes gramineus
White-throated sparrow	Zonotrichia albicollis
Song Sparrow	Melospiza melodia
Swamp Sparrow	Melospiza georgiana
Red-winged Blackbird	Agelaius phoeniceus
Common Grackle	Ouiscalus guiscula
Brown-headed Cowbird	Molothrus ater
Orchard Oriole	Icterus spurius
Pine Siskin	Carduelis pinus
American Goldfinch	Carduelis tristis

Observed Butterfly List

<u>COMMON NAME</u>

Pipe-vine swallowtail
Black swallowtail
Tiger swallowtail
Spice-bush swallowtail
Zebra swallowtail
Dog-face
Cloudless sulfur
Little sulphur
Sleepy sulphur
Red-banded hairstreak
Gray hairstreak
Spring azure
Red-spotted purple
Viceroy
American painted lady
Buckeye
Seminole crescent
Variegated fritillary
Gulf fritillary
Queen
Pearly-eye
Eyed brown
Gemmed satyr
Carolina satyr
Wood nymph

SELECTED SUBSURFACE DATA

```
WELL NO: GGS 757                    ALTITUDE:          229 ft.
WELL NAME:   Wade Chastain          TOTAL DEPTH:       240 ft.
COUNTY:  Thomas                     (Data from McFadden, et al, 1986)
LATITUDE:      30 50 00
LONGITUDE:     84 01 20
```

SUMMARY:

FORMATION	DESCRIPTION	THICKNESS IN FEET	DEPTH IN FEET
In Pliocene Miccosukee 0	Sand: very pale orange to light olive-gray, fine coarse-grained, poorly sorted, subangular to sub-rounded quartz, argillaceous at top of interval, 10YR8/2 to 5Y6/1-------------- 50		50
Miocene Hawthorne Undif. 50	Clay: white, calcareous, sandy (X-ray diffraction shows that the clay is sepiolite with some montmorillonite)-------------------------- 20		70
	Sand: white to light greenish-gray, fine- to medium-grained, well sorted, subrounded quartz, argillaceous cement, N9 to 5GY8/1----------- 80		150
	Limestone: yellowish-gray, molds and casts of megafossils common; 5Y8/1------------------ 55		205
	Silt: white to light gray, calcareous, argillaceous, with interbedded Limestone; sandy, molds and casts of megafossils common; N9 to N7------- 30		235
	No Samples------------------------------------- 5		240

T.D. 240

```
WELL NO: GGS 784                        ALTITUDE:          170 ft.
WELL NAME:    H. D. Burton              TOTAL DEPTH:       182 ft.
COUNTY:  Thomas                         (Data from McFadden, et al, 1986)
LATITUDE:      30 49 25
LONGITUDE:     83 54 17
```

SUMMARY:

FORMATION	DESCRIPTION	THICKNESS IN FEET	DEPTH IN FEET
In Miocene Hawthorne Undif. 0	Sand: mottled, white to moderate red to grayish-purple, fine- to medium-grained, well sorted, subangular quartz, with abundant iron minerals at top of interval, 5R4/6 to 5P4/2--------------------------------------	40	40
	Clay: grayish-yellow green, slightly calcareous, with Sand; medium- to coarse-grained, moderately sorted, subangular quartz, 5GY7/2---------------------------------------	45	85
Oligocene	No samples-------------------------------------	25	110
Suwannee 85	Limestone: white, pure, fossiliferous, with foraminifers common-----------------------	5	115
T.D. 182	No samples-------------------------------------	67	182

```
WELL NO: GGS 801                    ALTITUDE:        163 ft.
WELL NAME:   Robert C. Balfour      TOTAL DEPTH:     226 ft.
COUNTY: Grady                       (Data from McFadden, et al, 1986)
LATITUDE:      30 45 46
LONGITUDE:     84 13 14
```

SUMMARY:

FORMATION	DESCRIPTION	THICKNESS IN FEET	DEPTH IN FEET
In Pleistocene Fluvial Terrace	Sand: yellowish-orange, poorly sorted, fine- to coarse-grained, with fine pebble gravel common, argillaceous, silty, 10YT7/4--------	20	20
Miocene Hawthorne Undif. 20	Clay: light greenish-gray, silty to sandy, and Limestone; white, sandy, 5GY8/1------------	15	35
	Sand: white to very light gray, somewhat indurated, with calcite cement, and interbedded Limestone; white, sandy, N9 to N8--------------	10	45
	Limestone: white to light gray, sandy, dense, N9 to N7 -----------------------------------	35	80
	Limestone: white to light gray, sandy, dolomitic fossiliferous, at certain levels abundantly fossiliferous (coquina) and Sand; interbedded N9 to N7----------------------------------	85	165
	Sand: white, fine-grained, well sorted, subangular grains, calcareous fragments common, N9-----	5	170
	Dolomite: light brown to light olive-gray, saccharoidal, sandy, 5TR66/4 to 5Y6/1-------	15	185
	Limestone: light gray, sandy, somewhat re-crystallized, fossiliferous, with smaller foraminifers, and Dolomite, as above, N7----	5	190
Oligocene Suwannee 190	Limestone: light olive-gray, granular, calcarenitic, fossiliferous, with macroshell impressions, echinoid fragments, and miliolids, 5Y6/1--------------------------	25	215
	No samples--------------------------------	11	226

T.D. 226

```
WELL NO: GGS 807                    ALTITUDE:           178 ft.
WELL NAME:    W. D. Cox            TOTAL DEPTH:         213 ft.
COUNTY:  Thomas                    (Data from McFadden, et al, 1986)
LATITUDE:        30 46 50
LONGITUDE:       83 55 15
```

SUMMARY:

FORMATION	DESCRIPTION	THICKNESS IN FEET	DEPTH IN FEET
In Pliocene Miccosukee 0	Sand: mottled, light brown to very pale orange, medium- to coarse-grained, moderately sorted, subangular quartz, argillaceous, accessory iron minerals common, 5YR5/6 to 10YR8/2--------------------------------	40	40
Miocene Hawthorne Undif. 40	Sand: light greenish-gray, fine- to medium-grained, well sorted, subangular quartz, silty, slightly phosphatic, with Limestone; white sandy, thinly interbedded, 5GY8/1---------	55	95
Oligocene Suwannee 95	No samples-------------------------------------	10	105
	Limestone: white fossilferous _Quinqueloculina_ sp. at 9-100'------------------------------	65	170
	Dolomite: grayish-orange, saccharoidal, 10YR7/4--	35	205
	No samples-------------------------------------	8	213

T.D. 213

```
WELL NO: GGS 817                        ALTITUDE:         195 ft.
WELL NAME:    H. B. Burton              TOTAL DEPTH:      250 ft.
COUNTY:  Thomas                         (Data from McFadden, et al, 1986)
LATITUDE:       30 49 12
LONGITUDE:      83 54 45
```

SUMMARY:

FORMATION	DESCRIPTION	THICKNESS IN FEET	DEPTH IN FEET
In Miocene Hawthorne Undif. 0	Sand: very light gray, medium-grained, moderately sorted, subrounded quartz, argillaceous, slightly calcareous, N8------------------------------------	30	30
	Sand: mottled, white to moderate greenish-yellow, fine- to medium-grained, moderately sorted, subangular quartz, slightly calcareous, with accessory iron minerals common, 10Y7/4 to 5YR/6------------------	15	45
Oligocene Suwannee 45	Limestone: white, granular, with abundant foraminifers, Quinqueloculina sp. at 45-50'---------------------------------	205	250

T.D. 250

```
WELL NO: GGS 914                    ALTITUDE:        285 ft.
WELL NAME:   Earl Sanders           TOTAL DEPTH:     275 ft.
COUNTY: Thomas                      (Data from McFadden, et al, 1986)
LATITUDE:     30 47 50
LONGITUDE:    84 01 25
```

SUMMARY:

FORMATION	DESCRIPTION	THICKNESS IN FEET	DEPTH IN FEET
In Pliocene Miccosukee-Miocene Hawthorne Undif. 0	Sand: varicolored, fine-grained (0.2 mm), very well sorted, subrounded quartz, argillaceous, with Limestone; rounded fragments common, accessory iron minerals abundant--------------------------	70	70
Miocene Hawthorne Undif. 65	Sand: Sand: white to very pale orange, fine- to medium-grained, moderately sorted subangular to subrounded quartz, calcareous, fossiliferous, phosphatic (?), 10YR8/2 Ostracods common at 65-70'--------------------------	65	130
Miocene Chattahoochee	Limestone: very pale orange, sandy, with rare fossil impressions, 10YRB/2 Archaias sp. at 145-150'----------------------------------	35	165
Oligocene Suwannee 165	Chert: white to yellowish-gray, calcareous, 5Y7/2--	5	170
	No samples---	15	185
	Limestone: white, with abundant foraminifers-----	5	190
	No samples---	15	205
	Limestone: white, loosely cemented, with saccharoidal dolomite at bottom of interval-----------------------------------	65	270

T.D. 270

```
WELL NO: GGS 916                    ALTITUDE:           233 ft.
WELL NAME:   Ira Lee                TOTAL DEPTH:        210 ft.
COUNTY: Grady                       (Data from McFadden, et al, 1986)
LATITUDE:        30 43 44
LONGITUDE:       84 12 20
```

SUMMARY:

FORMATION	DESCRIPTION	THICKNESS IN FEET	DEPTH IN FEET
In Miocene to Pleistocene Undif. 0	Sand: yellowish-gray, fine- to very coarse-grained, poorly sorted, subrounded, clear quartz, 5Y7/2--------------------	60	60
	Sand: yellowish-gray, fine- to very coarse-grained, poorly sorted, subrounded quartz, argillaceous, with Limestone; white, sandy, and sparse lignite, 5Y7/2--	10	70
Oligocene Suwannee 70	Limestone: white, fossiliferous, recrystallized. Asterigerina subacuta, Pararotalia mexicana, Sphaerogypsina globula, Lepidocyclina sp., Nummulites sp., Dictyoconus sp., at 70-80'--------------------------------	115	185
Oligocene Undif. 185	Limestone: grayish-orange pink, dolomitic, saccharoidal, 5YR7/2--------------------	20	205
T.D. 210			

```
WELL NO: GGS 1446                      ALTITUDE (MSL):   242 ft.
WELL NAME:   Mistletoe Plantation      TOTAL DEPTH:
COUNTY:  Grady                         (Data from McFadden, et al, 1986)
LATITUDE:        30 41 08
LONGITUDE:       84 15 22
```

SUMMARY:

Depth to Top of Oligocene: 310 feet (by McFadden, et al, based on lithology).   Other information not available.

```
WELL NO: GGS 3114                      ALTITUDE (MSL):   267 ft.
WELL NAME:   Sedgewick #1              TOTAL DEPTH:      More than 2000 ft.
COUNTY:  Thomas                        (Data from McFadden, et al, 1986)
LATITUDE:        30 47 11
LONGITUDE:       83 57 44
```

SUMMARY:

Depth to Top of Oligocene: Greater than 120 feet (by McFadden, et al, based on lithology). Other information not available.

```
WELL NO: GGS 3121                      ALTITUDE:         269 ft.
WELL NAME:   Fed. Regional Center      TOTAL DEPTH:
COUNTY:  Thomas                        (Data from McFadden, et al, 1986)
LATITUDE:        30 48 20
LONGITUDE:       83 59 15
```

SUMMARY:

Depth to Top of Oligocene: 190 feet (by McFadden, et al, based on Paleontology).   Other information not available.

```
WELL NO: FGS Core 6927          ALTITUDE:        201 ft.
WELL NAME:    Wooten #2         TOTAL DEPTH:     162 ft.
COUNTY: Jefferson               (Data from Johnson, 1986)
LATITUDE:     30 36 09
LONGITUDE:    83 50 52
```

SUMMARY:

FORMATION	DESCRIPTION

0-56 ft.
Miccosukee
Formation

Poorly indurated, reddish brown to pale orange,
clayey, silty sand.

56-129.5 ft.
Hawthorn
Group
Undifferentiated

Moderately indurated, greenish yellow to yellowish
gray, phosphatic, silty, sandy clay

129.5-152 ft.
St. Marks
Formation

Moderately indurated, light gray to yellowish
brown, sandy calcilutite. Intervals of chert
present.

152-162 ft.
Suwannee
Limestone

Well indurated, pale orange, microfossilierous,
recrystallized calcarenite.

```
WELL NO: FGS Core 6933          ALTITUDE:        214 ft.
WELL NAME:    Sasser #1          TOTAL DEPTH:     270 ft.
COUNTY: Jefferson                (Data from Johnson, 1986)
LATITUDE:      30 37 05
LONGITUDE:     83 59 00
```

SUMMARY:

FORMATION	DESCRIPTION

0-48 ft.
Miccosukee
Formation

Predominately clay, very sandy to sandy, silty, grayish orange to light yellow, trace heavies, thin sand beds, also sand-soil horizon.

48-103 ft.
Hawthorn
Group
Undifferentiated

Clay, sandy, silty, white to yellowish gray, poor to moderate induration. Limestone, sandy, clayey, mudstone to wackestone, very light orange.

103-224 ft.
St. Marks
Formation

Limestone, sandy, clayey, clay beds, moderate to good induration, very light orange, fossiliferous.

224-270 ft.
Suwannee
Limestone

Limestone, grainstone to wackestone, poor to good induration, very light orange, fossilferous.

```
WELL NO: FGS Core 16736          ALTITUDE:         190 ft.
WELL NAME:    Tall Timbers       TOTAL DEPTH:      404 ft.
COUNTY: Leon                     (Well Log by Frank Rupert, F.G.S., 1994)
LATITUDE:        30 39 50
LONGITUDE:       84 12 49
```

SUMMARY:

```
  0.0 -     1.2     Undifferentiated Sand and Clay
  1.2 -    47.8     Miccossukee FM.
 47.8 -   130.0     Torreya FM.
130.0 -   173.0     Chattahoochee FM.
173.0 -   189.7     St. Marks FM.
189.7 -   404.0     Suwannee Limestone
```

Miccosukee

0 -   1.2   Sand: brownish gray. 30% porosity: intergranular. Grain size: fine.
                    Range: very fine to medium. Roundness: sub-angular to rounded;
                    medium sphericity. Poor induration. Accessory minerals: clay-
                    02% Fossils: no fossils, organics.

1.2 -   5.5   Sand: grayish orange to moderate yellowish brown. 28% porosity:
                    intergranular. Grain size: fine. Range: very fine to medium.
                    Roundness: sub-angular to rounded. medium sphericity.   Poor
                    induration. Accessory minerals: clay-05%; Fossils: no fossils.

5.5 -   8   Sand: grayish orange to very light orange. 28% porosity: intergranular.
                    Grain size: fine. Range: very fine to medium. Roundness: sub-
                    angular to rounded; medium sphericity.   Poor induration.
                    Accessory minerals: clay-01%. Fossils: no fossils.

8 -   15.2   Sand: light brown. 28% porosity: intergranular. Grain size: medium.
                    Range: very fine to coarse. Roundness: sub-angular to rounded;
                    medium sphericity. Poor induration. Sedimentary structures:
                    mottled. Accessory minerals: clay-02%. Fossils: no fossils.

15.2-   18.9   Sand: light brown. 25% porosity: intergranular. Grain size: fine.
                    Range: fine to coarse. Roundness: sub-angular to rounded; medium
                    sphericity. Poor induration. Accessory minerals: clay-05%.
                    Fossils: no fossils. Interval contains missing section.

18.9-   20.7   Clay: very light orange to grayish orange. 15% porosity: intergranular
                    Poor induration. Accessory minerals: quartz sand-10%. Fossils:
                    no fossils.

20.7-   21.8   Clay: dark yellowish orange. 10% porosity: intergranular. Poor
                    induration. Accessory minerals: quartz sand-01%. Fossils: no
                    fossils.

SUMMARY:

21.8-	26	Sand: grayish orange. 25% porosity: intergranular. Grain size: fine; Range: very fine to medium. Roundness: sub-angular to rounded; medium sphericity. Poor induration. Accessory minerals: clay-05 Fossils: no fossils.
26 -	28.3	Clay: grayish orange to very light orange. 20% porosity: intergranular; poor induration. Accessory minerals: quartz sand-02%. Fossils: no fossils.
28.3-	32	Sand: very light orange to grayish orange. 20% porosity: intergranular Grain size: fine; Range: very fine to fine. Roundness: sub-angular to rounded; medium sphericity. Poor induration. Accessory minerals: clay-10%. Fossils: no fossils.
32 -	37	Sand: dark yellowish orange to grayish orange. 20% porosity: intergranular Grain size: fine; Range: very fine to fine. Roundness: sub-angular to rounded; medium sphericity. Poor induration. Accessory minerals: clay-10%. Fossils: no fossils.
37 -	45	Sand: dark yellowish orange to grayish orange. 15% porosity: intergranular. Grain size: very fine. Range:: very fine to fine. Roundness: sub-angular to rounded; medium sphericity. Poor induration. Accessory minerals: clay-10%. Fossils: no fossils.
45 -	46.5	Clay: moderate yellowish brown to dark yellowish orange. 10% porosity: intergranular. Poor induration. Accessory minerals: quartz sand-01%. Fossils: no fossils.
46.5-	47.8	Sand: grayish orange to very light orange. 20% porosity: intergranular. Grain size: very fine. Range: very fine to fine. Roundness: sub-angular to rounded; medium sphericity. Poor induration. Accessory minerals: clay-05%. Fossils: no fossils.

Torreya

47.8-	55.5	Clay: yellowish gray. 10% porosity: intergranular. poor induration. Accessory minerals: quartz sand-05%. Fossils: no fossils.
55.5-	57	Sand: very light orange to yellowish gray. 30% porosity: intergranular. Grain size: fine. Range: very fine to medium. Roundness: sub-angular to rounded; medium sphericity. Poor induration. Accessory minerals: clay-01%. Fossils: no fossils.
57 -	58.2	Clay: dark yellowish orange to moderate yellowish brown. 10% porosity: intergranular. Poor induration. Accessory minerals: quartz sand-01 Fossils: no fossils.

58.2-   61   Sand: very light orange to yellowish gray. 20% porosity:
                    intergranular. Grain size: fine. Range: very fine to fine.
                    Roundness: Sub-angular to rounded; medium sphericity. Poor
                    induration. Accessory minerals: clay-05%. Fossils: no fossils.

61 -   64.5   Clay: moderate yellowish brown to dark yellowish orange. 10% porosity:
                    intergranular. Poor induration. Accessory minerals: quartz sand-
                    01 Fossils: no fossils.

64.5-   65   Clay: yellowish gray. 10% porosity: intergranular. poor induration.
                    Accessory minerals: quartz sand-02%. Fossils: no fossils.

65 -   92.5   Sand: Yellowish gray to grayish yellow. 20% porosity: intergranular.
                    Grain size: very fine. Range: very fine to fine. Roundness: sub-
                    angular to rounded; medium sphericity. Poor induration.
                    Accessory minerals: clay-05%. Fossils: no fossils.

92.5-   109.3   Sand: very light gray to yellowish gray. 20% porosity: intergranular.
                    Grain size: very fine. Range: very fine to fine. Roundness: sub-
                    angular to rounded; medium sphericity. Poor induration.
                    Accessory minerals: clay-01%. Fossils: no fossils.

109.3-110.5   Sand: grayish orange. 20% porosity: intergranular. Grain size: very
                    fine. Range: very fine to fine. Roundness: sub-angular to
                    rounded; medium sphericity. Poor induration. Accessory
                    minerals: clay-05%. Fossils: no fossils.

110.5-114.5   Sand: yellowish gray. 20% porosity: intergranular. Grain size: very
                    fine; Range: very fine to fine. Roundness: sub-angular to
                    rounded; medium sphericity. Poor induration. Accessory
                    minerals: clay-10%. Fossils: no fossils.

114.5-116.2   Clay: light olive gray. 10% porosity: intergranular. poor induration.
                    Accessory minerals: quartz sand-05%. Fossils: no fossils.

116.2-130   Silt-size dolomite: white to yellowish gray. 10% porosity:
intergranular,
                    intragranular. Moderate induration. Cement type(s): dolomite
                    cement. Accessory minerals: quartz sand-10%. Other features:
                    calcareous. Fossils: no fossils. Top of Chattahoochee based on
                    litho change. Top is likely in interval 130-138.

Chattahoochee

130-133.5   Limestone: yellowish gray to white. 10% porosity: intergranular,
                    intragranular, moldic. Grain type: calcilutite, skeletal. 10%
                    allochemical constituents. Grain size: microcrystalline.
                    Range: microcrystalline to medium; moderate induration. Fossils:
                    fossil fragments.

SUMMARY:

133.5-	153	Silt-size dolomite: very light orange to white. 05% porosity: intergranular, intercrystalline. Moderate induration. Cement type(s): dolomite cement. Other features: high recrystallization. Fossils: Benthic Foraminifera, fossil fragments.
153-	157	Silt-size dolomite: yellowish gray. 05% porosity: intergranular, intercrystalline. Moderate induration. Cement type(s): dolomite cement. Fossils: benthic foraminifera, fossil fragments.
157-	162	Silt-size dolomite: very light orange. 05% porosity: intergranular. intercrystalline. Moderate induration. Cement type(s): dolomite cement. Fossils: benthic foraminifera, fossil fragments.
162-	173	Silt-size dolomite: very light orange to yellowish gray. 05% porosity: intergranular, intercrystalline. Moderate induration. Cement type(s): dolomite cement. Fossils: benthic foraminifera, fossil fragments.

St. Marks

173-	189.7	Limestone: white to yellowish gray. 10% porosity: intergranular, intragranular, moldic. Grain type: skeletal, calcilutite, biogenic. 40% allochemical constituents. Grain size: microcrystalline. Range: microcrystalline to very coarse. Accessory minerals: quartz sand -15%. Fossils: benthic foraminifera, fossil fragments, mollusks.

Suwannee

189.7-	253	Limestone:; white to yellowish gray. 10% porosity: intergranular, intragranular, moldic. Grain type: skeletal, calcilutite, biogenic. 70% allochemical constituents. Grain size: microcrystalline. Range: microcrystalline to very coarse. Cement type(s): gypsum cement. Fossils: benthic foraminifera, mollusks, bryozoa, coral fossil fragments. Top of Suwannee picked on decreased sand, fossil increase, and apparent hardground at 189.7 feet. Highly molluscan moldic in some intervals.
253-	404	Dolostone: dark yellowish brown to grayish orange. 15% porosity: intergranular, moldic. 10-50% altered subhedral. Grain size: microcrystalline. Range: microcrystalline to very fine. Moderate induration. Cement type(s): dolomite cement. Other features: high recrystallization. Fossils: mollusks, fossil fragments.
404		Total depth

APPENDIX V

SOILS INFORMATION

Table V-1
Soil Permeability Groups by Map Symbol and Name (Thomas County)

High	Medium	Low
Ch - Chipley	FaB,FaD,FdC2 - Faceville	Ap - Alapaha
LaB - Lakeland	LmB,LmC - Lucy	Bm - Bayboro
[1]MO - Myatt-Osier	Mn - Mascotte	CaB^2, CaC^2 - Carnegie
Oc - Ochlockonee	NoA,NoB - Norfolk	Cn - Clarendon
[1]WA - Wahee	Od - Ocilla	Co - Coxville
[1]Da - Dasher	Oe - Olustee	Do - Dothan
	OrB,OrD,OsC2 - Orangeburg	EuB, EuD - Esto
	Ra - Rains	Gr - Grady
	Se - Stilson	Le - Leefield
	TaA,TfB,TsC2 - Tifton	NkB,NkC - Nankin
	TuB - Tifton Urban	
	[2]FsB - Fuquay	

[1]Permeability range in map unit is variable from rapid to slow

[2]Permeability range in this map unit is variable from excessive to moderate.

Table V-2
Soil Permeability Groups by Map Symbol and Name (Grady County)[1]

High	Medium	Low
33B1 - Bigbee	10A1,10B1,10C1 - Norfolk	19A1 - Rembert
54B1 - Chipola	21B1,21C1 - Wicksburg-Esto	17B1 - Hornsville-Wahee
733Ba-733D1 - Lakeland	34A1 - Coosaw	27A1,717A - Hornsville
770A1 - Osier	36B1,36C1-Chisolm	70A - Megget
	37B1 - Eddings	716A1,716B1 - Freemanville
	49E2 - Orangeburg-Esto	719A1 - Grady
	749A1,749B1,749C1, 749D1 - Orangeburg	747B1 - Fuquay[1]
	56C2,56D2 - Cowarts-Gritney	758A1,758B1 - Varina
	158C1 - Tifton-Lucy	760B2,760C2 - Carnegie-Wahee
	58A1,58B1,58C1-Tifton	810A1,810B1 - Dothan
	154B1-Lucy	821C2,821D2 - Esto
	707B - Kolomoki	
	715B1,715C1,715D1 - Troup	
	718A1 - Goldsboro	
	734A1 - Ocilla	
	736B1 - Bonneau	
	737B1,737C1 - Blanton	
	745A1 - Rains	
	751A1,752A1 - Pelham. frequently flooded	
	813 - Lynchburg	

[1]The Grady survey is unpublished, and no map unit descriptions were available.

Interpretations are based solely on characteristic soil descriptions and interpretations and are not as specific to Grady County as the Thomas County data is to Thomas County.

Table V-3

PHYSICAL AND CHEMICAL PROPERTIES OF SOILS

[The symbol < means less than; > means more than. Entries under "Erosion factors--T" apply to the entire profile. Absence of an entry indicates that data were not available or were not estimated]

Soil name and map symbol	Depth	Permeability	Available water capacity	Soil reaction	Shrink-swell potential	Risk of corrosion		Erosion factors	
						Uncoated steel	Concrete	K	T
	In	In/hr	In/in	pH					
Alapaha:									
Ap————————	0-32	6.0-20	0.05-0.08	4.5-5.5	Low————	High——————	High——————	———	———
	32-44	0.6-2.0	0.10-0.13	4.5-5.5	Low————	High———— ————	High——————	———	
	44-65	0.2-0.6	0.08-0.10	4.5-5.5	Low————	High——————	High——————	———	
Bayboro:									
Bm———————	0-15	0.6-2.0	0.15-0.20	4.5-5.5	Low————	High——————	High——————	———	———
	15-62	0.06-0.2	0.14-0.18	4.5-5.5	Moderate	High——————	High——————	———	
Carnegie:									
CaB2, CaC2————	0-7	2.0-6.0	0.05-0.08	4.5-6.0	Low————	Low————	Moderate————	0.28	3
	7-21	0.6-2.0	0.10-0.14	4.5-6.0	Low————	Low————	Moderate————	0.24	
	21-35	0.2-0.6	0.10-0.13	4.5-5.5	Low————	Low————	Moderate————	0.20	
	35-65	0.2-0.6	0.10-0.14	4.5-5.5	Low————	Low————	Moderate————	0.24	
Chipley:									
Ch———————	0-8	6.0-20	0.05-0.10	4.5-6.0	Very low———	Low————	High——————	0.15	5
	8-80	6.0-20	0.03-0.08	4.5-6.0	Very low———	Low————	High——————	———	
Clarendon:									
Cn———————	0-13	2.0-6.0	0.08-0.12	4.5-6.5	Low————	Moderate————	High——————	0.15	5
	13-32	0.6-2.0	0.10-0.15	4.5-5.5	Low————	Moderate————	High——————	0.20	
	32-62	0.2-0.6	0.08-0.12	4.5-5.5	Low————	Moderate————	High——————	0.15	
Coxville:									
Co———————	0-14	0.6-2.0	0.12-0.17	4.5-6.0	Low————	High——————	High——————	———	———
	14-62	0.2-0.6	0.14-0.18	4.5-5.5	Moderate	High——————	High——————	———	
Dasher:									
Da———————	0-8	———	———	———	———————	———————	———————	———	———
	8-65	———	———	———	———————	———————	———————	———	
Dothan:									
DoA, DoB————	0-9	2.0-6.0	0.06-0.10	4.5-5.5	Very low———	Moderate————	Moderate————	0.24	4
	9-42	0.6-2.0	0.10-0.14	4.5-5.5	Low————	Moderate————	Moderate————	0.20	
	42-62	0.2-0.6	0.08-0.12	4.5-5.5	Low————	Moderate————	Moderate————	0.10	
Esto:									
EuB, EuD—————	0-7	2.0-6.0	0.11-0.15	4.5-5.5	Low————	Low————	High——————	0.17	3
	7-12	0.6-2.0	0.12-0.17	4.5-5.5	Moderate	High——————	High——————	0.28	
	12-62	0.06-0.2	0.12-0.18	4.5-5.5	Moderate	High——————	High——————	0.32	
Faceville:									
FaB, FaD, FdC2————	0-8	6.0-20	0.06-0.09	4.5-5.5	Low————	Low————	Moderate————	0.28	5
	8-11	0.6-2.0	0.12-0.15	4.5-5.5	Low————	Low————	Moderate————	———	
	11-68	0.6-2.0	0.12-0.18	4.5-5.5	Low————	Low————	Moderate————	———	
Fuquay:									
FsB———————	0-28	>6.0	0.04-0.09	4.5-5.5	Low————	Low————	High——————	0.20	5
	28-50	0.6-2.0	0.12-0.15	4.5-5.5	Low————	Low————	High——————	0.20	
	50-65	0.06-0.2	0.10-0.13	4.5-5.5	Low————	Low————	High——————	0.20	
	96-99	>6.0	0.04-0.09	4.5-5.5	Low————	Low————	High——————	0.20	
Grady:									
Gr———————	0-5	0.6-2.0	0.10-0.18	3.6-5.5	Low————	High——————	High——————	———	———
	5-65	0.06-0.2	0.12-0.16	3.6-5.5	Moderate	High——————	High——————	———	
Lakeland:									
LaB———————	0-42	>20	0.05-0.08	4.5-6.0	Very low———	Low————	Moderate————	0.17	5
	42-80	>20	0.03-0.08	4.5-6.0	Very low———	Low————	Moderate————	———	
Leefield:									
Le———————	0-28	6.0-20	0.04-0.07	4.5-6.0	Low————	Low————	Low————	———	———
	28-32	0.6-2.0	0.10-0.13	4.5-5.5	Low————	Moderate————	High——————	———	
	32-65	0.2-0.6	0.08-0.12	4.5-5.5	Low————	Moderate————	High——————	———	

See footnote at end of table.

Soil name and map symbol	Depth	Permeability	Available water capacity	Soil reaction	Shrink-swell potential	Risk of corrosion		Erosion factors	
						Uncoated steel	Concrete	K	T
	_In_	_In/hr_	_In/in_	_pH_					
Lucy:									
LmB, LmC----------	0-32	>6.0	0.06-0.10	5.1-5.5	Low--------	Low------------	High------------	0.20	5
	32-40	2.0-6.0	0.10-0.12	4.5-5.5	Low--------	Low------------	High------------	----	
	40-65	0.6-2.0	0.12-0.14	4.5-5.5	Low--------	Low------------	High------------	----	
Mascotte:									
Mn----------------	0-14	6.0-20	0.03-0.08	4.5-5.5	Very low---	High-----------	High-----------	----	----
	14-23	0.6-2.0	0.10-0.15	4.5-5.5	Very low---	High-----------	High-----------	----	
	23-35	6.0-20	0.03-0.08	4.5-5.5	Very low---	High-----------	High-----------	----	
	35-65	0.6-2.0	0.10-0.15	4.5-5.5	Low--------	High-----------	High-----------	----	
Myatt:									
[1]MO:									
Myatt part------	0-12	0.6-2.0	0.11-0.24	4.5-5.5	Low--------	High-----------	High-----------	----	----
	12-55	0.2-2.0	0.12-0.20	3.6-5.5	Low--------	High-----------	High-----------	----	
	55-65	>6.0	0.06-0.10	3.6-5.0	Very low---	High-----------	High-----------	----	
Osier part------	0-4	6.0-20	0.10-0.15	4.5-6.0	Low--------	High-----------	High-----------	----	----
	4-43	6.0-20	0.03-0.10	4.5-6.0	Low--------	High-----------	High-----------	----	
	43-65	>20	0.02-0.05	4.5-6.0	Low--------	High-----------	High-----------	----	
Nankin:									
NkB, NkC----------	0-8	2.0-6.0	0.05-0.08	4.5-5.5	Low--------	Low------------	High------------	0.28	3
	8-13	0.6-2.0	0.10-0.15	4.5-5.5	Low--------	Moderate------	High------------	0.24	
	13-38	0.2-0.6	0.11-0.16	4.5-5.5	Low--------	High-----------	High------------	0.24	
	38-65	0.2-0.6	0.10-0.15	4.5-5.5	Low--------	High-----------	High------------	0.24	
Norfolk:									
NoA, NoB---------	0-12	2.0-6.0	0.06-0.10	4.5-6.0	Low--------	Moderate------	High------------	0.17	5
	12-65	0.6-2.0	0.10-0.15	4.5-5.5	Low--------	Moderate------	High------------	0.24	
Ochlockonee:									
Oc----------------	0-6	2.0-6.0	0.07-0.14	4.5-5.5	Low--------	Low------------	High-----------	----	----
	6-65	2.0-6.0	0.06-0.12	4.5-5.5	Low--------	Low------------	High-----------	----	
Ocilla:									
Od----------------	0-28	2.0-20	0.05-0.08	4.5-5.5	Low--------	High-----------	Moderate--------	----	----
	28-65	0.6-2.0	0.09-0.12	4.5-5.5	Low--------	High-----------	Moderate--------	----	
Olustee:									
Oe----------------	0-6	6.0-20	0.05-0.10	4.5-5.5	Very low---	High-----------	High-----------	----	----
	6-19	0.6-2.0	0.10-0.15	4.5-5.5	Very low---	High-----------	High-----------	----	
	19-35	6.0-20	0.03-0.08	4.5-5.5	Very low---	High-----------	High-----------	----	
	35-60	0.6-2.0	0.10-0.15	4.5-5.5	Low--------	High-----------	High-----------	----	
Orangeburg:									
OrB, OrD---------	0-13	2.0-6.0	0.06-0.08	4.5-6.0	Low--------	Moderate------	Moderate--------	0.20	5
	13-18	2.0-6.0	0.07-0.10	4.5-5.5	Low--------	Moderate------	Moderate--------	0.24	
	18-65	0.6-2.0	0.10-0.13	4.5-5.5	Low--------	Moderate------	Moderate--------	0.24	
OsC2--------------	0-5	2.0-6.0	0.07-0.10	4.5-6.0	Low--------	Moderate------	Moderate--------	0.24	5
	5-18	2.0-6.0	0.07-0.10	4.5-5.5	Low--------	Moderate------	Moderate--------	0.24	
	18-65	0.6-2.0	0.10-0.13	4.5-5.5	Low--------	Moderate------	Moderate--------	0.24	
Osier:									
[1]OS:									
Osier part------	0-4	6.0-20	0.10-0.15	4.5-6.0	Low--------	High-----------	High-----------	----	----
	4-43	6.0-20	0.03-0.10	4.5-6.0	Low--------	High-----------	High-----------	----	
	43-65	>20	0.02-0.05	4.5-6.0	Low--------	High-----------	High-----------	----	
Pelham part-----	0-28	6.0-20	0.05-0.08	4.5-5.5	Very low---	High-----------	High-----------	----	----
	28-64	0.6-2.0	0.10-0.13	4.5-5.5	Low--------	High-----------	High-----------	----	
Ousley:									
Ou----------------	0-14	6.0-20	0.05-0.10	4.5-5.5	Low--------	Low------------	High-----------	0.15	5
	14-80	6.0-20	0.02-0.06	4.5-5.5	Low--------	Low------------	High-----------	0.15	
Rains:									
Ra----------------	0-16	6.0-20	0.07-0.10	4.5-6.5	Low--------	High-----------	High-----------	----	----
	16-65	0.6-2.0	0.10-0.15	4.5-5.5	Low--------	High-----------	High-----------	----	

See footnote at end of table.

Soil name and map symbol	Depth	Permea-bility	Available water capacity	Soil reaction	Shrink-swell potential	Risk of corrosion		Erosion factors	
						Uncoated steel	Concrete	K	T
	In	In/hr	In/in	pH					
Stilson:									
Se------------------	0-36	6.0-20	0.06-0.09	4.5-5.5	Low--------	Low------------	High------------	0.17	5
	36-46	0.6-2.0	0.09-0.12	4.5-5.5	Low--------	Moderate-------	High------------	0.24	
	46-62	0.6-2.0	0.08-0.10	4.5-5.5	Low--------	Moderate-------	High------------	0.17	
Tifton:									
TfA, TfB, TsC2,									
[1]TuB--------------	0-11	6.0-20	0.03-0.08	4.5-5.5	Low--------	Low------------	Moderate--------	0.24	4
	11-14	6.0-20	0.08-0.12	4.5-5.5	Low--------	Low------------	Moderate--------	---	
	14-42	0.6-2.0	0.12-0.15	4.5-5.5	Low--------	Low------------	Moderate--------	---	
	42-65	0.6-2.0	0.10-0.13	4.5-5.5	Low--------	Low------------	Moderate--------	---	
Wahee:									
[1]WA--------------	0-10	0.6-2.0	0.10-0.15	4.5-5.5	Low--------	Moderate-------	High------------	---	---
	10-52	0.06-0.2	0.12-0.20	4.5-5.5	Moderate	High-----------	High------------	---	
	52-65	0.2-0.6	0.12-0.20	4.5-5.5	Moderate	High-----------	High------------	---	

[1]This map unit is made up of two or more dominant kinds of soil. See map unit description for the composition and behavior characteristics of the map unit.

Table V-4

PHYSICAL AND CHEMICAL PROPERTIES OF THE SOILS

Survey Area- DECATUR AND GRADY COUNTIES, GEORGIA

Map Symbol	Soil Name	Depth (In)	Clay (pct)	Moist Blk Density (g/cm3)	Permeab- ility (In/hr)	Available water cap (In/in)	Soil React (ph)	Shrink Swell Pot.	Erosion Factor K	T	Wind Erod. Group	Organic Matter (pct)
10A1	NORFOLK	0-14	2- 8	1.55-1.70	6.00-20.00	0.06-0.11	3.6-6.0	LOW	.17	5	2	0.5- 2.0
		14-38	18-35	1.30-1.65	0.60- 2.00	0.10-0.18	3.6-5.5	LOW	.24			0.0- 0.0
		38-70	20-43	1.20-1.65	0.60- 2.00	0.12-0.18	3.6-5.5	LOW	.24			0.0- 0.0
		70-99	-	0.00-0.00	0.00- 0.00	0.00-0.00	0.0-0.0					0.0- 0.0
10B1	NORFOLK	0-14	2- 8	1.55-1.70	6.00-20.00	0.06-0.11	3.6-6.0	LOW	.17	5	2	0.5- 2.0
		14-38	18-35	1.30-1.65	0.60- 2.00	0.10-0.18	3.6-5.5	LOW	.24			0.0- 0.0
		38-70	20-43	1.20-1.65	0.60- 2.00	0.12-0.18	3.6-5.5	LOW	.24			0.0- 0.0
		70-99	-	0.00-0.00	0.00- 0.00	0.00-0.00	0.0-0.0					0.0- 0.0
10C2	NORFOLK	0-14	2- 8	1.55-1.70	6.00-20.00	0.06-0.11	3.6-6.0	LOW	.17	5	2	0.5- 2.0
		14-38	18-35	1.30-1.65	0.60- 2.00	0.10-0.18	3.6-5.5	LOW	.24			0.0- 0.0
		38-70	20-43	1.20-1.65	0.60- 2.00	0.12-0.18	3.6-5.5	LOW	.24			0.0- 0.0
		70-99	-	0.00-0.00	0.00- 0.00	0.00-0.00	0.0-0.0					0.0- 0.0
17B1	HORNSVILLE	0- 9	6-15	1.44-1.68	6.00-20.00	0.08-0.12	4.5-6.0	LOW	.20	5	3	1.0- 4.0
		9-43	35-60	1.58-1.63	0.20- 0.60	0.12-0.16	4.5-6.0	LOW	.28			0.0- 0.0
		43-76	12-35	1.62-1.69	0.60- 2.00	0.10-0.14	4.5-6.0	LOW	.24			0.0- 0.0
	WAHEE	0-11	5-20	1.30-1.60	0.60- 2.00	0.10-0.15	4.5-6.0	LOW	.24	5	3	0.5- 5.0
		11-56	35-60	1.40-1.60	0.06- 0.20	0.12-0.20	3.6-5.5	MODER	.28			0.0- 0.5
		56-65	-	0.00-0.00	0.00- 0.00	0.00-0.00	0.0-0.0					0.0- 0.0
19A1	REMBERT	0- 5	5-18	1.40-1.60	0.60- 2.00	0.10-0.14	4.5-6.5	LOW	.20	5	3	1.0- 5.0
		5-33	35-60	1.20-1.50	0.06- 0.20	0.12-0.16	4.5-5.5	LOW	.20			0.0- 0.5
		33-54	22-45	1.30-1.50	0.60- 2.00	0.12-0.15	4.5-5.5	LOW	.17			0.0- 0.5
		54-65	8-25	1.30-1.60	0.60- 6.00	0.07-0.12	4.5-5.5	LOW	.17			0.0- 0.5
21B1	WICKSBURG	0-26	4-12	1.30-1.70	6.00-20.00	0.05-0.11	4.5-6.0	LOW	.10	5	2	0.5- 1.0
		26-30	25-40	1.40-1.60	0.06- 2.00	0.12-0.18	4.5-5.5	LOW	.20			0.0- 0.0
		30-65	35-45	1.30-1.50	0.06- 0.20	0.14-0.18	4.5-5.5	MODER	.24			0.0- 0.0
	ESTO	0- 8	7-12	1.45-1.65	6.00-20.00	0.06-0.10	3.6-5.5	LOW	.17	4	2	0.5- 1.0
		8-13	26-45	1.55-1.65	0.60- 2.00	0.12-0.17	3.6-5.5	MODER	.32			0.0- 0.0
		13-62	35-60	1.50-1.65	0.06- 0.20	0.12-0.18	3.6-5.5	MODER	.32			0.0- 0.0
21C1	WICKSBURG	0-26	4-12	1.30-1.70	6.00-20.00	0.05-0.11	4.5-6.0	LOW	.10	5	2	0.5- 1.0
		26-30	25-40	1.40-1.60	0.06- 2.00	0.12-0.18	4.5-5.5	LOW	.20			0.0- 0.0
		30-65	35-45	1.30-1.50	0.06- 0.20	0.14-0.18	4.5-5.5	MODER	.24			0.0- 0.0
	ESTO	0- 8	7-12	1.45-1.65	6.00-20.00	0.06-0.10	3.6-5.5	LOW	.17	4	2	0.5- 1.0
		8-13	26-45	1.55-1.65	0.60- 2.00	0.12-0.17	3.6-5.5	MODER	.32			0.0- 0.0
		13-62	35-60	1.50-1.65	0.06- 0.20	0.12-0.18	3.6-5.5	MODER	.32			0.0- 0.0
27A1	HORNSVILLE	0- 9	6-15	1.44-1.68	6.00-20.00	0.08-0.12	4.5-6.0	LOW	.20	5	3	1.0- 4.0
		9-43	35-60	1.58-1.63	0.20- 0.60	0.12-0.16	4.5-6.0	LOW	.28			0.0- 0.0
		43-76	12-35	1.62-1.69	0.60- 2.00	0.10-0.14	4.5-6.0	LOW	.24			0.0- 0.0
33B1	BIGBEE	0-17	4-10	1.40-1.50	6.00-20.00	0.05-0.10	4.5-6.0	LOW	.10	5		0.5- 2.0
		17-80	1-10	1.40-1.50	6.00-20.00	0.05-0.08	4.5-6.0	LOW	.17			0.0- 0.0
34A1	COOSAW	0-32	5-12	1.55-1.70	6.00-20.00	0.08-0.11	4.5-6.0	LOW	.10	5	2	0.5- 2.0
		32-35	15-20	1.55-1.70	2.00- 6.00	0.12-0.14	4.5-6.0	LOW	.24			0.0- 0.5
		35-72	18-35	1.50-1.75	0.60- 2.00	0.11-0.14	4.5-5.5	LOW	.24			0.0- 0.5
		72-99	2-20	1.55-1.80	2.00- 6.00	0.06-0.14	4.5-5.5	LOW	.10			0.0- 0.5
36B1	CHISOLM	0-25	5-12	1.40-1.70	6.00-20.00	0.04-0.10	4.5-6.0	LOW	.15	5	2	0.5- 1.0
		25-36	18-35	1.30-1.50	0.60- 2.00	0.10-0.15	4.5-6.0	LOW	.15			0.0- 0.5

PHYSICAL AND CHEMICAL PROPERTIES OF THE SOILS

Survey Area- DECATUR AND GRADY COUNTIES, GEORGIA

Map Symbol	Soil Name	Depth (In)	Clay (pct)	Moist Blk Density (g/cm3)	Permeab- ility (In/hr)	Available water cap (In/in)	Soil React (ph)	Shrink Swell Pot.	Erosion Factor K	Erosion Factor T	Wind Erod. Group	Organic Matter (pct)
		36-45	20-45	1.30-1.50	0.60- 2.00	0.10-0.16	4.5-6.0	LOW	.15			0.0- 0.5
		45-57	15-35	1.30-1.50	0.60- 6.00	0.08-0.15	4.5-6.0	LOW	.15			0.0- 0.5
		57-80	2-20	1.40-1.70	6.00-20.00	0.03-0.08	4.5-5.5	LOW	.15			0.0- 0.5
36C1	CHISOLM	0-25	5-12	1.40-1.70	6.00-20.00	0.04-0.10	4.5-6.0	LOW	.15	5	2	0.5- 1.0
		25-36	18-35	1.30-1.50	0.60- 2.00	0.10-0.15	4.5-6.0	LOW	.15			0.0- 0.5
		36-45	20-45	1.30-1.50	0.60- 2.00	0.10-0.16	4.5-6.0	LOW	.15			0.0- 0.5
		45-57	15-35	1.30-1.50	0.60- 6.00	0.08-0.15	4.5-6.0	LOW	.15			0.0- 0.5
		57-80	2-20	1.40-1.70	6.00-20.00	0.03-0.08	4.5-5.5	LOW	.15			0.0- 0.5
37B1	EDDINGS	0-44	1-10	1.50-1.70	6.00-20.00	0.05-0.11	4.5-6.5	LOW	.10	5	2	0.5- 2.0
		44-66	15-25	1.30-1.50	0.60- 2.00	0.10-0.17	4.5-6.5	LOW	.15			0.0- 0.5
		66-84	15-40	1.30-1.50	0.60- 2.00	0.11-0.18	4.5-5.5	LOW	.10			0.0- 0.5
49E2	ORANGEBURG	0- 7	4-10	1.35-1.55	2.00- 6.00	0.06-0.09	4.5-6.0	LOW	.10	5	2	0.5- 1.0
		7-12	7-18	1.50-1.65	2.00- 6.00	0.09-0.12	4.5-6.0	LOW	.20			0.0- 0.0
		12-54	18-35	1.60-1.75	0.60- 2.00	0.11-0.14	4.5-5.5	LOW	.24			0.0- 0.0
		54-64	20-45	1.60-1.75	0.60- 2.00	0.11-0.14	4.5-5.5	LOW	.24			0.0- 0.0
	ESTO	0- 8	8-20	1.45-1.65	2.00- 6.00	0.11-0.15	3.6-5.5	LOW	.28	4	3	0.5- 1.0
		8-13	26-45	1.55-1.65	0.60- 2.00	0.12-0.17	3.6-5.5	MODER	.32			0.0- 0.0
		13-62	35-60	1.50-1.65	0.06- 0.20	0.12-0.18	3.6-5.5	MODER	.32			0.0- 0.0
54B1	CHIPOLA	0-35	2- 8	1.30-1.65	6.00-20.00	0.06-0.10	4.5-6.0	LOW	.17	5	2	0.5- 1.0
		35-56	10-35	1.55-1.70	2.00- 6.00	0.10-0.17	4.5-5.5	LOW	.24			0.0- 0.0
		56-75	5-15	1.55-1.70	2.00-20.00	0.06-0.14	4.5-5.5	LOW	.20			0.0- 0.0
		75-94	1-10	1.55-1.70	6.00-20.00	0.02-0.06	4.5-5.5	LOW	.10			0.0- 0.0
56C2	COWARTS	0- 8	5-20	1.30-1.65	2.00- 6.00	0.08-0.13	4.5-5.5	LOW	.24	4	3	1.0- 3.0
		8-19	10-30	1.30-1.50	0.60- 2.00	0.10-0.16	4.5-5.5	LOW	.28			0.2- 1.0
		19-25	25-40	1.30-1.50	0.20- 2.00	0.10-0.16	4.5-5.5	LOW	.28			0.0- 0.5
		25-60	18-35	1.45-1.75	0.06- 0.60	0.10-0.14	4.5-5.5	LOW	.24			0.0- 0.5
	GRITNEY	0- 7	8-30	1.50-1.60	6.00-20.00	0.10-0.15	4.5-5.5	LOW	.20	3	3	1.0- 4.0
		7-12	30-45	1.55-1.65	0.60- 2.00	0.10-0.15	4.5-5.5	MODER	.32			0.0- 0.0
		12-31	35-60	1.55-1.70	0.06- 0.20	0.10-0.15	4.5-5.5	HIGH	.32			0.0- 0.0
		31-50	20-35	1.50-1.65	0.20- 0.60	0.10-0.15	4.5-5.5	HIGH	.28			0.0- 0.0
		50-68	-	0.00-0.00	2.00-20.00	0.00-0.00	0.0-0.0					0.0- 0.0
56D2	COWARTS	0- 8	5-20	1.30-1.65	2.00- 6.00	0.08-0.13	4.5-5.5	LOW	.24	4	3	1.0- 3.0
		8-19	10-30	1.30-1.50	0.60- 2.00	0.10-0.16	4.5-5.5	LOW	.28			0.2- 1.0
		19-25	25-40	1.30-1.50	0.20- 2.00	0.10-0.16	4.5-5.5	LOW	.28			0.0- 0.5
		25-60	18-35	1.45-1.75	0.06- 0.60	0.10-0.14	4.5-5.5	LOW	.24			0.0- 0.5
	GRITNEY	0- 7	8-30	1.50-1.60	6.00-20.00	0.10-0.15	4.5-5.5	LOW	.20	3	3	1.0- 4.0
		7-12	30-45	1.55-1.65	0.60- 2.00	0.10-0.15	4.5-5.5	MODER	.32			0.0- 0.0
		12-31	35-60	1.55-1.70	0.06- 0.20	0.10-0.15	4.5-5.5	HIGH	.32			0.0- 0.0
		31-50	20-35	1.50-1.65	0.20- 0.60	0.10-0.15	4.5-5.5	HIGH	.28			0.0- 0.0
		50-68	-	0.00-0.00	2.00-20.00	0.00-0.00	0.0-0.0					0.0- 0.0
58A1	TIFTON	0-10	3- 8	1.30-1.55	6.00-20.00	0.03-0.08	4.5-6.0	LOW	.10	4	2	0.5- 1.0
		10-18	13-22	1.45-1.65	6.00-20.00	0.08-0.12	4.5-6.0	LOW	.24			0.5- 1.0
		18-33	20-35	1.50-1.70	0.60- 2.00	0.12-0.16	4.5-6.0	LOW	.24			0.0- 0.5
		33-64	25-40	1.55-1.80	0.20- 0.60	0.10-0.13	4.5-5.5	LOW	.17			0.0- 0.5
		64-85	25-45	1.60-1.85	0.20- 0.60	0.10-0.12	4.5-5.5	LOW	.17			0.0- 0.5

U.S. Department of Agriculture
Soil Conservation Service

PHYSICAL AND CHEMICAL PROPERTIES OF THE SOILS

Survey Area- DECATUR AND GRADY COUNTIES, GEORGIA

Map Symbol	Soil Name	Depth (In)	Clay (pct)	Moist Blk Density (g/cm3)	Permeability (In/hr)	Available water cap (In/in)	Soil React (ph)	Shrink Swell Pot.	Erosion Factor K	Erosion Factor T	Wind Erod. Group	Organic Matter (pct)
58B1	TIFTON	0-10	3- 8	1.30-1.55	6.00-20.00	0.03-0.08	4.5-6.0	LOW	.10	4	2	0.5- 1.0
		10-18	13-22	1.45-1.65	6.00-20.00	0.08-0.12	4.5-6.0	LOW	.24			0.5- 1.0
		18-33	20-35	1.50-1.70	0.60- 2.00	0.12-0.16	4.5-6.0	LOW	.24			0.0- 0.5
		33-64	25-40	1.55-1.80	0.20- 0.60	0.10-0.13	4.5-5.5	LOW	.17			0.0- 0.5
		64-85	25-45	1.60-1.85	0.20- 0.60	0.10-0.12	4.5-5.5	LOW	.17			0.0- 0.5
58C2	TIFTON	0-10	10-20	1.30-1.50	6.00-20.00	0.06-0.10	4.5-6.0	LOW	.17	4	3	1.0- 2.0
		10-18	13-22	1.45-1.65	6.00-20.00	0.08-0.12	4.5-6.0	LOW	.24			0.5- 1.0
		18-33	20-35	1.50-1.70	0.60- 2.00	0.12-0.16	4.5-6.0	LOW	.24			0.0- 0.5
		33-64	25-40	1.55-1.80	0.20- 0.60	0.10-0.13	4.5-5.5	LOW	.17			0.0- 0.5
		64-85	25-45	1.60-1.85	0.20- 0.60	0.10-0.12	4.5-5.5	LOW	.17			0.0- 0.5
70A1	MEGGETT	0- 8	5-20	1.20-1.40	2.00- 6.00	0.10-0.15	4.5-6.5	LOW	.24	5	3	2.0- 8.0
		8-16	30-60	1.45-1.60	0.06- 0.20	0.13-0.18	5.1-8.4	HIGH	.32			0.0- 0.0
		16-52	35-60	1.50-1.75	0.06- 0.20	0.13-0.18	6.1-8.4	HIGH	.32			0.0- 0.0
		52-65	25-50	1.40-1.60	0.06- 0.60	0.12-0.18	6.1-8.4	MODER	.28			0.0- 0.0
154B1	LUCY	0-24	1-12	1.30-1.70	6.00-20.00	0.08-0.12	5.1-6.0	LOW	.10	5	2	0.5- 1.0
		24-35	10-30	1.40-1.60	2.00- 6.00	0.10-0.12	4.5-5.5	LOW	.24			0.0- 0.0
		35-70	20-45	1.40-1.60	0.60- 2.00	0.12-0.14	4.5-5.5	LOW	.28			0.0- 0.0
158C1	TIFTON	0-10	3- 8	1.30-1.55	6.00-20.00	0.03-0.08	4.5-6.0	LOW	.10	4	2	0.5- 1.0
		10-18	13-22	1.45-1.65	6.00-20.00	0.08-0.12	4.5-6.0	LOW	.24			0.5- 1.0
		18-33	20-35	1.50-1.70	0.60- 2.00	0.12-0.16	4.5-6.0	LOW	.24			0.0- 0.5
		33-64	25-40	1.55-1.80	0.20- 0.60	0.10-0.13	4.5-5.5	LOW	.17			0.0- 0.5
		64-85	25-45	1.60-1.85	0.20- 0.60	0.10-0.12	4.5-5.5	LOW	.17			0.0- 0.5
	LUCY	0-24	1-12	1.30-1.70	6.00-20.00	0.08-0.12	5.1-6.0	LOW	.10	5	2	0.5- 1.0
		24-35	10-30	1.40-1.60	2.00- 6.00	0.10-0.12	4.5-5.5	LOW	.24			0.0- 0.0
		35-70	20-45	1.40-1.60	0.60- 2.00	0.12-0.14	4.5-5.5	LOW	.28			0.0- 0.0
	TIFTON	0-10	3- 8	1.30-1.55	6.00-20.00	0.03-0.08	4.5-6.0	LOW	.10	4	2	0.5- 1.0
		10-18	13-22	1.45-1.65	6.00-20.00	0.08-0.12	4.5-6.0	LOW	.24			0.5- 1.0
		18-33	20-35	1.50-1.70	0.60- 2.00	0.12-0.16	4.5-6.0	LOW	.24			0.0- 0.5
		33-64	25-40	1.55-1.80	0.20- 0.60	0.10-0.13	4.5-5.5	LOW	.17			0.0- 0.5
		64-85	25-45	1.60-1.85	0.20- 0.60	0.10-0.12	4.5-5.5	LOW	.17			0.0- 0.5
707B1	KOLOMOKI	0- 8	10-14	1.35-1.45	2.00- 6.00	0.06-0.09	4.5-6.5	LOW	.24	4	3	0.5- 3.0
		8-28	35-55	1.60-1.70	0.60- 2.00	0.13-0.16	4.5-6.0	LOW	.32			0.0- 0.0
		28-35	20-35	1.50-1.60	0.60- 2.00	0.10-0.13	4.5-6.0	LOW	.28			0.0- 0.0
		35-42	10-35	1.50-1.60	0.60- 2.00	0.06-0.11	4.5-6.0	LOW	.24			0.0- 0.0
		42-65	2-15	1.50-1.60	6.00-20.00	0.05-0.08	4.5-6.0	LOW	.20			0.0- 0.0
715B1	TROUP	0-53	2-12	1.30-1.70	6.00-20.00	0.08-0.12	4.5-6.0	VERY	.10	5	2	0.5- 1.0
		53-80	15-35	1.40-1.60	0.60- 2.00	0.10-0.13	4.5-5.5	LOW	.20			0.0- 0.0
715C1	TROUP	0-53	2-12	1.30-1.70	6.00-20.00	0.08-0.12	4.5-6.0	VERY	.10	5	2	0.5- 1.0
		53-80	15-35	1.40-1.60	0.60- 2.00	0.10-0.13	4.5-5.5	LOW	.20			0.0- 0.0
715D1	TROUP	0-53	2-12	1.30-1.70	6.00-20.00	0.08-0.12	4.5-6.0	VERY	.10	5	2	0.5- 1.0
		53-80	15-35	1.40-1.60	0.60- 2.00	0.10-0.13	4.5-5.5	LOW	.20			0.0- 0.0
716A1	FREEMANVILLE	0-10	7-20	1.30-1.60	0.60- 2.00	0.11-0.18	5.1-6.0	LOW	.24	5	3	0.5- 1.0
		10-17	15-35	1.30-1.60	0.60- 2.00	0.12-0.18	5.1-6.0	LOW	.28			0.0- 0.0
		17-72	35-45	1.25-1.55	0.20- 0.60	0.12-0.16	4.5-5.5	LOW	.28			0.0- 0.0
716B1	FREEMANVILLE	0-10	7-20	1.30-1.60	0.60- 2.00	0.11-0.18	5.1-6.0	LOW	.24	5	3	0.5- 1.0

PHYSICAL AND CHEMICAL PROPERTIES OF THE SOILS

Survey Area- DECATUR AND GRADY COUNTIES, GEORGIA

Map Symbol	Soil Name	Depth (In)	Clay (pct)	Moist Blk Density (g/cm3)	Permeab- ility (In/hr)	Available water cap (In/in)	Soil React (ph)	Shrink Swell Pot.	Erosion Factor K	Erosion Factor T	Wind Erod. Group	Organic Matter (pct)
		10-17	15-35	1.30-1.60	0.60- 2.00	0.12-0.18	5.1-6.0	LOW	.28			0.0- 0.0
		17-72	35-45	1.25-1.55	0.20- 0.60	0.12-0.16	4.5-5.5	LOW	.28			0.0- 0.0
717A1	HORNSVILLE	0- 9	6-15	1.44-1.68	6.00-20.00	0.08-0.12	4.5-6.0	LOW	.20	5	3	1.0- 4.0
		9-43	35-60	1.58-1.63	0.20- 0.60	0.12-0.16	4.5-6.0	LOW	.28			0.0- 0.0
		43-76	12-35	1.62-1.69	0.60- 2.00	0.10-0.14	4.5-6.0	LOW	.24			0.0- 0.0
718A1	GOLDSBORO	0-15	2- 8	1.55-1.75	6.00-20.00	0.06-0.11	3.6-5.5	LOW	.17	5	2	0.5- 2.0
		15-45	18-30	1.30-1.50	0.60- 2.00	0.11-0.17	3.6-5.5	LOW	.24			0.0- 0.0
		45-65	20-34	1.30-1.40	0.60- 2.00	0.11-0.20	3.6-5.5	LOW	.24			0.0- 0.0
		65-76	-	0.00-0.00	0.00- 0.00	0.00-0.00	0.0-0.0					0.0- 0.0
719A1	GRADY	0- 5	15-20	1.25-1.45	0.60- 2.00	0.10-0.15	3.6-5.5	LOW	.10	5	3	1.0- 4.0
		5-11	20-35	1.40-1.55	0.20- 0.60	0.10-0.15	3.6-5.5	LOW	.10			0.0- 0.0
		11-62	45-65	1.50-1.60	0.06- 0.20	0.12-0.16	3.6-5.5	MODER	.10			0.0- 0.0
733B1	LAKELAND	0-43	2- 8	1.35-1.65	6.00-20.00	0.05-0.09	4.5-6.0	LOW	.10	5	1	0.5- 1.0
		43-80	1- 6	1.50-1.60	6.00-20.00	0.02-0.08	4.5-6.0	LOW	.10			0.0- 0.5
733D1	LAKELAND	0-43	2- 8	1.35-1.65	6.00-20.00	0.05-0.09	4.5-6.0	LOW	.10	5	1	0.5- 1.0
		43-80	1- 6	1.50-1.60	6.00-20.00	0.02-0.08	4.5-6.0	LOW	.10			0.0- 0.5
734A1	OCILLA	0-28	4-10	1.45-1.65	2.00-20.00	0.05-0.08	4.5-5.5	LOW	.10	5	2	1.0- 2.0
		28-59	15-35	1.55-1.70	0.60- 2.00	0.09-0.12	4.5-5.5	LOW	.24			0.0- 0.0
		59-67	15-40	1.55-1.70	0.20- 2.00	0.09-0.12	4.5-5.5	LOW	.24			0.0- 0.0
736B1	BONNEAU	0-22	5-15	1.30-1.70	6.00-20.00	0.05-0.11	4.5-6.0	LOW	.10	5	2	0.5- 2.0
		22-50	13-35	1.40-1.60	0.60- 2.00	0.10-0.15	4.5-5.5	LOW	.20			0.0- 0.5
		50-74	15-40	1.40-1.60	0.60- 2.00	0.10-0.16	4.5-5.5	LOW	.20			0.0- 0.5
736C1	BONNEAU	0-22	5-15	1.30-1.70	6.00-20.00	0.05-0.11	4.5-6.0	LOW	.10	5	2	0.5- 2.0
		22-50	13-35	1.40-1.60	0.60- 2.00	0.10-0.15	4.5-5.5	LOW	.20			0.0- 0.5
		50-74	15-40	1.40-1.60	0.60- 2.00	0.10-0.16	4.5-5.5	LOW	.20			0.0- 0.5
737B1	BLANTON	0-58	5-13	1.35-1.60	6.00-20.00	0.05-0.10	4.5-6.0	LOW	.10	5	2	0.5- 2.0
		58-62	10-18	1.50-1.65	2.00- 6.00	0.10-0.15	4.5-5.5	LOW	.15			0.0- 0.5
		62-80	12-40	1.60-1.70	0.20- 2.00	0.10-0.15	4.5-5.5	LOW	.20			0.0- 0.5
737C1	BLANTON	0-58	5-13	1.35-1.60	6.00-20.00	0.05-0.10	4.5-6.0	LOW	.10	5	2	0.5- 2.0
		58-62	10-18	1.50-1.65	2.00- 6.00	0.10-0.15	4.5-5.5	LOW	.15			0.0- 0.5
		62-80	12-40	1.60-1.70	0.20- 2.00	0.10-0.15	4.5-5.5	LOW	.20			0.0- 0.5
745A1	RAINS	0-12	5-20	1.30-1.60	2.00- 6.00	0.10-0.14	3.6-6.5	LOW	.20	5	3	1.0- 6.0
		12-40	18-35	1.30-1.60	0.60- 2.00	0.11-0.15	3.6-5.5	LOW	.24			0.5- 1.0
		40-62	18-40	1.30-1.50	0.60- 2.00	0.10-0.15	3.6-5.5	LOW	.28			0.5- 1.0
		62-79	15-45	1.30-1.60	0.60- 2.00	0.10-0.15	3.6-5.5	LOW	.28			0.5- 1.0
747B1	FUQUAY	0-34	2-10	1.60-1.70	6.00-20.00	0.04-0.09	4.5-6.0	LOW	.15	5	2	0.5- 2.0
		34-45	10-35	1.40-1.60	0.60- 2.00	0.12-0.15	4.5-6.0	LOW	.20			0.0- 0.0
		45-96	20-35	1.40-1.60	0.06- 0.20	0.10-0.13	4.5-6.0	LOW	.20			0.0- 0.0
		96-99	-	0.00-0.00	0.00- 0.00	0.00-0.00	0.0-0.0					0.0- 0.0
747C1	FUQUAY	0-34	2-10	1.60-1.70	6.00-20.00	0.04-0.09	4.5-6.0	LOW	.15	5	2	0.5- 2.0
		34-45	10-35	1.40-1.60	0.60- 2.00	0.12-0.15	4.5-6.0	LOW	.20			0.0- 0.0
		45-96	20-35	1.40-1.60	0.06- 0.20	0.10-0.13	4.5-6.0	LOW	.20			0.0- 0.0
		96-99	-	0.00-0.00	0.00- 0.00	0.00-0.00	0.0-0.0					0.0- 0.0
749A1	ORANGEBURG	0- 7	4-10	1.35-1.55	2.00- 6.00	0.06-0.09	4.5-6.0	LOW	.10	5	2	0.5- 1.0
		7-12	7-18	1.50-1.65	2.00- 6.00	0.09-0.12	4.5-6.0	LOW	.20			0.0- 0.0

PHYSICAL AND CHEMICAL PROPERTIES OF THE SOILS

Survey Area- DECATUR AND GRADY COUNTIES, GEORGIA

Map Symbol	Soil Name	Depth (In)	Clay (pct)	Moist Blk Density (g/cm3)	Permeab- ility (In/hr)	Available water cap (In/in)	Soil React (ph)	Shrink Swell Pot.	Erosion Factor K	T	Wind Erod. Group	Organic Matter (pct)
		12-54	18-35	1.60-1.75	0.60- 2.00	0.11-0.14	4.5-5.5	LOW	.24			0.0- 0.0
		54-64	20-45	1.60-1.75	0.60- 2.00	0.11-0.14	4.5-5.5	LOW	.24			0.0- 0.0
749B1	ORANGEBURG	0- 7	4-10	1.35-1.55	2.00- 6.00	0.06-0.09	4.5-6.0	LOW	.10	5	2	0.5- 1.0
		7-12	7-18	1.50-1.65	2.00- 6.00	0.09-0.12	4.5-6.0	LOW	.20			0.0- 0.0
		12-54	18-35	1.60-1.75	0.60- 2.00	0.11-0.14	4.5-5.5	LOW	.24			0.0- 0.0
		54-64	20-45	1.60-1.75	0.60- 2.00	0.11-0.14	4.5-5.5	LOW	.24			0.0- 0.0
749C2	ORANGEBURG	0- 7	4-10	1.35-1.55	2.00- 6.00	0.06-0.09	4.5-6.0	LOW	.10	5	2	0.5- 1.0
		7-12	7-18	1.50-1.65	2.00- 6.00	0.09-0.12	4.5-6.0	LOW	.20			0.0- 0.0
		12-54	18-35	1.60-1.75	0.60- 2.00	0.11-0.14	4.5-5.5	LOW	.24			0.0- 0.0
		54-64	20-45	1.60-1.75	0.60- 2.00	0.11-0.14	4.5-5.5	LOW	.24			0.0- 0.0
749D2	ORANGEBURG	0- 7	4-10	1.35-1.55	2.00- 6.00	0.06-0.09	4.5-6.0	LOW	.10	5	2	0.5- 1.0
		7-12	7-18	1.50-1.65	2.00- 6.00	0.09-0.12	4.5-6.0	LOW	.20			0.0- 0.0
		12-54	18-35	1.60-1.75	0.60- 2.00	0.11-0.14	4.5-5.5	LOW	.24			0.0- 0.0
		54-64	20-45	1.60-1.75	0.60- 2.00	0.11-0.14	4.5-5.5	LOW	.24			0.0- 0.0
751A1	PELHAM	0-27	5-10	1.50-1.70	6.00-20.00	0.05-0.08	4.5-5.5	LOW	.10	5	8	1.0- 2.0
		27-56	15-30	1.30-1.60	0.60- 2.00	0.10-0.13	4.5-5.5	LOW	.24			0.0- 0.0
		56-68	15-40	1.30-1.60	0.20- 2.00	0.10-0.16	4.5-5.5	LOW	.24			0.0- 0.0
752A1	PELHAM	0-27	5-10	1.50-1.70	6.00-20.00	0.05-0.08	4.5-5.5	VERY	.10	5	2	1.0- 2.0
		27-56	15-30	1.30-1.60	0.60- 2.00	0.10-0.13	4.5-5.5	LOW	.24			0.0- 0.5
		56-68	15-40	1.30-1.60	0.20- 2.00	0.10-0.16	4.5-5.5	LOW	.24			0.0- 0.5
754B1	LUCY	0-24	1-12	1.30-1.70	6.00-20.00	0.08-0.12	5.1-6.0	LOW	.10	5	2	0.5- 1.0
		24-35	10-30	1.40-1.60	2.00- 6.00	0.10-0.12	4.5-5.5	LOW	.24			0.0- 0.0
		35-70	20-45	1.40-1.60	0.60- 2.00	0.12-0.14	4.5-5.5	LOW	.28			0.0- 0.0
754C1	LUCY	0-24	1-12	1.30-1.70	6.00-20.00	0.08-0.12	5.1-6.0	LOW	.10	5	2	0.5- 1.0
		24-35	10-30	1.40-1.60	2.00- 6.00	0.10-0.12	4.5-5.5	LOW	.24			0.0- 0.0
		35-70	20-45	1.40-1.60	0.60- 2.00	0.12-0.14	4.5-5.5	LOW	.28			0.0- 0.0
756B1	NANKIN	0- 8	7-20	1.45-1.55	2.00- 6.00	0.08-0.12	4.5-5.5	LOW	.28	3	3	0.5- 1.0
		8-13	15-35	1.55-1.65	0.60- 2.00	0.10-0.15	4.5-5.5	LOW	.24			0.0- 0.0
		13-38	35-50	1.30-1.70	0.20- 0.60	0.11-0.16	4.5-5.5	LOW	.24			0.0- 0.0
		38-65	15-35	1.60-1.70	0.60- 2.00	0.10-0.15	4.5-5.5	LOW	.24			0.0- 0.0
756C2	NANKIN	0- 8	7-20	1.45-1.55	2.00- 6.00	0.08-0.12	4.5-5.5	LOW	.28	3	3	0.5- 1.0
		8-13	15-35	1.55-1.65	0.60- 2.00	0.10-0.15	4.5-5.5	LOW	.24			0.0- 0.0
		13-38	35-50	1.30-1.70	0.20- 0.60	0.11-0.16	4.5-5.5	LOW	.24			0.0- 0.0
		38-65	15-35	1.60-1.70	0.60- 2.00	0.10-0.15	4.5-5.5	LOW	.24			0.0- 0.0
756D2	NANKIN	0- 8	7-20	1.45-1.55	2.00- 6.00	0.08-0.12	4.5-5.5	LOW	.28	3	3	0.5- 1.0
		8-13	15-35	1.55-1.65	0.60- 2.00	0.10-0.15	4.5-5.5	LOW	.24			0.0- 0.0
		13-38	35-50	1.30-1.70	0.20- 0.60	0.11-0.16	4.5-5.5	LOW	.24			0.0- 0.0
		38-65	15-35	1.60-1.70	0.60- 2.00	0.10-0.15	4.5-5.5	LOW	.24			0.0- 0.0
	COWARTS	0- 8	5-20	1.30-1.65	2.00- 6.00	0.08-0.13	4.5-5.5	LOW	.24	4	3	1.0- 3.0
		8-19	10-30	1.30-1.50	0.60- 2.00	0.10-0.16	4.5-5.5	LOW	.28			0.2- 1.0
		19-25	25-40	1.30-1.50	0.20- 2.00	0.10-0.16	4.5-5.5	LOW	.28			0.0- 0.5
		25-60	18-35	1.45-1.75	0.06- 0.60	0.10-0.14	4.5-5.5	LOW	.24			0.0- 0.5
758A1	VARINA	0-14	8-18	1.40-1.60	2.00- 6.00	0.08-0.13	4.5-6.5	LOW	.17	4		0.5- 2.0
		14-38	35-60	1.30-1.50	0.60- 2.00	0.12-0.18	4.5-5.5	LOW	.28			0.0- 0.0
		38-80	30-55	1.30-1.50	0.06- 0.20	0.06-0.09	4.5-5.5	LOW	.28			0.0- 0.0

PHYSICAL AND CHEMICAL PROPERTIES OF THE SOILS

Survey Area- DECATUR AND GRADY COUNTIES, GEORGIA

Map Symbol	Soil Name	Depth (In)	Clay (pct)	Moist Blk Density (g/cm3)	Permeability (In/hr)	Available water cap (In/in)	Soil React (ph)	Shrink Swell Pot.	Erosion Factor K	T	Wind Erod. Group	Organic Matter (pct)
758B1	VARINA	0-14	8-18	1.40-1.60	2.00- 6.00	0.08-0.13	4.5-6.5	LOW	.17	4		0.5- 2.0
		14-38	35-60	1.30-1.50	0.60- 2.00	0.12-0.18	4.5-5.5	LOW	.28			0.0- 0.0
		38-80	30-55	1.30-1.50	0.06- 0.20	0.06-0.09	4.5-5.5	LOW	.28			0.0- 0.0
760B2	CARNEGIE	0- 5	3- 8	1.45-1.65	2.00- 6.00	0.05-0.10	4.5-6.0	LOW	.28	3	3	1.0- 2.0
		5-20	36-43	1.40-1.65	0.20- 0.60	0.10-0.16	4.0-5.5	LOW	.32			0.0- 0.0
		20-32	36-51	1.40-1.65	0.20- 0.60	0.10-0.14	4.0-5.5	LOW	.28			0.0- 0.0
		32-65	36-55	1.40-1.65	0.20- 0.60	0.10-0.14	4.0-5.5	LOW	.28			0.0- 0.0
760C2	CARNEGIE	0- 5	3- 8	1.45-1.65	2.00- 6.00	0.05-0.10	4.5-6.0	LOW	.28	3	3	1.0- 2.0
		5-20	36-43	1.40-1.65	0.20- 0.60	0.10-0.16	4.0-5.5	LOW	.32			0.0- 0.0
		20-32	36-51	1.40-1.65	0.20- 0.60	0.10-0.14	4.0-5.5	LOW	.28			0.0- 0.0
		32-65	36-55	1.40-1.65	0.20- 0.60	0.10-0.14	4.0-5.5	LOW	.28			0.0- 0.0
763A1	WAHEE	0-11	5-20	1.30-1.60	0.60- 2.00	0.10-0.15	4.5-6.0	LOW	.24	5	3	0.5- 5.0
		11-56	35-60	1.40-1.60	0.06- 0.20	0.12-0.20	3.6-5.5	MODER	.28			0.0- 0.5
		56-65	-	0.00-0.00	0.00- 0.00	0.00-0.00	0.0-0.0					0.0- 0.0
770A1	OSIER	0- 8	10-15	1.35-1.60	6.00-20.00	0.10-0.15	3.6-6.0	LOW	.15	5	3	2.0- 5.0
		8-48	1-10	1.40-1.60	6.00-20.00	0.03-0.10	3.6-6.0	LOW	.10			0.0- 0.0
		48-75	2- 5	1.40-1.60	20.00-20.00	0.02-0.05	3.6-6.0	LOW	.05			0.0- 0.0
	BIBB	0-12	2-18	1.50-1.70	0.60- 2.00	0.12-0.18	3.6-5.5	LOW	.20	5	3	1.0- 3.0
		12-60	2-18	1.45-1.75	0.60- 2.00	0.10-0.20	3.6-5.5	LOW	.37			0.5- 1.0
810A1	DOTHAN	0-13	5-15	1.30-1.60	2.00- 6.00	0.06-0.10	4.5-6.0	VERY	.15	5	2	0.0- 0.5
		13-33	18-35	1.40-1.60	0.60- 2.00	0.12-0.16	4.5-6.0	LOW	.28			0.0- 0.0
		33-60	18-40	1.45-1.70	0.20- 0.60	0.08-0.12	4.5-6.0	LOW	.28			0.0- 0.0
810B1	DOTHAN	0-13	5-15	1.30-1.60	2.00- 6.00	0.06-0.10	4.5-6.0	VERY	.15	5	2	0.0- 0.5
		13-33	18-35	1.40-1.60	0.60- 2.00	0.12-0.16	4.5-6.0	LOW	.28			0.0- 0.0
		33-60	18-40	1.45-1.70	0.20- 0.60	0.08-0.12	4.5-6.0	LOW	.28			0.0- 0.0
813A1	LYNCHBURG	0-10	2-10	1.40-1.70	6.00-20.00	0.07-0.10	3.6-6.0	LOW	.15	5	2	0.5- 5.0
		10-62	18-35	1.30-1.50	0.60- 2.00	0.12-0.16	3.6-5.5	LOW	.20			0.0- 0.5
821C2	ESTO	0- 8	8-20	1.45-1.65	2.00- 6.00	0.11-0.15	3.6-5.5	LOW	.28	4	3	0.5- 1.0
		8-13	26-45	1.55-1.65	0.60- 2.00	0.12-0.17	3.6-5.5	MODER	.32			0.0- 0.0
		13-62	35-60	1.50-1.65	0.06- 0.20	0.12-0.18	3.6-5.5	MODER	.32			0.0- 0.0
821D2	ESTO	0- 8	8-20	1.45-1.65	2.00- 6.00	0.11-0.15	3.6-5.5	LOW	.28	4	3	0.5- 1.0
		8-13	26-45	1.55-1.65	0.60- 2.00	0.12-0.17	3.6-5.5	MODER	.32			0.0- 0.0
		13-62	35-60	1.50-1.65	0.06- 0.20	0.12-0.18	3.6-5.5	MODER	.32			0.0- 0.0

APPENDIX VI

OUTLINE OF FUTURE GEOLOGIC STUDY NEEDS

Basic Needs

In planning for future use and protection of the groundwater system in any area, certain basic information is required as a prerequisite to informed decision-making. The two basic categories of data needs are described below. These relate to the Floridan Aquifer, which is the primary water source in the project area.

A. <u>Aquifer Parameters:</u>

   1.   <u>Physical</u> - Depth, thickness and lithology of the aquifer, and areal variations in those factors, are necessary "boundary" conditions for sll other determinations. Natural recharge rates and other water-bearing characteristics of the aquifer (potentiometric levels, flow directions, permeability, specific capacities, transmissivity, and related factors), and areal and vertical changes in these characteristics are needed to compute the volume of available water that may be safely (and dependably) withdrawn in various areas and at various depths. This information also allows projection of changes in the aquifer system that may result from local withdrawals.

   2.   <u>Chemical</u> - The chemical quality of waters within the aquifer determines its suitability for use and is necessary information for documenting any future changes that may occur. The water quality is especially important when chemical acceptability deteriorates with depth in the aquifer (a common circumstance). Poor water quality at depth plainly limits the thickness of the aquifer that may be used to produce potable water, as well as limiting local pumping rates that could cause up-coning of undesirable waters into producing zones. Salt water and various other objectionable water characteristics are common at lower levels in the Floridan Aquifer and have been documented in many areas.

B. <u>Aquifer Protection Parameters:</u>

Aquifers are normally considered fairly well-protected (locally) if they are tightly confined (overlain by substantial impermeable material)--at least insofar as local contamination by surface sources is concerned. Unfortunately, in much of the project area the Floridan is described as "un-confined" or "semi-confined" and the aquifer is quite close to the surface as well. Given this situation, knowledge of the thickness, lithology, and, especially, the water-retarding characteristics of the overlying sediments becomes critical in determining areas in which the aquifer is most susceptible to surface contamination.

A high rate of local recharge to the aquifer has been projected for a large part of the project area; this provides an indication that the local confining beds may not function well as aquicludes, but documentation of the local competency of these beds is needed to adequately define the situation.

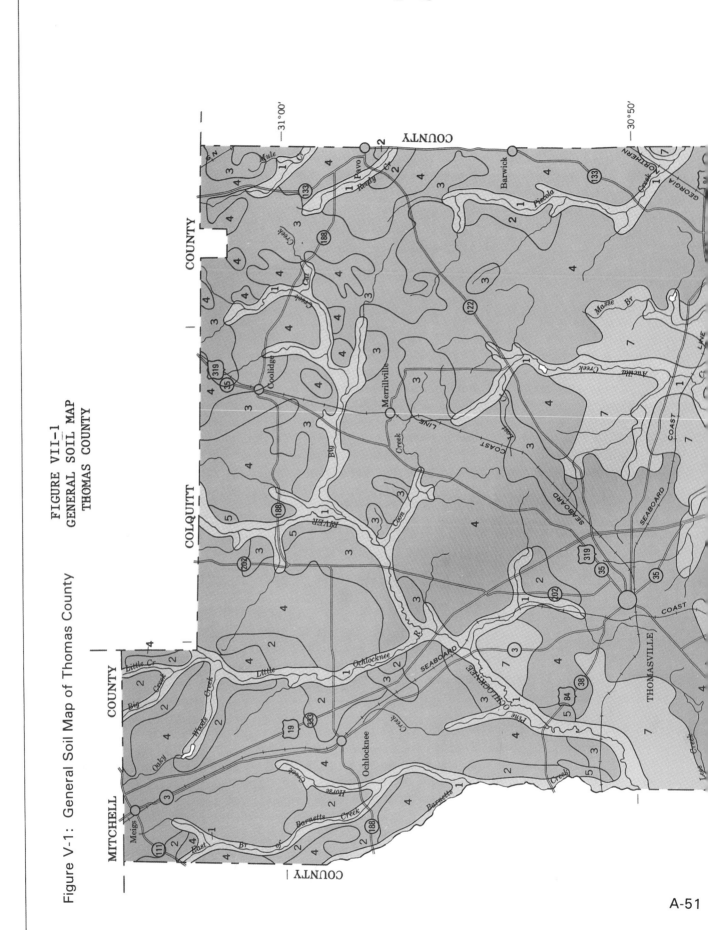

Figure V-1: General Soil Map of Thomas County

FIGURE VII-1
GENERAL SOIL MAP
THOMAS COUNTY

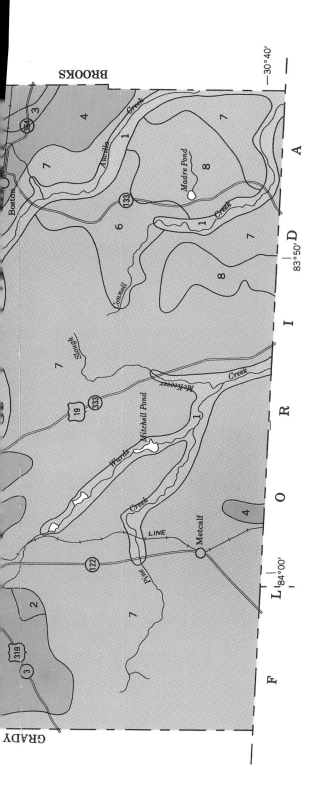

BROOKS

GRADY

F L 84°00'   O   R   I   83°50' D   A   —30°40'

SOIL ASSOCIATIONS

NEARLY LEVEL SOILS ON BOTTOM LANDS AND ON STREAM TERRACES OR ON LOW UPLANDS

1 OSIER-PELHAM-OCILLA: Nearly level soils that have predominantly a sandy surface layer and loamy or sandy underlying layers, on bottom lands and on stream terraces

NEARLY LEVEL TO GENTLY SLOPING SOILS ON UPLANDS, ALONG DRAINAGEWAYS, IN DEPRESSIONS, OR ON FLATS

2 TIFTON-CARNEGIE-ALAPAHA: Very gently sloping and gently sloping soils that have a sandy or loamy surface layer and loamy underlying layers, on uplands; and nearly level soils that have a sandy surface layer and loamy underlying layers, along drainageways of uplands

3 LEEFIELD-ALAPAHA-FUQUAY: Nearly level or very gently sloping soils that have a sandy surface layer and loamy underlying layers, in depressions and in drainageways of uplands, and in flat areas and on ridgetops of low uplands

4 TIFTON-ALAPAHA-DOTHAN: Nearly level to gently sloping soils that have a sandy surface layer and loamy underlying layers, on uplands; and nearly level soils that have a sandy surface layer and loamy underlying layers, in depressions and along drainageways of uplands

5 LAKELAND-ALAPAHA-FUQUAY: Nearly level or very gently sloping soils that have a sandy surface layer and sandy or loamy underlying layers, on uplands; and nearly level soils that have a sandy surface layer and loamy underlying layers, in depressions and in drainageways of uplands

NEARLY LEVEL TO SLOPING SOILS ON UPLANDS

6 ORANGEBURG-DOTHAN-FUQUAY: Nearly level to sloping soils that have a sandy surface layer and loamy underlying layers; on uplands

7 ORANGEBURG-FACEVILLE-TIFTON: Very gently sloping to sloping soils that have a loamy or sandy surface layer and loamy or clayey underlying layers, on uplands

8 DOTHAN-NORFOLK-FUQUAY: Nearly level or very gently sloping soils that have a sandy surface layer and loamy underlying layer, on uplands

Compiled 1977

Each area outlined on this map consists of more than one kind of soil. The map is thus meant for general planning rather than a basis for decisions on the use of specific tracts.

U. S. DEPARTMENT OF AGRICULTURE
SOIL CONSERVATION SERVICE
UNIVERSITY OF GEORGIA
COLLEGE OF AGRICULTURE
AGRICULTURAL EXPERIMENT STATIONS

GENERAL SOIL MAP
THOMAS COUNTY, GEORGIA

Scale 1:190,080

1   0   1   2   3   4 Miles

Conclusion

Simply stated, available information in the project area is insufficient to satisfy <u>any</u> of the described data needs. A few widely-spaced reference wells are available for determining depth to the top of the aquifer and some, very limited, lithologic characteristics. Some published data on water quality and ability of the aquifer to transmit water are available for a few sites near the project area (Thomasville and Cairo, for example), but otherwise this information is notably lacking. No information is available on competency of the local confining beds, other than some thickness and lithologic generalizations that may be drawn from reference wells and observation of surface exposures. Prevalence of local sinkholes provides some additional inferences as to the confining beds. Though local estimates are consistent with regional models, recharge rates have not been measured locally and obviously exceed the estimates in some areas.

Consequently, a fairly substantial data-gathering and analysis effort is needed to define the local groundwater situation in a dependable manner. Given that future land-use trends in the area are difficult to project, even for the short-term, it seems reasonable to move forward with the suggested work in as timely a manner as possible.

Future Study

No attempt is made here to define the exact details of the needed work. These details are more appropriately determined in a request-for-proposal/rfp-response process. However, certain project activities are obvious, at this point, and these are briefly summarized below.

A. <u>Lithologic Cores</u>: Several cores (probably three) are needed to assist in defining local geologic formations and aquifer and confining bed characteristics, especially as these factors change in the vicinity of the Apalachicola Embayment - Gulf Trough. In fact, one useful result would be better definition of the trough boundary. The Georgia Geological Survey can assist in determining the best core locations; however, it seems reasonable, at this point, to locate one in the Metcalf area, one south of the Meridian Road/U.S. Highway 319 intersection, and perhaps one close to Thomasville. Ideally, the cores would penetrate the full thickness of the Floridan Aquifer.

B. <u>Test Wells/Pump Tests</u>: Test wells to determine water quality, transmissivity and other aquifer characteristics, at appropriate depths, are needed in various locations. These tests can also provide definitive information as to the "leaky" nature of local confining beds. In some cases, existing wells may be used, but it is anticipated that a majority of the wells will have to be constructed. Later, the wells can be donated for use by local land-owners, with the stipulation that future use as part of a monitor well network is required. Much additional lithologic information can be acquired in the drilling process.

C. <u>Surface - Groundwater Intraction</u>: Although regional models have predicted recharge rates for the project area, and these generally seem compatible with local topographic features, no local work has been done to compute actual rates of recharge to the Floridan Aquifer. This information would contribute significantly to understanding of the local dynamics of the system and its vulnerability to contamination from surface sources.

Typical watersheds should be chosen in areas northwest and southeast of U.S. Highway 319/Meridian Road. Within each watershed, run-off (stream flow) should be monitored and quantified, over at least a year, and compared with local calculations of rainfall, evaporation and transpiration. Hopefully, monitoring could continue beyond the year period, to allow refinement of recharge calculation for periods of different rates of annual rainfall. Particular emphasis should be placed on selecting at least one watershed with high incidence of sink holes and one with very low incidence, or none.

D. Remainder of the Georgia Red Hills Area: The eastern portion of the Georgia Red Hills constitutes an area equivalent in size to that of the current study. It is similar geologically and hydrologically, suffers a comparable low level of available information, and may have an equally uncertain future, insofar as growth and development are concerned. Vulnerability of the natural systems seems at least equivalent, if not greater. Hence, extension of the current project into the eastern portion of the Red Hills seems a reasonable and prudent way to begin the process of developing environmental safe-guards in that area.

SEDGEFIELD
CONSERVATION EASEMENT

THIS SEDGEFIELD CONSERVATION EASEMENT
(herein "Easement") is made as of November 21, 1992, by and
between JOHN G. BUTLER and CAROL HUMPHREY BUTLER, husband
and wife (the "Grantors"; Carol Humphrey Butler is referred
to herein individually as "Grantor Carol Butler") of
Cleveland, Ohio, and TALL TIMBERS RESEARCH, INC. (the
"Grantee"), a nonprofit corporation organized and existing
under the laws of the State of Florida, with an address of
Route 1, Box 678, Tallahassee, Florida 32312-9712, an
eligible donee as described under Treasury Reg. 1.170A-
14(c)(1).

RECITALS

A.   The Grantors are the owners in fee
simple of certain real property as described on Exhibit A
attached hereto and by this reference incorporated herein,
and Grantor Carol Butler is the owner in fee simple of
certain real property as described on Exhibit B attached
hereto and by this reference incorporated herein (the real
property identified on Exhibits A and B is hereinafter
collectively referred to as the "Protected Property"),
which real property has aesthetic, scientific, educational,
and ecological value in its present state as a natural area
which has not been subject to development or exploitation.

B.   The Protected Property is a natural area
which contains upland longleaf pine forests, both natural
and old field stands; a seepage bog; the Wards Creek
drainage corridor.and associated mesic hardwood forests;
various wetlands including natural and man-made ponds; and
a habitat for rare species such as Red-cockaded woodpecker
(RCW), Gopher tortoise, Tallahassee hedge-nettle and other
species of special concern.

C.   The Grantee is a nonprofit corporation
whose purposes include scientific research, education, and
the preservation and conservation of culturally and
biologically significant lands.

D.   Section 44-10-1 et seq. of Georgia
Statutes permits the creation of conservation easements for
the purposes of, inter alia, retaining or protecting
natural, scenic or open space values of real property;
assuring its availability for open space use; and
protecting natural resources.

E.   The Grantors and Grantee recognize the
natural, scenic, aesthetic and special character of the
Protected Property, and have the common purpose of the

conservation and protection in perpetuity of the Protected
Property as "a relatively natural habitat of fish,
wildlife, or plants or similar ecosystem" as that phrase is
used in Public Law 96-541, 26 United States
Code 170(b)(4)(a)(ii), as amended and in regulations
promulgated thereunder, by placing voluntary restrictions
upon the use of the Protected Property and by providing for
the conveyance and transfer from the Grantors to Grantee of
affirmative rights for the protection of the Protected
Property.

     F. The condition of the Protected Property
at the time of this grant is evidenced by the Easement
Documentation Report for Sedgefield Plantation, dated
November, 1992 (the "Report"), a copy of which is on file
with both the Grantors and the Grantee, which documentation
establishes the condition of the property at the time of
the gift as provided in Treasury Reg. 1.170A-14(g)(5).

I. AFFIRMATIVE RIGHTS

     NOW, THEREFORE, the Grantors, for good and
valuable consideration, the receipt and sufficiency of
which are hereby acknowledged by the Grantors, and of the
covenants, mutual agreements, conditions and promises
herein contained, the Grantors do hereby freely give,
grant, bargain, sell and convey unto the Grantee, its
successors and assigns, forever, a conservation easement
over the Protected Property consisting of the following:

     1. The right of the Grantee to have visual
access to and view of the Protected Property in its
natural, scenic, open and undisturbed condition.

     2. The right of the Grantee to enter and
inspect the Protected Property, in a reasonable manner and
at reasonable times, in order to determine compliance with
the terms of this Easement, and to enforce, by proceedings
at law or in equity, the covenants herein set forth
including, but not limited to, the right to require the
restoration of the Protected Property to its condition at
the date of this Easement. The Grantee does not waive or
forfeit the right to take action as may be necessary to
insure compliance with the covenants and purposes of this
Easement by any prior failure of Grantee to act. Nothing
herein shall be construed to entitle the Grantee to
institute any proceedings against Grantors for any changes
to the Protected Property due to causes beyond the
Grantors' control such as changes caused by wildfire,
floods, storm or unauthorized wrongful acts of third
persons. Grantee's right of access hereunder shall include
the right, following approval from Grantors or their
representative, of access for (a) periodic site visits for
land management professionals, trainees or other adults to

observe various land management techniques, provided that an employee or associate of Grantee shall accompany such persons, and (b) scientific research, provided that Grantee shall have delivered to Grantors, at least thirty (30) days in advance of commencement of such research, a written description of the research proposed, in a form approved by Grantee, and a schedule of projected site visits; provided, that the right of approval by Grantors with respect to the access described in subparagraph (b) above may be withheld in Grantors' sole discretion and, without limiting the foregoing, Grantee shall have no right to conduct scientific research which adversely affects the Protected Property, as determined by Grantors in Grantors' sole discretion.

3. The right of the Grantee to assist the implementation of the Forest Management Plan, dated November, 1992, prepared by Mr. Leon Neel and Mr. James McKinley (the "Forest Management Plan"), the terms of which are incorporated herein by reference. The Forest Management Plan specifically includes a prescribed burn program and management recommendations for specific "Special Natural Areas". The Forest Management Plan shall not be amended except by agreement in writing, executed by both Grantors and Grantee. In the event that the Grantors are unable to implement crucial components of the Forest Management Plan (such as rare species management or prescribed burning), the Grantee shall have the right to implement activities using trained staff.

II. GENERAL COVENANTS

AND IN FURTHERANCE of the foregoing affirmative rights, the Grantors, on behalf of themselves, their heirs, successors and assigns, and with the intent that the same shall run with and bind the Protected Property in perpetuity, do hereby make, with respect to the Protected Property, the following general covenants, subject however, in each case, to the Reserved Rights (defined in Section IV below):

1. (Uses) There shall be no commercial or industrial activity undertaken or allowed, nor shall any right of passage across or upon the Protected Property be allowed or granted if that right of passage is used in conjunction with commercial or industrial activity. There shall be no agricultural activity.

2. (Structural) There shall be no construction of temporary or permanent residences, buildings, facilities, or placing of mobile homes, advertising signs, billboards or other advertising material. There shall be no construction or placing of

docks, bridges, piers or other structures excepting
maintenance and replacement of existing structures.

     3.   (Roads)   There shall be no building of
any new permanent roads, nor widening of existing roads.
Maintenance of roads shall be limited to (a) the removal of
dead vegetation, (b) necessary pruning or removal of
hazardous trees and plants, (c) the application of
permeable materials necessary to correct or impede erosion
(e.g. sand, gravel, crushed stone), (d) grading, (e) the
replacement of culverts, water control structures and
bridges and (f) maintenance of roadside ditches.

     4.   (Timber)   There shall be no timber
management or harvesting except in accordance with the
Forest Management Plan.

     5.   (Waters)   There shall be no dredging,
construction of new ponds, groins or dikes nor any
manipulation of natural water courses or Cochran Road Pond,
nor any activities or uses detrimental to water purity;
provided, however, that, without expanding the application
of the aforementioned restrictions, Grantor shall have the
right (a) to continue to divert water from Lake Bud along
the existing ditch to the existing planted field located to
the southeast of Lake Bud, (b) to maintain the spillway
located at the south end of Mitchell Pond (also known as
Sedgefield Lake) and the south end of Lake Bud and (c) to
perform such manipulation of the waters on the Protected
Property as may be reasonably necessary or appropriate for
the safeguard and proper protection of any dwellings,
buildings or other improvements on the Protected Property.

     6.   (Minerals and Topography)   There shall
be no filling, excavating, dredging, mining or drilling; no
removal of topsoil, sand, gravel, rock, peat, minerals or
other materials, nor any dumping of ashes, trash, garbage
or other unsightly or offensive material, and no change in
the topography of the land in any manner except as provided
for herein; provided, however, that (a) Grantors may
continue to use any existing sanitary landfill in
compliance with state, federal and local laws and
regulations; and (b) Grantors reserve to themselves, their
heirs and assigns, all interest in minerals found or to be
found in, on or under the Protected Property, provided that
there may not be at any time any extraction or removal of
the minerals by any surface mining method and there may not
at any time be used any method of mining that is
inconsistent with the particular conservation purpose of
this Easement, i.e. the protection of a relatively natural
habitat of fish, wildlife and plants, so that any permitted
method of mining may have only limited localized impact on
the real property and may not be irremediably destructive
of significant conservation interests. For example,
production facilities must be substantially concealed or

compatible with existing topography and landscape, and any surfaces which are altered must be restored substantially to their original state. Additionally, any mining shall be conducted in a manner consistent with any applicable regulations in effect from time to time governing qualified conservation contributions.

7. (Prohibited Use) Any use of the Protected Property and any activity thereon which, in the reasonable opinion of Grantee, is or may become inconsistent with this Easement, being the preservation of the Protected Property predominantly in its natural condition and the protection of environmental systems, is prohibited.

8. (Subdivision) There shall be no subdivision of the Protected Property.

III. SPECIAL NATURAL AREA COVENANTS

FURTHER, there are certain special natural areas within the boundaries of the Protected Property, (the "Special Natural Areas") harboring species or communities of special concern, as identified in the Report, which areas may be revised from time to time by Grantee, subject to approval by Grantors, which approval shall not be unreasonably withheld; provided, however, that Grantors shall have the absolute right not to consent to the designation of any Special Natural Areas within the Residential Development Land (defined below). Subject to the Reserved Rights, Grantors further agree that the Special Natural Areas shall (a) be managed in accordance with the pertinent provisions of the Forest Management Plan, and (b) be subject to the following additional covenants:

1. (Habitat) There shall be no removal, destruction or spraying with biocides of any vegetation, nor any disturbance or change in such manner, including introduction of exotic animal or plant species and timber harvesting, in the Special Natural Areas or within 132 feet (2 chains) of any Special Natural Areas, or any future such area established on the Protected Property, except in accordance with the Forest Management Plan.

2. (Topography and Minerals) There shall be no filling, excavating or dredging, no removal of topsoil, sand, gravel, rock, peat, minerals or other materials, nor dumping of ashes, trash, garbage or of any other material, nor any mineral activity and no changes of the topography of the land in any manner within 660 feet (10 chains) of any Special Natural Areas, excepting maintenance of existing canals and wetland impoundments.

3.   (Soil)   No major soil disturbing activities, including, without limitation, installation of new firebreaks and new food plots, will be undertaken within any Special Natural Areas, except in accordance with the pertinent provisions of the Forest Management Plan.

In the event that a breach of the restrictions set forth in Article II or III by the Grantors or by a third party comes to the attention of the Grantee, the Grantee shall notify the Grantors in writing of such a breach. If Grantors shall not, within thirty (30) days after receipt of such notice, undertake appropriate action reasonably calculated to correct promptly the conditions constituting such a breach, then the Grantee may, in its discretion, undertake such action, including appropriate legal proceedings. If, in any legal proceedings it is finally determined that the Grantors are responsible for the breach, the cost of such action, including the Grantee's reasonable expenses, court costs and legal fees, shall be paid by the Grantors.

IV.   RESERVED RIGHTS

NEVERTHELESS, and notwithstanding any of the foregoing provisions to the contrary, the Grantors reserve for themselves, their heirs, successors and assigns, the following reserved rights (herein, the "Reserved Rights"), which may be exercised at any time, subject to any notice requirements set forth below:

1.   The right to use and to maintain, repair, add to, restore and replace any existing houses, buildings and other improvements on the Protected Property, subject to applicable building codes and regulations.

2.   The right to construct, maintain, alter, repair, reconstruct and replace up to three (3) additional single family residences (herein "Main Dwellings") together with ancillary structures and related improvements including, without limitation, guest houses, tenant houses, farm manager houses and seasonal cabins (herein "Ancillary Structures"), and access drives and roads within that portion of the Protected Property identified as the "Residential Development Land" on Exhibit C attached hereto and made a part hereof, comprising approximately eighty (80) acres of land (herein, the "Residential Development Land"); provided, however, that Grantors shall provide to Grantee at least forty-five (45) days advance written notice of the proposed commencement of any new construction, or other work preparatory to new construction, including notice of the proposed location of any Main Dwellings or Ancillary Structures, and the location of all such improvements shall be subject to the prior written approval of Grantee, which approval shall not be unreasonably withheld, conditioned or delayed.

3. The right of Grantors, following prior written notice to Grantee, to subdivide the Residential Development Land into not more than three (3) separate parcels, and the right to grant easements to the owners of any portion of the Residential Development Land for ingress and egress from the public right of way to the Residential Development Land through any existing roads on the Protected Property.

4. The right to hunt and fish on the Protected Property, and the right to lease all or any portion of the Protected Property for hunting and fishing, provided that all such activity is conducted in accordance with state and federal regulations and shall not materially impair the conservation value of the Special Natural Areas.

5. The right to maintain existing wetland impoundments and dikes, whether man-made or natural, such impoundments being recognized by both Grantors and Grantee as conducive to waterfowl enhancement, all subject to state and federal rules and regulations. Impoundment reserves shall be managed for the primary purpose of providing feeding and nesting habitat for waterfowl and wading bird species and other wildlife species which the Grantee may determine in the future to warrant management, which determination shall be effective upon written notification thereof by Grantee to Grantors.

6. The right (a) to conduct agricultural and grazing activities on any portion of the Residential Development Land and to sell the produce and product therefrom, provided that, in consideration of the sensitive nature of the aquatic resources of Mitchell Pond and of its scenic and erodible shoreline, the clearing of forested acreage for agricultural and grazing activities within the Residential Development Land shall be subject to the prior written approval of Grantee, which approval shall not be unreasonably withheld, conditioned or delayed, and (b) as to the balance of the Protected Property (i.e. excluding the Residential Development Land), the right to continue agricultural and grazing activity on acreage not in excess of the acreage under such agricultural or grazing use at the time of this grant, and the right to sell the produce and product therefrom, provided that (i) the location of any additional tract for such activity shall be subject to the prior approval of Grantee, which approval shall not unreasonably be withheld (provided that Grantee may withhold such approval in its sole discretion with respect to the Special Natural Areas), and (ii) no naturally forested area therein shall be cleared for agricultural or grazing activity.

7. The right to selective timber management by thinning and harvesting; provided, however, that all timbering activities shall be conducted only in accordance

with the Forest Management Plan. The parties acknowledge that the Forest Management Plan includes Special Natural Areas management prescriptions and a prescribed burn schedule.

8. The right to allow archaeological research and work at any historical site or human burial site, provided that there is no adverse impact to any of the Special Natural Areas identified hereinabove and provided further that Grantee shall have approved of any such excavation, which approval shall not unreasonably be withheld.

The parties agree that all rights reserved by Grantor, or not prohibited or restricted by this Easement, are consistent with the conservation purposes of this Easement and, except as expressly provided herein, require no prior notification to or approval by Grantee other than the notification set forth above that such activities shall be undertaken.

V. GENERAL PROVISIONS

The Grantors agree that the terms, conditions, restrictions and purposes of this Easement will be included, or incorporated by reference, in any subsequent deed or other legal instrument by which the Grantors divest themselves of either fee simple, or their possessory interest, in all or any portion of the Protected Property and that the Grantors will notify the Grantee, its successors or assigns, of any such conveyance.

Grantors acknowledge that, by the terms of this Easement, Grantee has no obligation to maintain the Protected Property. The parties may, however, enter into a separate agreement regarding the allocation of responsibility for the maintenance of the Protected Property, subject, in any event, to the terms and provisions of this Easement.

Any notice required in this Easement shall be sent by registered or certified mail, postage prepaid, to the following addresses or such address as may be hereafter specified by notice in writing:

GRANTORS:

Mr. & Mrs. John Butler
c/o Advisory Services,
  Inc.
1010 The Hanna Bldg.
Cleveland, Ohio 44115

GRANTEE:

Tall Timbers Research, Inc.
Route 1, Box 678
Tallahassee, FL 32312-9712

With copy to:

Oliver C. Henkel, Esq.
Thompson, Hine and Flory
1100 National City Bank Bldg.
Cleveland, Ohio 44114

With a copy to:

Camilla M. Herlevich, Esq.
The Cotton Exchange
321 North Front Street
Wilmington, NC 28401

In the event any provision of this Easement is determined by any court having jurisdiction hereof to be void and unenforceable, all remaining terms shall remain valid and binding.

The burdens of this Easement shall run with the Protected Property and shall be enforceable against the Grantors and all future owners and tenants thereof in perpetuity. The benefits shall be in gross and assignable subject to the following restrictions: (a) no assignment shall be effective unless to an eligible donee under applicable federal laws, rules and regulations, as the same may be amended from time to time (the parties acknowledge that, at the time of this grant, the term "eligible donee" is defined in Treasury Reg. 1.170A-14(c)(1)); (b) any assignment must require the Assignee to carry out the purposes of this Easement; and (c) any assignment shall be subject to the prior written approval of Grantors, which approval shall not be unreasonably withheld, except that, provided that the requirements of items (a) and (b) of this paragraph are satisfied, an assignment to The Nature Conservancy (through its Georgia Field Office) shall not require the consent of Grantors, but Grantee shall have no right to make an assignment to The Nature Conservancy until the expiration of thirty (30) days prior notification to Grantors of the proposed assignment.

If a subsequent, unexpected change in the condition of the Protected Property or the surrounding property make impossible or impractical the continued use of the Protected Property for conservation purposes, this Easement shall be extinguished by judicial proceeding (and any proceeds received by Grantee from a subsequent sale or exchange of the Protected Property shall be used in a manner consistent with the conservation purposes of this Easement).

Whenever all or part of the Protected Property is taken in exercise of eminent domain by public, corporate or other authority so as to abrogate the restrictions imposed by this Easement, the Grantors and the Grantee shall join in appropriate actions at the time of such taking to recover the full value of the taking and all incidental or direct damages resulting from the taking. The net proceeds (including, for purposes of this subparagraph, proceeds from any lawful sale of the Protected Property unencumbered by the restrictions hereunder) shall be distributed among the Grantors and the Grantee in shares in proportion to the fair market value of their interests in the premises on the date of execution of this Easement. Any share received by the Grantee shall be used in a manner consistent with the conservation purposes set forth herein.

The Grantor and Grantee agree that the terms of this Easement shall survive any merger of the fee and easement interest in the Protected Property.

The Grantor agrees to pay any real estate taxes or other assessments levied on the Protected Property.

The Grantor hereby agrees that this Easement gives rise to a real property right, immediately vested in the Grantee, with a fair market value that is at least equal to the proportionate value that this Easement, at the time of conveyance, bears to the fair market value of the property as a whole at such time. That proportionate value of the Grantee's property rights shall remain constant. Accordingly, when a change in conditions makes impossible or impractical any continued protection of the Protected Property for conservation purposes, and the restrictions contained herein are extinguished by judicial proceeding, the Grantee, upon a subsequent sale, exchange or involuntary conversion of the Protected Property, shall be entitled to a portion of the proceeds at least equal to that proportionate value of the Easement, unless applicable state law provides that Grantor is entitled to the full proceeds from the conversion without regard to the prior perpetual conservation restriction. The Grantee shall use its share of the proceeds in a manner consistent with the conservation purposes set forth herein.

TO HAVE AND TO HOLD this Easement, together with all and singular the appurtenances and privileges belonging or in any way pertaining thereto, either in law or in equity, either in possession or expectancy, for the proper use and benefit of the Grantee, its successors and assigns, forever.

GRANTORS HEREBY WARRANT and represent that the Grantors are seized in fee simple of that portion of the Protected Property as described on Exhibit A, and that Grantor Carol Butler is seized in fee simple of that portion of the Protected Property as described on Exhibit B, and that Grantors and Grantor Carol Butler, respectively, have good right to grant and convey this

Easement, that the Protected Property is free and clear of any and all encumbrances, except easements of record and prescriptive easements, if any, and that the Grantee and its successors and assigns shall have the use and enjoyment of all of the benefits derived from and arising out of this Easement.

IN WITNESS WHEREOF, the Grantors and Grantee have executed this instrument as of the day and year first above written.

As to Grantors, signed,
sealed and delivered in
our presence:

Julie H. Moore
Witness

Glenda Shealey
Witness

GRANTORS:

John G. Butler (SEAL)
John G. Butler

Carol Humphrey Butler (SEAL)
Carol Humphrey Butler

As to Grantee, signed,
sealed and delivered
in our presence

Julie H. Moore
Witness

Glenda Shealey
Witness

GRANTEE: TALL TIMBERS
RESEARCH, INC., a Florida
non-profit corporation

By: _____

STATE OF GEORGIA)
) SS.
COUNTY OF THOMAS)

The foregoing instrument was acknowledged before me this 21st day of November, 1992, by John G. Butler and Carol Humphrey Butler.

Glenda Shirley
NOTARY PUBLIC

Notary Public, Thomas County, Georgia
My Commission Expires January 22, 1995

(SEAL)

STATE OF GEORGIA)
) SS.
COUNTY OF THOMAS)

I HEREBY CERTIFY that on this day, before me, an officer duly authorized in the State and County aforesaid to take acknowledgements, personally appeared _____Walter C. Sedgwick_____, the _____Chairman, Board of Trustees_____, of TALL TIMBERS RESEARCH, INC., known to me to be Grantee in the foregoing instrument, and that he acknowledged executing the same in the presence of two subscribing witnesses freely and voluntarily under authority duly vested in him by said corporation.

WITNESS my hand and official in the County and State last aforesaid, this 21st day of November, 1992.

Glenda Shirley
NOTARY PUBLIC

My Commission Expires:
Notary Public, Thomas County, Georgia
My Commission Expires January 22, 1995

(SEAL)

LIST OF EXHIBITS

Exhibit A	Legal Description of property owned jointly by Grantors John and Carol Butler.
Exhibit B	Legal Description of property owned by Grantor Carol Humphrey Butler.
Exhibit C	Diagram of Residential Development Land.

Greenways

Apalachee Greenways Network
Project Synopsis

Project "Handle"

This project will assess important natural and cultural resources within the Apalachee region, examine potential greenway linkages and scenic corridors, identify threats associated with the area's growth and devise a strategy to protect and manage critical features as a part of a regional network of green. By documenting the region's important natural and cultural sites and significant associated linear features (e.g., rivers, historic routes), the project will help increase the effectiveness of the region's resource protection efforts. As Florida's capital region, this project will serve to educate elected officials and involve senior agency staff in a greenways initiative in their own "backyard". In addition, the natural and cultural features of the region that transcend the Florida/Georgia border offer a chance to address bi-state greenways planning efforts.

Study Area

The study area focuses on lands within a six-county region of North Florida and South Georgia stretching from the Aucilla River on the east to the Ochlockonee River on the west. This geographic region has many outstanding features including the Red Hills area between Tallahassee and Thomasville, Georgia, the pine flatwoods of the Apalachicola National Forest, and the coastal wetlands of the St. Marks National Wildlife Refuge.

Project Partners

The Florida Greenways Program directs and administers all project activities, provides professional direction and assistance and serves as the liaison with all project participants. The Red Hills Conservation Association and the Apalachee Land Conservancy serve with Florida Greenways as lead project partners. A variety of additional project participants will be solicited including The Nature Conservancy, the Coastal Plains Institute, the Trust for Public Land, other area nonprofits and appropriate government agencies. Faculty and graduate students from Florida State University's Department of Urban and Regional Planning may be utilized to assist in data gathering and preparing greenway design concepts.

(continued)

The Florida Greenways Program
926 East Park Avenue
Post Office Box 5948
Tallahassee, Florida 32314-5948
(904) 222-6277
Fax (904) 222-1117

1000 Friends of Florida/The Conservation Fund
Partners in Land and Water Conservation

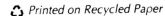 *Printed on Recycled Paper*

Project Area Actions to Date

The Red Hills Conservation Association has been active over the past years working with private landowners to conserve the landscapes and historic uses of the rural Red Hills region (the south Georgia and north Florida sections of the project area). For the past two years, the Apalachee Land Conservancy has advocated the creation of a scenic byway system centered upon Meridian Road in Leon County, Florida. The Nature Conservancy for nearly a decade has focused on protection of vital natural areas within the region. The Trust for Public Land in conjunction with the University of Florida has studied the scenic qualities of the roadways in the Red Hills Regions and will be shortly publishing a resource guide and tour book. The St. Marks Rail-Trail and the Phipps-Overstreet greenway represent important natural and recreational linkages that will be incorporated into the network of green.

Proposed Work Program

The three- to five-year Apalachee Greenways Project consists of three distinct phases: **Phase I** (1993), Regional Assessment and Visioning; **Phase II** (1994) Network Planning, Strategy Development and Demonstration Project; and **Phase III** (1995 and beyond), Resource Protection Implementation. Phase I activities will directly benefit the protection of natural and cultural resources within the six-county project area.

Phase I products will include: (1) a summary of the results of the natural/cultural resources assessment including a series of maps and a list of project area agencies and/or organizations currently involved in resource planning and protection activities; (2) an analysis of immediate and potential threats to identified natural/cultural features and an annotated listing of tools available to address these threats; and (3) a synopsis of prototype workshops discussions and recommendations. Each of these products will also directly aid Florida Greenways in carrying out Phase II and Phase III network planning and implementation activities.

Start-up Date

January 1, 1993

Prototype Project Staffing

The prototype project is directed by Mark Benedict, Ph.D., Director of Florida Greenways, and assisted by Kent Wimmer, Florida Greenways Program Planner. The project's lead partners are represented by Mr. Curt Blair who is president of the Apalachee Land Conservancy and Mr. Jim McKinley who is the Red Hills Conservation Association's Assistant Director for Inventory and Easements.

Funding Source(s)

The Elizabeth Ordway Dunn Foundation with matches from other private foundations and governmental entities as appropriate.

For further information please write to Florida Greenways Program, Post Office Box 5948, Tallahassee, FL 32314, or call (904) 222-6277.

Apalachee Greenways Prototype

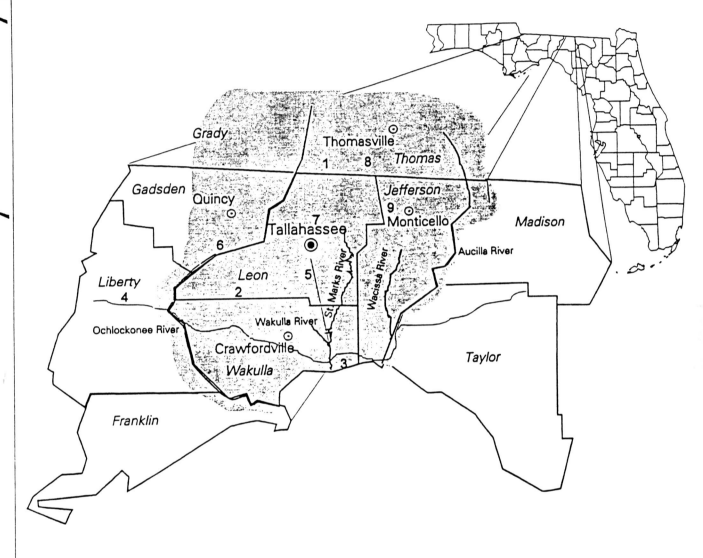

1. Red Hills Area
2. Apalachicola National Forest
3. St. Marks National Wildlife Refuge
4. Florida National Scenic Trail
5. St. Marks State Rail Trail
6. Lake Talquin State Forest & Joe Bud Wildlife Management Area
7. Lake Jackson - Phipps - Overstreet - Maclay Gardens greenway
8. Canopy Roads
9. Lake Miccossukee

The numbers are keyed to significant resource areas.

N

Greenways

Grant Proposal

APALACHEE GREENWAYS PROJECT

Submitted To

The Elizabeth Ordway Dunn Foundation, Inc.
c/o Ann Fowler Wallace
Grants Management Associates
230 Congress Street
Boston, Massachusetts 02110

From

1000 Friends of Florida
Florida Greenways Program
Post Office Box 5948
Tallahassee, Florida 32314-5948
Dr. Mark A. Benedict, Program Director

In Cooperation With

The Conservation Fund
1800 North Kent Street, Suite 1120
Arlington, Virginia 22209
Mr. Patrick F. Noonan, President

September 15, 1992

The Florida Greenways Program
524 East College Avenue
Post Office Box 5948
Tallahassee, Florida 32314-5948
(904) 222-6277
Fax (904) 222-1117

1000 Friends of Florida/The Conservation Fund
Partners in Land and Water Conservation
♲ *Printed on Recycled Paper*

Case Statement

Table of Contents

Introduction

The Florida Greenways Program is a cooperative effort of 1000 Friends of Florida and The Conservation Fund. The program is dedicated to the creation of a statewide network of green, a network composed of protected natural area "hubs" and greenways used as corridors for habitat linkages and/or public recreation. In addition to its efforts to promote a comprehensive greenways initiative statewide, the Florida Greenways Program identifies unique local or regional projects that can benefit from a coordinated approach to the protection of wildlife habitat and open space and can serve as prototypes for similar efforts statewide. The Apalachee Greenways Project has been designed as one of these local/regional prototypes.

The Apalachee Greenways Project will focus on lands within a six-county region of north Florida and south Georgia stretching from the Aucilla River to the Ochlockonee River (Figure 1). This geographic area has many outstanding features including the Red Hills area between Tallahassee, Florida and Thomasville, Georgia, the pine flatwoods of the Apalachicola National Forest and the coastal wetlands of the St. Marks National Wildlife Refuge.

The Apalachee region was selected for four main reasons:

1) The region possesses existing natural and cultural features (e.g., state and federal conservation lands, working landscapes and local/regional trail segments) that represent important building blocks of Florida's statewide network of green.

2) A number of private and public initiatives are currently underway to protect natural and cultural sites from threats associated with the region's ever-expanding growth infrastructure (e.g., roads, utility lines).

3) As Florida's capital region, many opportunities are provided to educate elected officials and involve senior agency staff in a greenways initiative in their own "backyard".

4) The natural and cultural features of the region that transcend the Florida/Georgia border offer a chance to address bi-state greenways planning efforts.

Because of the region's attributes and ongoing conservation efforts, Florida Greenways believes that the Apalachee Greenways Project has great potential to gain the momentum and funding necessary to carry a north Florida "network of green" initiative forward. In addition, the project as designed represents the many facets needed for successful, community-based greenways projects statewide.

The Apalachee Greenways Project will be directed by the Florida Greenways Program with the Apalachee Land Conservancy and the Red Hills Conservation Association serving as the project's lead partners. Additional project participants will be solicited including the Coastal Plains Institute, The Nature Conservancy, the Trust for Public Land, other area nonprofits and appropriate government agencies.

Project Design

Under the leadership and administration of the Florida Greenways Program, 1000 Friends of Florida will work together with the Apalachee Land Conservancy, the Red Hills Conservation Association and other project participants to assess important natural and cultural resources within the Apalachee region, identify threats associated with the area's growth and devise a strategy to protect and manage critical features as a part of a regional network of green. With Florida Greenways serving as a catalyst and facilitator, the Apalachee Greenways Project will bring the participants together in a coordinated and open consensus-building process that will result in short- and long-term protection for important natural and cultural resources within the project area.

The Apalachee Greenways Project has been designed to generally follow the established process for Florida Greenways' prototype projects. The project will be conducted in a series of three phases over a three to five year period: Phase I, Regional Assessment and Visioning; Phase II, Network Planning, Strategy Development and Demonstration Project; and Phase III, Resource Protection Implementation. Florida Greenways will play a leadership role in Phases I and II. Guiding concepts and a generalized work program for Florida Greenways prototype projects are described in Attachment F, Item 2c.

1993 Phase I Activities

Using funds obtained from the Elizabeth Ordway Dunn Foundation, 1000 Friends of Florida, in cooperation with the Apalachee Land Conservancy and the Red Hills Conservation Association, will undertake the following six tasks in 1993:

Task 1:   **Establish an Apalachee Greenways Project steering committee and operational framework.**

In this task, a project steering committee will be set up. It will consist of appropriate staff from 1000 Friends of Florida, the Apalachee Land Conservancy and the Red Hills Conservation Association, the project's lead partners. The steering committee, which will be chaired by the Florida Greenways Program Director, will be active throughout the project and will meet periodically to coordinate project activities. It is anticipated that the Red Hills Conservation Association will provide guidance in assessing the region's natural resources while the Apalachee Land Conservancy will help in addressing the project area's cultural/recreational features. 1000 Friends of Florida will play a major role in identifying future development pressures and threats. The Florida Greenways office will direct and administer all project activities and provide staffing for the project. Informal working sub-committees will be established as appropriate to provide additional technical assistance. These working sub-committees would consist of representatives from other organizations and agencies in the project area that are involved in relevant natural and/or cultural resource protection activities.

Task 2:   **Hold a project initiation workshop.**

Under this task, a workshop will be held during the second or third month of the project. The workshop will involve 25 to 50 representatives from key project area resource agencies, nonprofit organizations and the private sector. The workshop will be designed to inform participants about project objectives and tasks and obtain initial recommendations regarding project area resources and threats. The workshop will most likely include introductory remarks by 1000 Friends, the Red Hills Conservation Association and the Apalachee Land Conservancy, a panel on project area resource features and concerns, a break-out session to address specific project-related issues and a moderated closing discussion. This workshop will be modeled after similar workshops held in Gainesville in March 1992 and in Live Oak in August 1992 (Attachment F, Item 1c). Through this workshop, we will also identify resource people that could serve on the steering committee's working sub-committees and significantly expand the project's data gathering and assessment capabilities.

2

Task 3:   Conduct a natural and cultural resource assessment for the project area.

With the assistance of the project's lead partners, important natural and cultural resource features within the project area will be assessed during months two through ten. The assessment will focus on highlighting key components and linkages that would make up a future north Florida greenways network. To this end, Florida Greenways will identify the natural and cultural infrastructure that is essential to the project area's long-term prosperity. Identified natural features will include critical natural resource sites (e.g., red cockaded woodpecker habitat) and key natural linkages (e.g., the area's undisturbed river floodplains). Identified cultural resource features will include important cultural/historic sites (e.g., working landscapes, structures) and corridors (e.g., canopy roads, historic/modern trail segments). Through background research and field surveys, the assessment will identify "holes" in existing data as well as other agencies' and organizations' work within the project to supply needed resource information.

Task 4:   Identify growth-related resource threats in the project area.

In addition to assessing key natural and cultural resources in the project area, it is essential to also address current and potential threats to these features posed by modern, growth-related infrastructure. Under this task, proposed roads, gas and utility lines, and proposed land uses (as detailed in comprehensive plans and other documents) that represent threats to the project area's key natural and cultural resources will be identified. Mapping these features as overlays to the natural/cultural assessment will help highlight future threats and facilitate region-wide planning to minimize their impact. Tools that are available to address such threats will also be identified during this task.

Task 5:   Hold a phase I visioning workshop.

In Task 5, we will hold a preliminary visioning workshop for the region's network of green. This workshop, which will be held in the fall of 1993, will be designed as a follow-up to the project initiation workshop and involve the same public and private sector representatives that participated in the initial meeting. The workshop will give participants the opportunity to view the results of the natural/cultural assessment and the analysis of future threats. Through breakout discussions and a moderated final session, participants will help determine key sites and linkages that would make up the project area's network of green, explore ideas on how to deal with immediate and potential threats to network components and develop strategies and procedures for ongoing efforts. The results of this workshop will serve as the basis for further planning and implementation activities in Phase II and Phase III.

Task 6:   Prepare Project Resource Document.

Tasks 1 through 5 are designed to compile the resource information necessary to support a community-wide greenways network initiative. Phase I activities will result in a resource document that will include: the results of the natural and cultural resource assessment in the form of an overlay map series identifying the location and relationship of key project area features; an annotated listing of project area agencies and organizations currently involved in resource planning and protection, highlighting each agency's or organization's current focus and activities; the results of the analysis of immediate and potential threats

3

to identified natural and cultural resource features keyed to the overlay map series; and a synopsis of tools currently available to protect natural and cultural resources in the project area and address threats associated with the region's growth. The Phase I resource document is the critical first step in any holistic, community greenways initiative. The resource document will help direct Florida Greenways' Phase II and Phase III network planning and implementation activities.

Future Project Phases

Phase II of the Apalachee Greenways Project will be undertaken in 1994. During this phase, Florida Greenways and the three lead partners will undertake a series of activities to plan and build consensus for the project area's greenways network and develop a specific strategy and action plan for its implementation. Phase II activities will include:

* a network mapping charrette to develop an optimum, resource-based blueprint for the Apalachee region's network of green. This charrette may be undertaken in concert with and supported by a spring 1994 graduate student studio project by Florida State University's Department of Urban and Regional Planning;

* a demonstration project focused either on the establishment or completion of a recreational greenway (e.g., the extension of the St. Marks Trail or the Meridian Road "canopy" project) or the protection of one of the regions important conservation linkages through fee-simple or less-than-fee acquisition;

* the development and implementation of a public education/outreach program to build broader public understanding and to obtain public input and support for a regional greenways network. This activity would include the preparation of education/outreach materials, including a citizens' resource guide, and the holding of community workshops;

* the preparation of a detailed, multi-year network implementation strategy and associated action agenda. This activity would specifically identify a wide variety of network implementation tasks needed to move the project forward and the agencies, organizations and/or individuals that would take the lead in carrying out each task.

It is envisioned that Phase II activities would involve a broader spectrum of participants than Phase I by including local officials and community activists. Through their involvement in Phase II, not only will we be able to garner additional technical and socio-political information, but we will also be able to gauge citizen response to the proposed network of green and adjust our activities to achieve community consensus. The steering committee will use the additional Phase II resource data, the demonstration project and the community response to visioning documents to develop long-term implementation strategies for activities in Phase III of the project. The final product of Phase II will include a refined network resource map that has achieved community consensus and a series of implementation strategies for the succeeding three or more years.

Phase III of the Apalachee Greenways Project will commence in 1995 and focus on the specific Greenway network protection activities identified in Phase II planning. This multi-year phase will involve fee-simple acquisition of targeted sites, less-than-fee simple protection efforts including protective easements and covenants, and implementation of resource management techniques. In addition, regional and local comprehensive plans and other agency documents will be amended to support the greenways network. Funding for Phase III will be raised from a variety of governmental and private sources identified during

Phase II. Florida Greenways will provide general oversight to these activities and periodically evaluate and report on the success of network implementation efforts.

Project Evaluation

1000 Friends of Florida has achieved substantial, measurable success in its efforts to ensure full and effective implementation of Florida's Growth Management Act. The Conservation Fund, 1000 Friends' partner in the Florida Greenways Program, is a results-oriented organization, as is evident by far-reaching successes in land and water conservation initiatives nationwide.

Grant results will be evaluated against overall Florida Greenways Program goals and prototype tasks contained in the program's multi-year Tactical Plan (Attachment E). The Tactical Plan has been endorsed as the Florida Greenways work program by the Board of Directors of 1000 Friends of Florida and The Conservation Fund. Progress on meeting the objectives of the Apalachee Greenways Project will be evaluated based on the completion of the above-listed Phase I tasks and associated products. The Board of 1000 Friends of Florida and The Conservation Fund will be briefed on project activities and accomplishments as a part of Florida Greenways' quarterly activity reports. At the end of the year, a project summary report will be prepared by Florida Greenways' program staff. This prototype status report, which will provide a qualitative evaluation of the project's Phase I accomplishments, will be delivered to the Elizabeth Ordway Dunn Foundation in the fall of 1993 with the project's assessment and planning products.

The Proposed 1993/Phase I Budget

1000 Friends of Florida anticipates that a minimum of $50,000 is needed from the Elizabeth Ordway Dunn Foundation to provide base-level support for Phase I of the Apalachee Greenways Project. 1000 Friends of Florida would also like to return to the Dunn Foundation in September 1993 to request second year funding for Phase II of the project.

It is the intent of 1000 Friends of Florida, in cooperation with The Conservation Fund, the Apalachee Land Conservancy and the Red Hills Conservation Association, to seek additional funding to supplement the Dunn Foundation's grant. A $40,000 grant that has been received from the Knight Foundation will enable the Apalachee Land Conservancy to provide an in-kind match for their help with the cultural/historic assessment. A $16,900 grant proposal is currently under consideration by the Florida Department of Agriculture. If approved, funds from this grant will be used to help cover costs for Phase I project workshops. Additional funding proposals are being considered for this project including one to the Turner Foundation to cover the costs associated with digitizing assessment data and producing an overlay map series.

INDEX

Figure 5.16: Average Annual Rainfall in the Project Area, from Bush and Johnston, 1988.

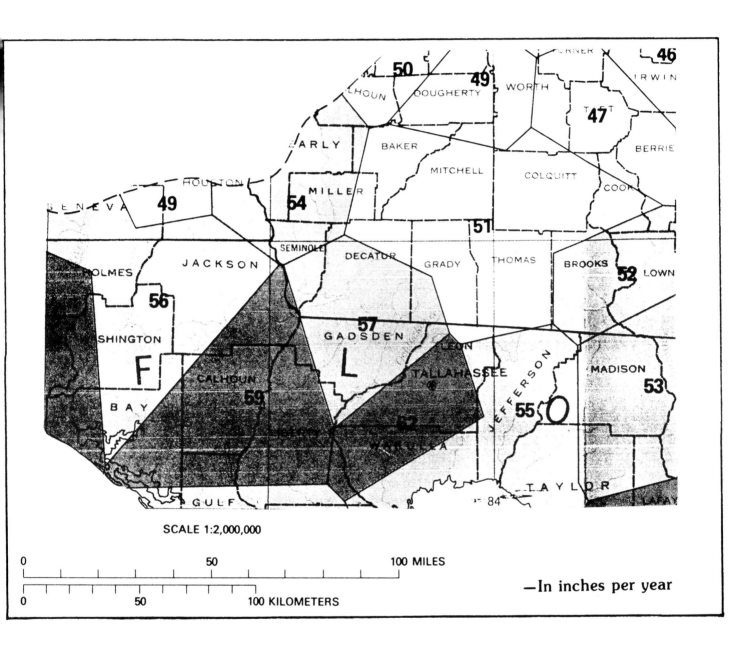

SCALE 1:2,000,000

—In inches per year

Figure 5.17: Generalized Hydrologic Budget (does not reflect high rates of internal drainage in parts of project area), after Bush and Johnston, 1988.

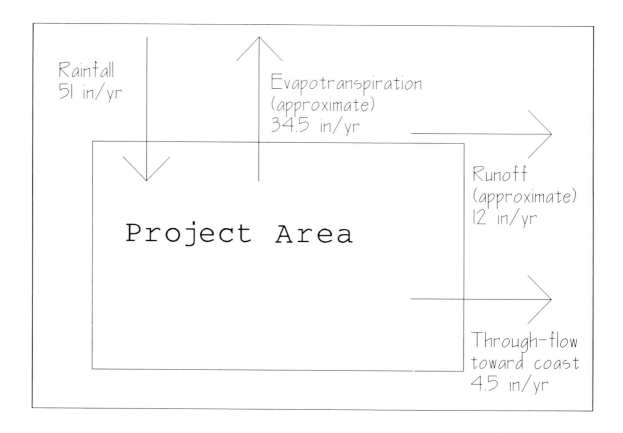

Patterns of groundwater flow that evolved within the Floridan prior to development are divided into three groups by Bush and Johnston (1988). The local, intermediate and regional systems coincide with the model developed by Toth (1963), which apportioned flow among three types of flows. Toth defined the local flow as that which directly resulted from basin topography and which is recharged at the top of local topographic highs and discharges at nearby lows. The intermediate system circulates deeper than the local system, and one or more topographic highs and lows may occur between areas of recharge and discharge. The regional system is deeper yet, and discharges at the down-gradient terminus of the original basin (the Gulf of Mexico).

Pre-development flow within the project area and present post-development flow, to a large extent, is dominated by large springs near the Florida Coast. Most of the recharge needed to sustain the high discharges of these springs occurs in the "virtually unconfined, highly transmissive area just to the north around Tallahassee, Florida, and extending northeast to about Thomasville, Georgia." (Bush and Johnston, 1988).

Water Use

Groundwater development in the project area began in the late 1880's, and by the turn of the century several hundred wells tapped the Floridan system across south and central Georgia. Monitoring of water use and development by state and federal agencies is relatively modern. In the mid-1950's the U. S. Geological Survey (USGS) began cooperative programs with the states, compiling surface and groundwater use data across the nation. These surveys are compiled at five-year intervals. In 1978 the Georgia Geological Survey and the USGS began a comprehensive inventory of major water users in Georgia. The data included in this report are obtained from the most recently published, available water use report and are provided by county (V.P. Trent, J.L. Fanning, and G.A. Doonan, 1990).

In 1987, all public water supplies within the two project area counties were withdrawn from the Floridan Aquifer system. Rural domestic water supplies are also from groundwater, generally from the Floridan in both counties (Trent, et al., 1990), but may be withdrawn from the surficial aquifer system in some areas of Grady County. Public and private domestic water supplies total nearly 5.8 million gallons per day (MGPD) (includes 4.18 MGPD for the City of Thomasville) or ~59% of Thomas County water use and 2.5 MGPD or ~17% of Grady's water use in 1987.

Agricultural water use may be divided into two use classes: livestock water and irrigation water. Stock water may come from surface water or ground water sources. Only about two percent of total water use in the area is stock water. Irrigation water is another matter, constituting about 25% of Thomas County's water use and about 80% of that in Grady County. However, although supplies are again divided between surface and ground water, the amount used from each varies. Grady County obtains 62% of its irrigation water from groundwater while Thomas County obtains 70% of its irrigation water from that source. Relatively large increases in irrigation water use have occurred in Grady County since 1970; however, most of the irrigated land lies west of the Ochlockonee River and the project area.

Finally, industrial water use is varied in both counties and the project area, consuming about 1.39 MGPD or ~14% of Thomas County's water use. Most Thomas County industrial uses lie outside the project boundary. In Grady County, industrial use is very low, at 0.50% of total use or about 80,000 gpd. (See Table 5.1, Water Use Data by County).

Table 5.1: Water Use Data By County
(From Trent, et al., 1990)

Type of Use	Thomas County		Grady County	
	Ground-Water (MGPD)	Surface Water (MGPD)	Ground- Water (MGPD)	Surface Water (MGPD)
Public Supply	4.79	0.00	1.57	0.00
Domestic and Commercial	.98	0.00	0.97	0.00
Industry and Mining	1.39	0.00	0.08	0.00
Irrigation	1.72	0.74	7.38	4.52
Livestock	0.10	0.12	0.16	0.13
Thermo-electric	0.00	0.00	0.00	0.00
TOTAL	8.98	0.86	10.16	4.65

Discussion

Detailed data on groundwater supply and use is limited for the project area. Most recent studies of the hydrology and geologic framework of major Georgia water sources collected no data in either Thomas or Grady Counties. This means that regional analysis and data are extrapolated in order to arrive at reasonable values for the project area. There is a real need for more data collection within the project area in order to better relate the local water system and its use to the regional framework.

LOCAL FEATURES

Sink Hole Assessment

A prominent feature of the project area is its abundance of sink holes. In fact, the topographic expression of the features has become so accepted in the area that the name of at least one geographic portion of Thomas County reflects the topography (Sinkola, Sinkola Plantation, Sinkola Cemetery: see U.S.G.S. 1:24,000 Pine Park Quadrangle, southern portion).

In that sink holes often reflect a direct conduit between land surface and the local groundwater system, these features were designated as a part of the overall project to receive special emphasis. The location and density of the sinks were of primary interest. These factors may be generally known locally, but a search of the literature revealed no published effort to map the features. Without such a compilation, it would have been difficult to assess the geologic and topographic factors that affect the areas subject to sinks and, in fact, sometimes probably mask the surface expression of the sinks.